# *A COURSEBOOK* ON SCIENTIFIC AND PROFESSIONAL WRITING FOR *SPEECH-LANGUAGE PATHOLOGY*

*Fifth Edition*

# A COURSEBOOK ON SCIENTIFIC AND PROFESSIONAL WRITING FOR *SPEECH-LANGUAGE PATHOLOGY*

*Fifth Edition*

**M. N. Hegde, PhD**

*California State University–Fresno*

5521 Ruffin Road
San Diego, CA 92123

e-mail: information@pluralpublishing.com
Website: http://www.pluralpublishing.com

Copyright 2018 © by Plural Publishing, Inc.

Typeset in 10.5/12 Adobe Garamond Pro by Flanagan's Publishing Services, Inc.
Printed in the United States of America by McNaughton & Gunn
20 19 18    2 3 4 5

All rights, including that of translation, reserved. No part of this publication may be reproduced, stored in a retrieval system, or transmitted in any form or by any means, electronic, mechanical, recording, or otherwise, including photocopying, recording, taping, Web distribution, or information storage and retrieval systems without the prior written consent of the publisher.

For permission to use material from this text, contact us by
Telephone: (866) 758-7251
Fax: (888) 758-7255
e-mail: permissions@pluralpublishing.com

*Every attempt has been made to contact the copyright holders for material originally printed in another source. If any have been inadvertently overlooked, the publishers will gladly make the necessary arrangements at the first opportunity.*

**Library of Congress Cataloging-in-Publication Data:**

Names: Hegde, M. N. (Mahabalagiri N.), 1941- author.
Title: A coursebook on scientific and professional writing for
  speech-language pathology / M. N. Hegde.
Other titles: Scientific and professional writing for speech-language
  pathology | Based on (expression): Publication manual of the American
  Psychological Association. 6th ed.
Description: Fifth edition. | San Diego, CA : LOGO Plural Publishing, [2018]
  | This edition is based on the sixth edition of the Publication Manual of
  the American Psychological Association (2010). | Includes bibliographical
  references and index.
Identifiers: LCCN 2017032802| ISBN 9781944883089 (alk. paper) | ISBN
  1944883088 (alk. paper)
Subjects: | MESH: Medical Writing | Speech-Language Pathology
Classification: LCC RC428.5 | NLM WZ 345 | DDC 616.85/5--dc23
LC record available at https://lccn.loc.gov/2017032802

# Contents

*Preface to the Fifth Edition* .................................................................. *xv*
*About the Author* ............................................................................. *xviii*

## PART A
## FOUNDATIONS OF SCIENTIFIC AND PROFESSIONAL WRITING .......... 1

### A.1. BASIC RULES OF USAGE .................................................. 2

**Ampersand**

A.1.1. Use the Ampersand Correctly ................................................. 2

**Apostrophe**

A.1.2. Do Not Turn a Possessive Into a Plural ..................................... 2
A.1.3. Do Not Turn a Plural Into a Possessive ..................................... 4
A.1.4. Use the Correct Forms of Possessive Nouns ............................... 6
A.1.5. Use the Possessive Forms of Pronouns Correctly .......................... 12
A.1.6. Distinguish Contractions From Possessives ................................ 12

**Unusual Plurals**

A.1.7. Use Unusual Singulars and Plurals Correctly .............................. 14

**Comma**

A.1.8. Use a Serial Comma ............................................................ 18
A.1.9. Do Not Use a Serial Comma When You Write Only Two Parallel Terms and ............. 18
       Connect Them With a Conjunction

A.1.10. Use a Comma to Separate Parenthetic Expressions When You Do Not Use Parentheses. . . . . . . 20

A.1.11. Place a Comma Before a Conjunction Introducing an Independent Clause. . . . . . . . . . . . . . . 20

A.1.12. Do Not Use a Comma Before a Conjunction That Is Followed by a Dependent Clause . . . . . . 20

**Dash**

A.1.13. Prefer an *em dash* to a Comma to Set Off an Abrupt Break or Interruption . . . . . . . . . . . . . . . 22

**Semicolon**

A.1.14. Join Independent Clauses With a Semicolon When the Clauses Are . . . . . . . . . . . . . . . . . . . . . 22
Not Joined by a Conjunction

**Agreement**

A.1.15. Follow the Rules of Agreement . . . . . . . . . . . . . . . . . . . . . . . . . . . . . . . . . . . . . . . . . . . . . . . . 24

**Modifiers**

A.1.16. Use Modifiers Correctly. . . . . . . . . . . . . . . . . . . . . . . . . . . . . . . . . . . . . . . . . . . . . . . . . . . . . . 32

**Pronouns**

A.1.17. Clarify the Referents of Pronouns . . . . . . . . . . . . . . . . . . . . . . . . . . . . . . . . . . . . . . . . . . . . . . 34

A.1.18. Let the Pronoun Agree in Number With Its Antecedent . . . . . . . . . . . . . . . . . . . . . . . . . . . . . 34

A.1.19. Use the Proper Case of Pronoun . . . . . . . . . . . . . . . . . . . . . . . . . . . . . . . . . . . . . . . . . . . . . . . 34

**Sentence Fragments**

A.1.20. Do Not Break a Single Sentence Into Two Parts. . . . . . . . . . . . . . . . . . . . . . . . . . . . . . . . . . . 36

A.1.21. Do Not Write Sentence Fragments as a Series of Declarative Statements . . . . . . . . . . . . . . . . . 36

A.1.22. Do Not Punctuate Appositives . . . . . . . . . . . . . . . . . . . . . . . . . . . . . . . . . . . . . . . . . . . . . . . . 36

**Nouns and Adjectives**

A.1.23. Use Certain Terms Only in Their Adjectival Forms . . . . . . . . . . . . . . . . . . . . . . . . . . . . . . . . . 38

A.1.24. Do Not Turn a Noun Into a Verb . . . . . . . . . . . . . . . . . . . . . . . . . . . . . . . . . . . . . . . . . . . . . . 38

**Participial Phrase**

A.1.25. Let a Participial Phrase at the Beginning of a Sentence Refer to the Grammatical Subject . . . . . 40

## A.2 BASIC RULES OF COMPOSITION . . . . . . . . . . . . . . . . . . . . . . . . . . . . . . . . . . . . . . . . . . **42**

**Structure of Research Papers**

A.2.1. Design a Broad Outline of Your Paper. . . . . . . . . . . . . . . . . . . . . . . . . . . . . . . . . . . . . . . . . . . 42

A.2.2. Design Headings and Subheadings of Your Paper . . . . . . . . . . . . . . . . . . . . . . . . . . . . . . . . . . 44

**Composing Paragraphs**

A.2.3. Write Paragraphs That Express Related Ideas. . . . . . . . . . . . . . . . . . . . . . . . . . . . . . . . . . . . . . 46

A.2.4. Do Not Write Paragraphs That Are Too Long . . . . . . . . . . . . . . . . . . . . . . . . . . . . . . . . . . . . . 48

A.2.5. Do Not Write One-Sentence Paragraphs . . . . . . . . . . . . . . . . . . . . . . . . . . . . . . . . . . . . . . . . . 50

A.2.6. Begin and End Most Paragraphs With Transitionary Sentences . . . . . . . . . . . . . . . . . . . . . . . . 52

**Concise and Direct Writing**

| | | |
|---|---|---|
| A.2.7. | Prefer the Shorter to the Longer Sentences. | 54 |
| A.2.8. | Prefer the Active Voice. | 56 |
| A.2.9. | Say What It Is, Instead of What It Is Not. | 58 |
| A.2.10. | Avoid Too Many Qualifications. | 60 |
| A.2.11. | Use Definite, Specific, and Concrete Language | 62 |
| A.2.12. | Eliminate or Replace Unnecessary Phrases. | 64 |
| A.2.13. | Avoid Redundant Phrases. | 72 |
| A.2.14. | Avoid Wordiness. | 78 |
| A.2.15. | Avoid Jargon. | 80 |
| A.2.16. | Avoid Euphemism. | 82 |
| A.2.17. | Keep Related Words Together. | 84 |

**Parallelism**

| | | |
|---|---|---|
| A.2.18. | Write in Parallel Terms. | 86 |
| A.2.19. | Maintain Parallelism in Numbered or Bulleted Lists. | 88 |

**Misplaced or Dangling Modifiers**

| | | |
|---|---|---|
| A.2.20. | Avoid Dangling Modifiers. | 90 |

**Misplaced or Dangling Modifiers**

| | | |
|---|---|---|
| A.2.20. | Avoid Dangling Modifiers. | 91 |
| A.2.21. | Avoid Misplaced Modifiers. | 92 |

**Shifts Within and Between Sentences**

| | | |
|---|---|---|
| A.2.22. | Avoid Shifts Within and Between Sentences. | 94 |

**Quotations**

| | | |
|---|---|---|
| A.2.23. | Make Quotations Count. | 96 |
| A.2.24. | Do Not Overuse Quotations. | 98 |
| A.2.25. | Do Not Include Islands of Quotations. | 100 |
| A.2.26. | Do Not Begin a Sentence With a Quotation. | 102 |
| A.2.27. | Use Quotation and Punctuation Marks Correctly. | 104 |
| A.2.28. | Do Not Misuse Quotation Marks. | 106 |
| A.2.29. | Give References for All Direct Quotations. | 108 |
| A.2.30. | Reproduce Quotations Exactly. | 110 |
| A.2.31. | Integrate Quotations of Fewer Than 40 Words With the Text. | 110 |
| A.2.32. | Arrange Quotations as a *Block* When They Have 40 Words or More. | 112 |
| A.2.33. | Show Correctly the Changes in Quotations. | 114 |
| A.2.34. | Quote Correctly the Sources on the Internet. | 116 |

**Precision in the Use of Scientific Terms**

A.2.35. Use the Terms Ending in *-ology* Correctly ............................................. 118

A.2.36. Use Certain Terms Ending in *-ics* Correctly ............................................. 120

**Use of Fresh Language**

A.2.37. Avoid Clichés ............................................. 122

A.2.38. Avoid Colloquial or Informal Expressions ............................................. 122

### A.3. COMMONLY MISUSED WORDS AND PHRASES ............................................. 124

A.3.1. *Accept* and *Except* ............................................. 124

A.3.2. *Affect* and *Effect* ............................................. 124

A.3.3. *Alternate* and *Alternative* ............................................. 126

A.3.4. *Allusion* and *Illusion* ............................................. 126

A.3.5. *And/Or* ............................................. 126

A.3.6. *Baseline* and *Baserate* ............................................. 128

A.3.7. *Effect* and *Impact* ............................................. 128

A.3.8. *Elicit* and *Evoke* ............................................. 130

A.3.9. *Elicit* and *Illicit* ............................................. 130

A.3.10. *Farther* and *Further* ............................................. 132

A.3.11. *Focus* and *Analysis (Study)* ............................................. 132

A.3.12. *Incidence* and *Prevalence* ............................................. 134

A.3.13. *Inter-* and *Intra-* ............................................. 134

A.3.14. *Latter* and *Later* ............................................. 136

A.3.15. *Proof* and *Support* ............................................. 136

A.3.16. *Secondly* and *Thirdly* ............................................. 138

A.3.17. *Since* and *Because* ............................................. 138

A.3.18. *There* and *Their* ............................................. 138

## PART B
## SCIENTIFIC WRITING ............................................. 141

### B.1. INTRODUCTION TO SCIENTIFIC WRITING ............................................. 143

### B.2. WRITING WITHOUT BIAS ............................................. 145

B.2.1. Write Without Gender Bias ............................................. 146

B.2.2. Write Without Prejudicial Reference to Disabilities ............................................. 148

B.2.3. Write Without Prejudicial Reference to Ethnic or Racial Background ............................................. 150

B.2.4. Write Without Prejudicial Reference to People With Varied Sexual Orientation ............................................. 152

B.2.5. Use the Appropriate Gender Identity Terms ............................................. 154

## B.3. FORMAT OF SCIENTIFIC WRITING..................................................156

**Margins**

B.3.1. Leave Correct Margins............................................................. 156

**Title Page**

B.3.2. Type Correctly the Title Page of a Paper for Publication ............... 157
B.3.3. Type Correctly the Title Page of a Class (Term) Paper ................... 158

**Running Head**

B.3.4. Type the Manuscript Running Head Correctly .............................. 159

**Abstract Page**

B.3.5. Write an Abstract on the Second Page ........................................ 160

**Beginning of Text**

B.3.6. Begin the Text With an Untitled Introductory Section on Page Three ..................... 161

**Heading Levels**

B.3.7. Use the Headings Within the Text Consistently............................ 162

**Typefaces**

B.3.8. Use Acceptable Typefaces and Size............................................ 168
B.3.9. Use Boldface Correctly ............................................................ 168

**Page Numbers**

B.3.10. Number the Pages Correctly ................................................... 169
B.3.11. Reprint the Corrected Pages ................................................... 169

**Line Spacing and Line Length**

B.3.12. Use Appropriate Line Spacing ................................................. 170
B.3.13. Use Appropriate Line Length................................................... 170
B.3.14. Correct the Spelling Errors ..................................................... 170

## B.4. SELECTED MATTERS OF SCIENTIFIC STYLE...............................171

**Capitalization**

B.4.1. Capitalize the First Words ....................................................... 171
B.4.2. Capitalize the First and the Major Words.................................... 171
B.4.3. Capitalize the Words Correctly in Headings ................................ 172
B.4.4. Capitalize Proper Nouns and Trade Names ................................. 172
B.4.5. Capitalize the Chapters and Sections the Reader Is Referred To...... 172
B.4.6. Capitalize Nouns That Are Followed by a Number or Letter ........... 173
B.4.7. Capitalize Both Words in Otherwise Capitalized Hyphenated Compound .............. 173
B.4.8. Do Not Capitalize the Second Word of a Hyphenated Compound in Reference Lists ......... 173

**Italicization**

B.4.9. Use Italics Correctly Within the Body of Text .................................................. 174
B.4.10. Use Italics Correctly in the Reference List .................................................. 174

**Hyphenation**

B.4.11. Use the Hyphen Correctly .................................................. 175
B.4.12. Do Not Overuse the Hyphen .................................................. 177
B.4.13. Do Not Misuse the Hyphen .................................................. 177

**Indentation**

B.4.14. Use Correct Indentation .................................................. 178

**Space After Punctuation**

B.4.15. Give Correct Space or No Space After Punctuation .................................................. 179

**Abbreviations**

B.4.16. Write Out Abbreviations the First Time You Use the Term and Enclose the Abbreviations in Parentheses .................................................. 180
B.4.17. Do Not Start a Sentence With a Lowercase Abbreviation .................................................. 180
B.4.18. Use Latin Abbreviations Only in Parenthetical Constructions .................................................. 182
B.4.19. Add the Lowercase Plural Morpheme *s* to Plural Abbreviations Without an Apostrophe .................................................. 184
B.4.20. With Abbreviations, Use the Period Correctly .................................................. 184
B.4.21. Abbreviate Units of Measurement When a Number Is Specified .................................................. 184

**Numbers in Words or Numerals**

B.4.22. Write Out Units of Measurement When a Number Is Not Specified .................................................. 186
B.4.23. Use Roman Numerals Only When It Is an Established Practice .................................................. 186
B.4.24. Use Arabic Numerals for Numbers 10 and Above .................................................. 186
B.4.25. Use Numerals for Numbers Below 10 in Specified Contexts .................................................. 188
B.4.26. Write Out in Words Numbers Below 10 in Specified Contexts .................................................. 190
B.4.27. Write Out in Words Any Number That Begins a Sentence .................................................. 192
B.4.28. Combine Words and Numerals in Specified Contexts .................................................. 192

**Reference Citations Within the Text**

B.4.29. Cite the Author's Last Name and Year or Years of Publication in the Text .................................................. 194
B.4.30. Cite Both Names in the Text When a Work Has Two Authors .................................................. 194
B.4.31. Cite Works With Three to Five Authors Using All the Authors' Names Only the First Time .... 196
B.4.32. Cite Works of Six or More Authors by Only the First Author .................................................. 196
B.4.33. Distinguish Works of Multiple Authors Published in the Same Year .................................................. 198
B.4.34. Join Multiple Author Names With the Conjunction *and* or the Ampersand .................................................. 200
B.4.35. Distinguish the Different First Authors With the Same Surname .................................................. 200
B.4.36. Cite Multiple Works of the Same Author in a Temporally Ascending Order .................................................. 202

B.4.37. Attach Alphabetical Suffixes to the Same Author's Multiple Publications in the Same Year ..... 202

B.4.38. Within Parentheses, Arrange the Last Names of Multiple Authors in Alphabetical Order ..... 204

B.4.39. Cite Secondary Sources Sparingly and Correctly ..... 204

B.4.40. Cite Correctly the Works With No Author or an Anonymous Author ..... 206

B.4.41. Cite Correctly the Classical Works ..... 208

B.4.42. Cite Correctly the Year of Publication in Parenthetical Text ..... 210

B.4.43. Cite Correctly the Specific Parts of a Source ..... 210

**Reference List**

B.4.44. General Guidelines on Using Electronic Sources in Scientific Writing ..... 212

B.4.45. Guidelines on Referencing the Electronic Sources ..... 213

B.4.46. Begin the Reference List on a New Page With a Centered Heading ..... 216

B.4.47. In the Reference List, Arrange References in Alphabetical Order ..... 218

B.4.48. Arrange Multiple Works of the Same Single Author From the Earliest to the Latest Year ..... 218

B.4.49. Alphabetize the Titles of Several Works of the Same Author Published in the Same Year ..... 220

B.4.50. Arrange the Multiple Works of the Same Author Published in a Different Year, in a Temporally Ascending Order ..... 220

B.4.51. Alphabetize the Different Authors With the Same Last Name According to Their Initials ..... 220

B.4.52. Format Each Entry in the Reference List With a Hanging Indent of 5 Spaces ..... 222

B.4.53. Use the Specified Abbreviations in Reference Lists ..... 222

**Selected Examples of References** ..... **224**

**Printed Journal Articles**

B.4.54. Printed Journal Articles in Reference Lists ..... 224

B.4.55. Arrange Correctly the Articles With Multiple Authors ..... 226

B.4.56. Reference Correctly the Different Forms of Journal Publications ..... 226

**Magazines and Newspaper Articles**

B.4.57. Reference Correctly the Publications From Magazines and Newspapers ..... 228

**Abstracts**

B.4.58. Reference Correctly the Article Abstracts Used as the Primary Source ..... 228

**Books and Book Chapters**

B.4.59. Books in Reference Lists ..... 230

B.4.60. Edited Books and Chapters in Edited Books ..... 232

**Proceedings, Presentations, and Reports**

B.4.61. Proceedings of Conferences and Symposia ..... 234

B.4.62. Unpublished Convention Paper or Poster Presentations ..... 234

B.4.63. Reports From Organizations and Government Agencies ..... 236

B.4.64. Printed and Online Reference Works ..... 236

**Unpublished Articles, Dissertations, and Theses**

B.4.65. Unpublished Articles, Theses, or Dissertations............................................238

B.4.66. Theses and Dissertations in *Abstracts International*...................................238

## B.5. WRITING SECTIONS OF RESEARCH PAPERS AND PROPOSALS ......241

B.5.1. General Guidelines on Completed and Proposed Empirical Studies.......................241

B.5.2. Sections of a Research Paper ..........................................................241

## B.6. ELECTRONIC MANUSCRIPT PREPARATION, EDITING, ..............247 AND PROOFREADING

B.6.1. Electronic Manuscript Preparation ....................................................247

B.6.2. Electronic Manuscript Editing and Revising ..........................................253

B.6.3. Electronic Proofreading ...............................................................259

# PART C
# PROFESSIONAL WRITING...................................................................263

## C.1. INTRODUCTION TO PROFESSIONAL WRITING.........................264

## C.2. FORMATS OF DIAGNOSTIC REPORTS....................................265

**Elements of a Diagnostic Report**

C.2.1. Outline of a Typical Diagnostic Report on a *Child Client* ..............................266

C.2.2. Outline of a Typical Diagnostic Report on an *Adult Client* ............................268

C.2.3. Anatomy of a Diagnostic Report ......................................................270

## C.3. SAMPLE DIAGNOSTIC REPORTS..........................................277

C.3.1. Sample Diagnostic Report: *Speech Sound Disorder* ...................................*278*

C.3.2. Sample Diagnostic Report: *Voice Disorder*............................................*281*

C.3.3. Sample Diagnostic Report: *Aphasia and Apraxia*......................................*284*

C.3.4. Sample Diagnostic Report: *Stuttering*.................................................*288*

## C.4. PRACTICE IN DIAGNOSTIC REPORT WRITING ........................291

C.4.1. Diagnostic Report: *Speech Sound Disorder*...........................................*292*

C.4.2. Diagnostic Report: *Child Language Disorder*.........................................*306*

C.4.3. Diagnostic Report: *Stuttering*........................................................*320*

C.4.4. Diagnostic Report: *Voice Disorder*...................................................*334*

## C.5. COMPREHENSIVE TREATMENT PLANS ... 349
C.5.1. Comprehensive Treatment Plan: *Speech Sound Disorder* ... 350

## C.6. BRIEF TREATMENT PLANS ... 353
C.6.1. Brief Treatment Plan: *Fluency Disorder* ... 354
C.6.2. Brief Treatment Plan: *Speech Sound Disorder* ... 356
C.6.3. Brief Treatment Plan: *Child Language Disorder* ... 358
C.6.4. Brief Treatment Plan: *Voice Disorder* ... 360

## C.7. INDIVIDUALIZED EDUCATIONAL PROGRAMS ... 363
C.7.1. IEP: Treatment of Child Language Disorder ... 364
C.7.2. IEP: Treatment of Speech Sound Disorder ... 365
C.7.3. IEP: Treatment of Voice Disorder ... 366
C.7.4. IEP: Treatment of Fluency Disorder ... 367

## C.8. PRACTICE IN WRITING TREATMENT PLANS ... 369
C.8.1. Comprehensive Treatment Plan: *Child Language Disorder* ... 370
C.8.2. Brief Treatment Plan: *Fluency Disorder* ... 378
C.8.3. Brief Treatment Plan: *Speech Sound Disorder* ... 382
C.8.4. Brief Treatment Plan: *Child Language Disorder* ... 386
C.8.5. Brief Treatment Plan: *Voice Disorder* ... 390

## C.9. PROGRESS REPORTS ... 395
C.9.1. Progress Report: *Treatment of Stuttering* ... 396
C.9.2. Progress Report: *Treatment of Speech Sound Disorder* ... 399
C.9.3. Progress Report: *Treatment of Child Language Disorder* ... 401
C.9.4. Progress Report: *Treatment of Voice Disorder* ... 403

## C.10. PRACTICE IN WRITING PROGRESS REPORTS ... 407
C.10.1. Progress Report: *Treatment of Stuttering* ... 408
C.10.2. Progress Report: *Treatment of Speech Sound Disorder* ... 414
C.10.3. Progress Report: *Treatment of Child Language Disorder* ... 420
C.10.4. Progress Report: *Treatment of Voice Disorder* ... 426

*Selected References* ... 433
*Glossary* ... 437
*Index* ... 447

# Preface to the Fifth Edition

Teaching and learning to write in a technical and professional language is an important part of education in speech-language pathology. However, students often do not begin to acquire acceptable writing skills until they enroll in clinical practicums or in graduate research seminars in which professional and scientific writing are required. Unfortunately, because of limited instruction in scientific and professional writing, many graduate students are both challenged and frustrated in their research and clinical writing assignments.

Students in speech-language pathology programs who have taken courses on writing offered in other departments still do not have adequate technical and professional writing skills. Instructors know that merely extolling good writing and asking students to read some of the many available books on how to write well are not effective. Teaching writing skills is time- and effort-intensive because unless students have examples to follow and feedback to use, their skills do not improve. Students have to write, receive feedback, and rewrite. Although it does not obviate the need for writing and rewriting, this coursebook makes that task somewhat more practical for both the student and the instructor.

There are many books on writing, but few that give opportunities to practice writing as exemplars are given. Most instructors know that simply asking students to read various books on good writing does not generate writing skills. Writing courses are generally designed to teach rules of grammar, not writing. An explicit knowledge of grammar rules will help avoid grammatical mistakes. However, individuals who cannot recite rules of grammar can still write well. Exemplars of good writing and opportunities to practice writing are both essential to learn writing skills. Therefore I have designed this new type of book, which I call a *coursebook*.

The most important aspect of this coursebook is the way the left-hand and right-hand pages are designed (and keyed by icons). Most left-hand pages show specific examples of general, scientific, or professional writing (eyeglass icon). In many cases, both the incorrect and correct versions are shown. The corresponding right-hand pages require the student to write correctly (pencil icon). Typically, the facing pages contain the same rules or exemplars: one to read about, and the other to write on.

This coursebook is designed with the following assumptions:

- Students who simply memorize the rules of grammar do not necessarily write well; they need practice in writing.
- Students should have many examples of the skills they are expected to learn, including grammatically correct writing.
- Students should read an exemplar and write one immediately.
- Students should write multiple exemplars.
- Given exemplars and the student writing should go hand in hand.
- To the extent possible, students should receive feedback in the classroom.

This book has been used in a dedicated course on scientific and professional writing. Students actually wrote in the class. Students were randomly asked to read samples of their writing. The instructor then gave feedback, correcting any mistakes. The rest of the class then corrected their mistakes, if any. This act of writing was immediately followed by positive reinforcement or corrective feedback.

It was my hope that instructors and student clinicians would find it useful in teaching and learning writing skills in the classroom. The response of instructors around the country has been overwhelmingly positive. Many instructors have commented that there has been a need for this kind of book and that the coursebook method is more effective in teaching writing skills than are traditional books on writing.

Both clinical supervisors and academic course instructors can use this book to teach scientific and professional writing skills. The book can be used in the following contexts:

- A course on writing
- Courses on assessment and diagnosis
- Courses on research methods and introduction to graduate studies
- Clinical practicums and internships
- Independent studies in writing skills
- Informally assigned work to help individual students master good writing skills; students may be assigned selected sections to complete, depending on their deficiencies

## New to Fifth Edition

This fifth edition is based on the sixth edition of the *Publication Manual of the American Psychological Association* (2010), which is still the current edition at the time of this revision. Several new features were added or updated to this new edition, however. Changes in reference citations in the text and preparation of the reference list introduced in the sixth edition were incorporated into this revised edition of the coursebook. Sections on electronic manuscript preparation, review and revision, and copyediting were updated.

Electronic file management related to journal articles, books, and book chapters has become common in the publishing industry. Journal article submissions or convention presentation proposals are now electronically managed. Therefore electronic preparation of manuscripts, revisions in light of the copyeditor's comments, and responses to the copyeditor's queries were updated in this new edition. Furthermore, the topic of proofreading journal articles or books the authors receive as PDF documents was revised as found necessary. The topic of electronic submission of convention and conference proposals was updated. Additional reference examples of electronic sources of information were included as well.

The professional writing section of the new edition was also revised and updated to reflect current clinical terms.

## Acknowledgments

I am very pleased that this new edition is being published by Plural Publishing, the leading publishing house in communication disorders and related medical specialties. I would like to thank the editorial department headed by an able editor, Valerie Johns. Her kind and continuous help is greatly appreciated. I would also like to thank Kalie Koscielak for her excellent help throughout the development process. Angie Singh, the president of Plural, has been a friend and supporter for decades. I thank her and all her efficient staff at Plural.

# About the Author

M. N. (Giri) Hegde, PhD, Professor Emeritus of Communication Sciences and Disorders at California State University–Fresno, holds a master's degree in experimental psychology from the University of Mysore, India; a post-master's diploma in medical (clinical) psychology from Bangalore University, India; and a doctoral degree in speech-language pathology from Southern Illinois University Carbondale.

Dr. Hegde is a specialist in fluency disorders, language disorders, research methods, and treatment procedures in communicative disorders. He has made numerous presentations to national and international audiences on various basic and applied topics in communicative disorders and experimental and applied behavior analysis. With his deep and wide scholarship, Dr. Hegde has authored several highly regarded and widely used scientific and professional books, including *Assessment of Communication Disorders in Children (with F. Pomaville), Assessment of Communication Disorders in Adults (with D. Freed), Treatment Procedures in Communicative Disorders, Clinical Research in Communicative Disorders, Introduction to Communicative Disorders, A Coursebook on Aphasia and Other Neurogenic Language Disorders, Hegde's PocketGuide to Communication Disorders, Hegde's PocketGuide to Treatment in Speech-Language Pathology, Hegde's PocketGuide to Assessment in Speech-Language Pathology,* and several others. He has served on the editorial boards of scientific and professional journals and continues to serve as an editorial consultant to the *Journal of Fluency Disorders*.

Dr. Hegde is a recipient of various honors, including the Outstanding Professor Award from California State University–Fresno, CSU-Fresno Provost's Recognition for Outstanding Scholarship and Publication, Distinguished Alumnus Award from the Southern Illinois University Department of Communication Sciences and Disorders, and Outstanding Professional Achievement Award from District 5 of the California Speech-Language-Hearing Association. Dr. Hegde is a Fellow of the American Speech-Language-Hearing Association.

# PART A

# Foundations of Scientific and Professional Writing

# A.1. Basic Rules of Usage

## Ampersand

- The ampersand (&) stands for the conjunction *and*.
- It is used only with certain proper names and abbreviations.

### A.1.1a. Use the Ampersand Correctly

| Incorrect | Correct | Note |
|---|---|---|
| American Telephone and Telegraph<br>Charles Schwab & Co. | American Telephone & Telegraph<br>Charles Schwab & Co. | Use the ampersand only if the company itself uses it. |
| U.S. Department of Health & Human Services | U.S. Department of Health and Human Services | Such government agencies do not take an ampersand. |
| The local S and L may be helpful in getting a loan. | The local S & L may be helpful in getting a loan. | Ampersand used with an abbreviation, with one space on either side of it. |
| The R and D spokesman hinted at new products. | The R&D spokesman hinted at new products. | Some technical and scientific abbreviations take an ampersand without space on either side of it. |

*Note:* R&D refers to research and development [department].

## Apostrophe

### A.1.2a. Do Not Turn a Possessive Into a Plural

Use an apostrophe when needed.

| Incorrect | Correct | Note |
|---|---|---|
| The *patients* resistance to treatment was high. | The *patient's* resistance to treatment was high. | Singular possessives |
| The *clients* prognosis is good. | The *client's* prognosis is good. | |
| The *clinicians* motivation to treat matters. | The *clinicians'* motivation to treat matters. | Plural possessives |
| The *participants* socioeconomic status did not have an effect. | The *participants'* socioeconomic status did not have an effect. | |

# Ampersand

### A.1.1b. Use the Ampersand Correctly

| Incorrect | Write Correctly |
|---|---|
| Williams and Wilkins | |
| Johnson and Thomson Co. | |
| U.S. Department of Education & Human Development | |
| The local S and L gives loans. | |
| The R and D department is nonexistent | |

# Apostrophe

### A.1.2b. Do Not Turn a Possessive Into a Plural

| Incorrect | Write Correctly |
|---|---|
| I will train this clients mother. | |
| Ambiguous stimuli reduce a treatments effectiveness. | |
| The treatment settings influence cannot be ignored. | |
| Several clients progress was slow. | |
| The patients feelings should be considered. | |
| Pediatricians awareness of early language problems is limited. | |

*Hint:* Some examples contain a plural and a possessive.

## A.1.3a. Do Not Turn a Plural Into a Possessive

Do not use an unnecessary apostrophe.

| Incorrect | Correct | Note |
|---|---|---|
| The *characteristic's* of aphasia are well known. | The *characteristics* of aphasia are well known. | Common mistakes. |
| The *characteristics'* of aphasia are well known. | | |
| In the *1970's*, the clinicians began to treat language. | In the *1970s*, the clinicians began to treat language. | |
| I selected 10 *participants'*. | I selected 10 *subjects*. | |
| The *patients'* have rights. | The *patients* have rights. | |
| Twenty *clients'* were treated. | Twenty *clients* were treated. | |
| The *parents'* were not cooperative. | The *parents* were not cooperative. | |

## A.1.3b. Do Not Turn a Plural Into a Possessive

| Incorrect | Write Correctly |
|---|---|
| Patients' with dysarthria will have neurological problems. | |
| Many factors' affect the treatment outcome. | |
| The problems of the 1980's will persist into the 1990's. | |
| The clients are in their 60's. | |
| I studied several variables' related to the subjects' language skills. *Hint:* Contains a plural and a possessive. | |

## A.1.4a. Use the Correct Forms of Possessive Nouns

Several rules dictate the use of a variety of possessive forms. The simplest rule is to add the apostrophe and an *s*, as in *the man's hat*, *the girl's shoes*, and *the cat's tail*. Mistakes arise from the variable practice of adding or not adding *'s* to words that end in *s*.

| Incorrect | Correct | Note |
|---|---|---|
| The *boys's* room is large. | The *boys'* room is large. | Most regular plural words do not take an extra *s*; they only have an apostrophe. |
| The *ladies's* purses are small. | The *ladies'* purses are small. | |
| The *tigers's* look is ferocious. | The *tigers'* look is ferocious. | |
| The *mens* health history was not reported. | The *men's* health history was not reported. | Most irregular plurals take *'s*. |
| The *childrens* ages were not specified. | The *children's* ages were not specified. | |
| Those *womens* language skills are superior. | Those *women's* language skills are superior. | |
| The *oxens* hoofs are short. | The *oxen's* hoofs are short. | *Hooves* is acceptable. |
| The *horse'* skin is shiny. | The *horse's* skin is shiny. | Most words that end in *s* also take *'s*, as shown in later examples. |
| The *mouse'* tail is long. | The *mouse's* tail is long. | |
| This one is for old *times's* sake. | This one is for old *times'* sake. | However, a few words that end in *s* (sound) do not take an extra *s*. |
| He did it for *appearances's* sake. | He did it for *appearances'* sake. | |
| *Charles'* wedding was a grand event. | *Charles's* wedding was a grand event. | Most monosyllabic or disyllabic proper names that end in *s* also take *'s*; a common mistake is to omit the *s* after the apostrophe. |
| Mr. *Burns'* humor is wonderful. | Mr. *Burns's* humor is wonderful. | |
| *James'* novels are serious. | *James's* novels are serious. | |
| *Thomas'* acting is superb. | *Thomas's* acting is superb. | |
| *Keats'* poetry is beautiful. | *Keats's* poetry is beautiful. | |

## A.1.4b. Use the Correct Forms of Possessive Nouns

| Incorrect | Write Correctly |
|---|---|
| The boys's boots are here. | |
| The ladies's dresses are sold here. | |
| The mens educational status was unknown. | |
| The childrens language skills were not described. | |
| Womens professions are constantly changing. | |
| The horse' speed is unmatched. | |
| The mouse' manners are awful. | |
| Have one for old times's sake. | |
| She would not do it for appearances's sake. | |
| Charles' graduation party was enjoyable. | |
| Mr. Burns' 100th birthday celebration was cancelled. | |
| James' writings are philosophical. | |
| Thomas' lecture was boring. | |
| Keats' poetry is immortal. | |

A.1.4a., correct forms of possessive nouns *(continued)*

| Incorrect | Correct | Note |
|---|---|---|
| *Jesus's* story is moving. | *Jesus'* story is moving. | Names ending with *sus* or *ses*, that, when combined with *'s*, are awkward to pronounce, take only an apostrophe. |
| *Moses's* Ten Commandments. | *Moses'* Ten Commandments. | |
| Plato was *Socrates's* famous pupil. | Plato was *Socrates'* famous pupil. | Classical names that end with *es* also take only an apostrophe (Demosthenes', Euripides'). |
| The *Browns's* house is large. | The *Browns'* house is large.<br><br>(Correct: Browns's *shoes* are large.) | Only the apostrophe is used to form possessives in the case of plural forms of family names. |
| The *Thomas's* cars were stolen. | The *Thomas'* cars were stolen.<br><br>(Correct: Thomas's car *was* stolen.) | |

A.1.4b., correct forms of possessive nouns *(continued)*

| Incorrect | Write Correctly |
|---|---|
| Jesus's kindness was boundless. | |
| Moses's laws are ancient. | |
| The dialogue was Socrates's teaching method. | |
| The Jones's hospitality is wonderful. | |
| The Thomas's vacation was cut short. | |

A.1.4a., correct forms of possessive nouns *(continued)*

| Incorrect | Correct | Note |
|---|---|---|
| We went to *Tom's* and *Jerry's* Pizza Place. | We went to *Tom* and *Jerry's* Pizza Place.<br>*(Two owners of the place.)* | In the case of group possession, only the last name takes the *'s*. |
| We will take *Jim's* and *Jean's* car. | We will take *Jim* and *Jean's* car.<br>*(Two owners of the same car.)* | |
| *Lent's* and *Bent's* book is very interesting. | *Lent* and *Bent's* book is very interesting.<br>*(Coauthors of the same book.)* | |
| We will take *Linda* and *John's* cars. | We will take *Linda's* and *John's* cars.<br>*(Independent owners of two cars.)* | In the case of separate possessions of multiple objects or characteristics, each name takes the *'s*. |
| *Steinbeck* style is different from *Saroyan's*. | *Steinbeck's* style is different from *Saroyan's*.<br>*(Two authors, two styles.)* | |
| *Kent* book is interesting, but *Stein's* is boring. | *Kent's* book is interesting, but *Stein's* is boring.<br>*(Two authors, two books.)* | |

A.1 Basic Rules of Usage

A.1.4b., correct forms of possessive nouns *(continued)*

| Incorrect | Write Correctly |
|---|---|
| Dean's and Don's Italian restaurant is excellent.<br><br>*(Two owners of the place.)* | |
| We borrowed Tom's and Joan's car.<br><br>*(Two owners of the same car.)* | |
| Tent's and Nent's book on anatomy is fascinating.<br><br>*(Coauthors of the same book.)* | |
| We will take Jim and Kim's vans.<br><br>*(Independent owners of two vans.)* | |
| Hemingway style is different from Faulkner's.<br><br>*(Two authors, two styles.)* | |
| Knott book has drawings, but Steel's has color pictures.<br><br>*(Two authors, two books.)* | |

## A.1.5a. Use the Possessive Forms of Pronouns Correctly

The possessive personal pronouns *hers*, *his*, *its*, *ours*, *yours*, *theirs*, and *mine* are called *absolute* possessives, which do not take an apostrophe. Possessive forms of indefinite pronouns, on the other hand, take an apostrophe and *s* (*'s*).

| Incorrect | Correct | Note |
|---|---|---|
| This book is *her's*. | This book is *hers*. | Do not use an apostrophe to form absolute possessive pronouns. |
| This hat is *his'*. | This hat is *his*. | |
| *It's* tail is long. | *Its* tail is long. | |
| These are *ours'*. | These are *ours*. | |
| Isn't she a friend of *your's*? | Isn't she a friend of *yours*? | |
| This is *their's*. | This is *theirs*. | |
| That is *mine's*. | That is *mine*. | |
| *Anyones* money will do. | *Anyone's* money will do. | Use an apostrophe and *s* (*'s*) to form possessive forms of indefinite pronouns. |
| Who will be next is *anybodys* guess. | Who will be next is *anybody's* guess. | |
| Paying taxes is *everyones* responsibility. | Paying taxes is *everyone's* responsibility. | |
| *Someones* problems are not his concern. | *Someone's* problems are not his concern. | |

## A.1.6a. Distinguish Contractions From Possessives

Some contracted forms of words should not be confused with possessives.

| Incorrect | Correct | Note |
|---|---|---|
| *They're* cat is lost. | *They're* gone now. *Their* cat is lost. | *They're* is the contracted form of *they are*, and *their* is a possessive form. |
| *You're* office was closed. | *You're* not in your office. *Your* office was closed. | *You're* is the contracted form of *you are*, and *your* is a possessive form. |
| *Who's* wallet is this? | *Whose* wallet is this? | *Who's* is the contracted form of *who is*, and *whose* is the possessive form. |

A.1  Basic Rules of Usage

## A.1.5b. Use the Possessive Forms of Pronouns Correctly

| Incorrect | Write Correctly |
|---|---|
| Is it her's? | |
| I think it is his'. | |
| It's mouth is wide. | |
| Are these ours'? | |
| I met a friend of your's. | |
| It may be their's. | |
| Give me mine's. | |
| He will take anyones advice. | |
| He will use anybodys car. | |
| Taking care of the homeless is everyones responsibility. | |
| Those ethical concerns are someones problem. | |

## A.1.6b. Distinguish Contractions From Possessives

When appropriate, use the correct contracted form.

| Incorrect | Write Correctly |
|---|---|
| Their in London this summer. | |
| Your not home tomorrow? | |
| They're man is not here. | |
| You're home is big. | |
| Who's side are you on? | |

## Unusual Plurals

### A.1.7a. Use Unusual Singulars and Plurals Correctly

- Note that in popular usage, some unusual plurals are accepted as singulars (e.g., *data is* is often seen in print, although it is not accurate).
- In scientific and professional writing, these words are used more precisely.

| Incorrect | Correct | Note |
|---|---|---|
| Data *is* presented in Table 1. | Data *are* presented in Table 1. | *Data* is plural. |
| The *datum are* interesting. | The *datum is* interesting. | *Datum* is singular. |
| The *phenomena* of vocal abuse *is* widespread. | The *phenomenon* of vocal abuse *is* widespread. | *Phenomena* is plural. |
| These *phenomenon* have been recorded. | These *phenomena have* been recorded. | *Phenomenon* is singular. |
| There is no single *loci* of stuttering. | There is no single *locus* of stuttering. | *Locus* is singular. |
| The *loci* of stuttering *is* well known. | The *loci* of stuttering *are* well known. | *Loci* is plural. |
| The year of publication should be in *parenthesis*. | The year of publication should be in *parentheses*. | *Parentheses* is plural. |
| The closing *parentheses* is missing. | The closing *parenthesis* is missing. | The sentence requires the singular *parenthesis*. |
| I wrote a *theses*. | I wrote a *thesis*. | *Thesis* is singular. |
| I read *several thesis* before I selected my research topic. | I read *several theses* before I selected my research topic. | *Theses* is plural. |
| The participants were from the lower-socioeconomic *strata*. | The participants were from the lower-socioeconomic *stratum*. | *Stratum* is singular. |
| The participants were from *several* social *stratum*. | The participants were from *several* social *strata*. | *Strata* is plural. |
| The *papilloma* are benign growths. | *Papillomata* are benign growths. A *papilloma* is a benign growth. | *Papillomas* is an accepted plural form, however. |
| I will use a 90% correct *criteria*. | I will use a 90% correct *criterion*. | *Criterion* is singular. |
| I used two *criterion* of accuracy. | I used two *criteria* of accuracy. | *Criteria* is plural. |
| He removed *cortex* from several skulls. | He removed *cortices* from several skulls. | *Cortexes* also is an accepted plural. |

# Unusual Plurals

### A.1.7b. Use Unusual Singulars and Plurals Correctly

| Incorrect | Write Correctly |
|---|---|
| Her data is quite complex. | |
| Scientists cannot control many natural phenomenon. | |
| The phenomena of central auditory processing is a mystery. | |
| The loci of vocal nodules is variable within a small range. | |
| Check the closing parentheses of all quotations. | |
| Put that statement within parenthesis. | |
| I found no support for that theses. | |
| All of our thesis are in the library. | |
| Subjects should be drawn from at least three social stratum. | |
| The papillomata is a benign growth. | |

A.1.7a., use unusual singulars and plurals correctly *(continued)*

| Incorrect | Correct | Note |
|---|---|---|
| I found several scholarly *corpus* on the subject. | I found several scholarly *corpora* on the subject. | *Corpora* is plural. |
| The book has seven *appendix*. | The book has seven *appendixes*. | The APA *Manual* recommends *appendixes;* some other authorities recommend *appendices.* |
| The author and subject *index* are helpful. | The author and subject *indexes* are helpful. | The APA *Manual* recommends *indexes;* some other authorities recommend *indices.* |
| I have *several basis* for my argument. | I have *several bases* for my argument. | *Bases* is plural. |
| I had *many crisis*. | I had *many crises*. | *Crises* is plural. |
| The term *nucleus* refers to central *cores* of structures. | The term *nuclei* refers to central *cores* of structures. | *Nuclei* is the plural form of nucleus. |

### A.1 Basic Rules of Usage

A.1.7b., use unusual singulars and plurals correctly *(continued)*

| Incorrect | Write Correctly |
|---|---|
| Her grading criteria for an A is 90%. | |
| Good grades and high GRE scores are two criterion for admission. | |
| Lesion in a single cortices does not prove anything. | |
| Corpora means a single collection of scholarly writings. | |
| I found too many appendix in the book. | |
| He did not have a single bases for his statement. | |
| I can handle one crises in a semester. | |
| The term *nuclei* means a central core of structures. | |

# Comma

### A.1.8a. Use a Serial Comma

A **serial comma** separates parallel terms in a series. The comma after *men* and before *and* in *women, men, and children* is a serial comma. When you use three or more terms connected with a single conjunction, use a comma after each term that precedes the conjunction. Note that the print media may not use a serial comma.

| Incorrect | Correct | Note |
|---|---|---|
| The child had misarticulations, language delay and a hearing loss. | The child had misarticulations, language delay, and a hearing loss. | The use of conjunction *and*. |
| Our clinicians are intelligent, compassionate and competent. | Our clinicians are intelligent, compassionate, and competent. | |
| Each token may be exchanged for a sticker, a piece of gum or a small toy. | Each token may be exchanged for a sticker, a piece of gum, or a small toy. | The use of conjunction *or*. |
| Age, education, health, occupation or language skill may be a significant variable in this study. | Age, education, health, occupation, or language skill may be a significant variable in this study. | |

### A.1.9a. Do Not Use a Serial Comma When You Write Only Two Parallel Terms and Connect Them With a Conjunction

| Incorrect | Correct | Note |
|---|---|---|
| The patient with aphasia had naming, and comprehension problems. | The patient with aphasia had naming and comprehension problems. | In each case, only two terms are joined by a different conjunction (*and, or*). |
| I will recruit both male, and female subjects. | I will recruit both male and female subjects. | |
| Plastic tokens, or stickers will be used as reinforcers. | Plastic tokens or stickers will be used as reinforcers. | |
| The study revealed that age, or prior history of cancer may predict improvement. | The study revealed that age or prior history of cancer may predict improvement. | |

# Comma

### A.1.8b. Use a Serial Comma

| Incorrect | Write Correctly |
|---|---|
| I will teach the plural morpheme, the auxiliary and the copula. | |
| Sensory, neural and sensorineural hearing losses must be distinguished. | |
| The clients may choose counseling, syllable prolongation, time-out or response cost as treatment. | |
| Verbal praise, smiles or tokens will be reinforcers. | |

### A.1.9b. Do Not Use a Serial Comma When You Write Only Two Parallel Terms and Connect Them With a Conjunction

| Incorrect | Write Correctly |
|---|---|
| We noticed omissions, and distortions of speech sounds. | |
| Assessment revealed a large tongue, and missing canine teeth. | |
| Treatment may start at the word, or the phrase level. | |
| The client can select an analog, or digital hearing aid. | |

### A.1.10a. Use a Comma to Separate Parenthetic Expressions When You Do Not Use Parentheses

Parenthetic expressions interject an additional idea into a sentence.

| Incorrect | Correct |
| --- | --- |
| The woman who stuttered though she could not remember it had received treatment before. | The woman who stuttered, though she could not remember it, had received treatment before. |
| The client who was extremely dysfluent hesitated before starting to read aloud. | The client, who was extremely dysfluent, hesitated before starting to read aloud. |
| The patient a professional woman in her 50s had a stroke. | The patient, a professional woman in her 50s, had a stroke. |
| The mean length of utterance when calculated properly can be a good index of early language development. | The mean length of utterance, when calculated properly, can be a good index of early language development. |

### A.1.11a. Place a Comma Before a Conjunction Introducing an Independent Clause

An independent clause can stand alone as a sentence; the terms after the conjunction in the correct example form an independent clause.

| Incorrect | Correct |
| --- | --- |
| The clinician suggested a treatment program but the client was unresponsive. | The clinician suggested a treatment program, but the patient was unresponsive. |
| The man was diagnosed with aphasia and the prognosis for recovery was poor. | The man was diagnosed with aphasia, and the prognosis for recovery was poor. |
| Standardized tests should be administered properly or they will yield meaningless scores. | Standardized tests should be administered properly, or they will yield meaningless scores. |

### A.1.12a. Do Not Use a Comma Before a Conjunction That Is Followed by a Dependent Clause

A dependent clause like the one shown in the correct example (starting with a conjunction) cannot stand alone.

| Incorrect | Correct |
| --- | --- |
| The child was first assessed for speech and language, and then was referred to the psychologist. | The child was first assessed for speech and language and then was referred to the psychologist. |
| A treatment plan was developed, and then it was implemented. | A treatment plan was developed and then it was implemented. |

# A.1 Basic Rules of Usage

### A.1.10b. Use a Comma to Separate Parenthetic Expressions When You Do Not Use Parentheses

| Incorrect | Write Correctly |
|---|---|
| The child with misarticulations even though capable did not do well. | |
| The client who had aphasia could not readily name the objects shown. | |

### A.1.11b. Place a Comma Before a Conjunction Introducing an Independent Clause

| Incorrect | Write Correctly |
|---|---|
| The client's mother was asked to attend the sessions but her attendance was poor. | |
| The students were asked to make oral presentations but they were reluctant. | |
| The teacher cooperated with the clinician and the children benefited. | |
| The father conducted treatment sessions at home and the progress was excellent. | |

### A.1.12b. Do Not Use a Comma Before a Conjunction That Is Followed by a Dependent Clause

| Incorrect | Write Correctly |
|---|---|
| The client was treated first, and then was offered a follow-up assessment. | |
| Several goals were established, and will be discussed with the parents. | |

## Dash

### A.1.13a. Prefer an *em dash* to a Comma to Set Off an Abrupt Break or Interruption

*Note:* On a computer, if you type two dashes (--) with no space in between or on either side of the dashes, they will be converted to an *em dash* (printed as an unbroken line).

| Not Preferred | Preferred |
|---|---|
| The speech discrimination test, a standard portion of any audiological evaluation, revealed no significant problems. | The speech discrimination test—a standard portion of any audiological evaluation—revealed no significant problems. |
| The administration of a pure probe, if it is administered at all, requires much prior work. | The administration of a pure probe—if it is administered at all—requires much prior work. |

*Note:* No space separates the dashes (or *em dashes*) and the word that precedes or follows them.

## Semicolon

### A.1.14a. Join Independent Clauses With a Semicolon When the Clauses Are Not Joined by a Conjunction

The two independent clauses may be rewritten as two separate sentences.

| Incorrect | Correct |
|---|---|
| Stuttering is a speech problem, it should not be ignored. | Stuttering is a speech problem; it should not be ignored.<br><br>Stuttering is a speech problem. It should not be ignored. |
| Dysphagia can create serious concerns, it can be life-threatening. | Dysphagia can create serious concerns; it can be life-threatening.<br><br>Dysphagia can create serious concerns. It can be life-threatening. |
| Language disorders can lead to poor academic performance, they should be promptly treated. | Language disorders can lead to poor academic performance; they should be promptly treated.<br><br>Language disorders can lead to poor academic performance. They should be promptly treated. |

# Dash

### A.1.13b. Prefer a Dash to a Comma to Set Off an Abrupt Break or Interruption

| Not Preferred | Preferred |
|---|---|
| Modeling, a basic treatment procedure, will be used when the client fails to imitate. | |
| Treatment of stuttering, unless the clinician believes in spontaneous recovery, should be started as early as possible. | |
| The incidence of noise-induced hearing loss, a hazardous but controllable by-product of civilization, is on the increase. | |

# Semicolon

### A.1.14b. Join Independent Clauses With a Semicolon When the Clauses Are Not Joined by a Conjunction

Alternatively, write them as two separate sentences.

| Incorrect | Write Correctly |
|---|---|
| Dementia is a progressive disorder, it often is undetected in its early stages. | 1.<br>2. |
| Early treatment of stuttering is effective, this is unknown to some clinicians. | 1.<br>2. |
| Speech disorders may persist in some children, they should be promptly treated. | 1.<br>2. |
| Language acquisition is an interesting subject, I might do a thesis on it. | 1.<br>2. |

# Agreement

### A.1.15a. Follow the Rules of Agreement

- Subject and verb should agree in number.
- The terms that intervene between the noun phrase and the verb do not affect agreement.

| Incorrect | Correct | Note |
|---|---|---|
| No single dysfluency *type*—prolongations or sound repetitions—*justify* diagnosis. | No single dysfluency *type*—prolongations or sound repetitions—*justifies* diagnosis. | No single dysfluency *type justifies* diagnosis. |
| She is one of *those* clinicians who *is* always prepared for *her* sessions. | She is one of *those* clinicians who *are* always prepared for *their* sessions. | *clinicians* who *are* always prepared for their sessions. |
| A person *who stutters believes that they* cannot be treated. | A person who stutters believes that *he or she* cannot be treated.<br><br>or,<br><br>*People* who stutter believe that *they* cannot be treated. | *person* who stutters *believes* that *he or she* . . .<br><br>*people* who stutter *believe* that *they* . . . |
| Each *individual* is responsible for *their* actions. | Each *individual* is responsible for *his or her* actions. | Alternatively, *Individuals are* responsible for *their actions*. |
| The *patient*, who has had ineffective treatment, should have known that *they* are wasting money. | The *patient*, who has had ineffective treatment, should have known that *she* is wasting money. | The *patient* should have known that *she is* . . . |
| A responsible *student* knows that *they* should study hard. | A responsible *student* knows that *he or she* should study hard. | Alternatively, Responsible *students* know that *they* . . . |
| These *techniques*, when used correctly, *is* known to be effective. | These *techniques*, when used correctly, *are* known to be effective. | *Techniques are* known to be effective. |

# Agreement

### A.1.15b. Follow the Rules of Agreement

| Incorrect | Write Correctly |
|---|---|
| A speech disorder—whether it contains a few or many misarticulations—indicate a need for treatment. | |
| Naming problems, along with agrammatism, characterizes aphasia. | |
| He is one of those individuals who is always late. | |
| A client, who thinks that the clinician should do everything, may not self-monitor their skills. | |
| Each participant should be told what they will be expected to do. | |
| The clinician, who is knowledgeable about accountability, knows that they should document client progress. | |
| Tokens, when dispensed for a correct response, increases the rate of progress. | |

A.1.15a., follow the rules of agreement *(continued)*

| Incorrect | Correct | Note |
|---|---|---|
| Error *scores,* along with the correct score, *was* analyzed. | Error *scores,* along with the correct score, *were* analyzed. | Error *scores were* analyzed. |
| *Every* child and adult *go* through the same procedure. | *Every* child and adult *goes* through the same procedure. | A singular verb is used when *every* or *each* precedes a compound subject joined by *and.* |
| *Each* man and woman *consider* whether it is right. | *Each* man and woman *considers* whether it is right. | |
| *Either* verbal praise *or* informative feedback *are* combined with modeling. | *Either* verbal praise *or* informative feedback *is* combined with modeling. | When two subjects are linked by *or, either/or,* or *neither/nor,* the verb must be plural if both the subjects are plural and singular if both the subjects are singular. |
| *Either* words *or* morphemes *is* appropriate for calculating MLUs. | *Either* words *or* morphemes *are* appropriate for calculating MLUs. | |
| *Neither* he *nor* she *were* interested in the proposal. | *Neither* he *nor* she *was* interested in the proposal. | |
| *Neither* the stimuli *nor* the reinforcers *was* effective. | *Neither* the stimuli *nor* the reinforcers *were* effective. | |
| *Neither* the treatments *nor* the result *are* replicable. | *Neither* the treatments *nor* the result *is* replicable. | When a singular and a plural subject are linked by *neither/nor, either/or,* or *not only/but also,* the verb form is determined by the subject that is nearer to it. |
| *Either* the tokens *or* the verbal praise *are* appropriate. | *Either* the tokens or the verbal praise *is* appropriate. | |
| *Not only* the treatment, *but also* the *settings, tends* affect the outcome. | *Not only* the treatment *but also* the *settings tend* to affect the outcome. | |

# A.1 Basic Rules of Usage

A.1.15b., follow the rules of agreement *(continued)*

| Incorrect | Write Correctly |
|---|---|
| Every client and a family member receive training in treatment. | |
| Either time-out or response cost for incorrect responses are combined with positive reinforcement. | |
| Neither the procedure nor the outcome were clear. | |
| Neither the client nor his parents was cooperative. | |
| Neither stutterings nor the phonological processes is easily measured. | |
| Either verbal feedback or tokens is given to the client for her correct responses. | |
| Not only the client, but also his colleagues, tends to accept the suggestion. | |
| Percent dysfluency rates, along with the frequency of each dysfluency, is presented in Table 1. | |
| Either verbal feedback or tokens is given to the client for her correct responses. | |
| Either family support or teacher support are essential for maintenance of treatment effects. | |
| Neither the parents nor the grandparents was cooperative. | |
| Not only the rate of speech, but also the syllable prolongations, affects fluency. | |

A.1.15a., follow the rules of agreement *(continued)*

| Incorrect | Correct | Note |
|---|---|---|
| Mother *and* child was interviewed together. | Mother *and* child were interviewed together. | Compound subjects joined by *and* have plural verbs. |
| Who says *country and western* are dead? | Who says *country and western* is dead? | Expressions containing *and* that suggest a single concept (e.g., *country and western*) use singular verbs. |
| *Both* of us *is* busy. | *Both* of us *are* busy. | A few indefinite pronouns (*both, many, several, few, others*) are always plural and take plural verbs. |
| *Either* of them *are* acceptable. | *Either* of them *is* acceptable. | Most other indefinite pronouns (*another, anyone, everyone, each, either, neither, anything, everything, something,* and *somebody*) are singular and take singular verbs. |
| Some of *this* effect *are* understandable. | Some of *this* effect *is* understandable. | Some indefinite pronouns (*some, all, none, any, more,* and *most*) can be singular or plural. The verb form is singular or plural depending on the noun the pronoun refers to. |
| Some of *these* effects *is* understandable. | Some of *these* effects *are* understandable. | |
| The *group were* tested in a single session. | The *group was* tested in a single session. | Collective nouns can take singular verbs (if they refer to a single unit) or plural verbs (if they refer to individuals or elements of that unit). |
| Seven *individuals* in the group *was* retested. | Seven *individuals* in the group *were* retested. | |
| The *majority were* against the idea. | The *majority was* against the idea. | *The majority* is singular; *a majority of people* is plural. |
| A *majority* of people *was* against the idea. | A *majority* of people *were* against the idea. | |

A.1.15b., follow the rules of agreement *(continued)*

| Incorrect | Write Correctly |
|---|---|
| The experimental group were treated. | |
| Four participants in the control group was dropped from the study. | |
| The clinician and the client's sister was in the same treatment room. | |
| Who says rock 'n' roll are for the devils? | |
| Both of us is willing to do it. | |
| Several of the group is unhappy. | |
| Some of this mess are your responsibility. | |
| Some of these effects is unexplained. | |
| The majority were unimpressed. | |
| A majority of clinicians tends to agree. | |

A.1.15a., follow the rules of agreement *(continued)*

| Incorrect | Correct | Note |
|---|---|---|
| The *news are* bad. | The *news is* bad. | Some words that are typically in the plural form still take singular verbs. |
| *Statistics are* an exciting field. | *Statistics is* an exciting field. | |
| *Economics are* an inexact science. | *Economics is* an inexact science. | |
| *Statistics shows* that the county poverty rate is high. | *Statistics show* that the county poverty rate is high. | When *statistics* refers to numbers, it takes a plural verb. |
| A hurricane *is* a terrifying *phenomena*. | A hurricane *is* a terrifying *phenomenon*. | *Phenomenon* is singular, and *phenomena* is plural. |
| They offered *many thesis*, but none too exciting. | They offered *many theses*, but none too exciting. | *Theses* is plural, and *thesis* is singular. |
| His *data was* unconvincing. | His *data were* unconvincing. | *Data* is plural, and *datum* is singular. |

### A.1.15b., follow the rules of agreement *(continued)*

| Incorrect | Write Correctly |
|---|---|
| The local news tend to focus on crime. | |
| Statistics suggests fewer problems. | |
| Statistics are one the two courses. | |
| Politics are full of scoundrels. | |
| The phenomenon of earthquakes are poorly understood. | |
| It is a scary natural phenomena. | |
| My theses is as good as yours. | |
| The theses explaining language learning does not interest me. | |
| His data is a bit confusing. | |
| The datum are enlightening. | |

# Modifiers

## A.1.16a. Use Modifiers Correctly

To avoid confusion in the use of modifiers, keep the related words together.

| Incorrect | Correct | Note |
|---|---|---|
| The author and her assistants tested the hearing of all participants using the procedure described earlier. | The author and her assistants, using the procedure described earlier, tested the hearing of all participants. | Who used the procedure? Not the participants! |
| Distant and mysterious, he stared at the sky. | He stared at the distant and mysterious sky. | Who was mysterious and distant? Not he! |
| Several additional effects are observed using this technique in clients. | Several additional effects are observed in clients using this technique. | Who observed effects in whom? |
| Using the procedure, the participants were screened for hearing problems by the experimenter. | Using the procedure, the experimenter screened the participants for hearing problems. | Who used the standard procedure? |
| The study merely provided a partial support for the hypothesis. | The study provided merely a partial support for the hypothesis. | Place the following modifiers immediately before the words they modify: *almost, only, even, hardly, merely, nearly, exactly, scarcely, just,* and *simply*. |
| Teaching skills without concern for maintenance is hardly sufficient. | It is hardly sufficient to teach skills without concern for maintenance. | |
| Simply sampling language just once is not sufficient. | It simply is not sufficient to sample language just once. | |
| Several problems have been observed using negative reinforcement. | Several problems have been observed when clinicians used negative reinforcement. | *Using negative reinforcement* is a dangling modifier because it has no head word. |

# Modifiers

## A.1.16b. Use Modifiers Correctly

| Incorrect | Write Correctly |
|---|---|
| The clinician treated stuttering persons using the syllable stretching procedure. | |
| Consistent with other studies, Smith and Smith (1993) found that cochlear implants are beneficial.<br><br>*Hint:* What were consistent? Results or the authors? | |
| Using the Utah Test, the children's language was screened by the experimenter. | |
| The treatment only was partially effective. | |
| He said he was leaving, in a thundering voice. | |
| The client only had three tokens.<br><br>(The client had nothing other than three tokens.) | Rewrite the sentence to mean that the client had *no more than* three tokens. |
| Using tokens, the child was reinforced. | Rewrite to include a person who reinforced the child. |
| To get a better grade, a long paper was written. | Rewrite the sentence in the active voice and include a subject (e.g., a person's name). |
| The lecture was made interesting by including videos and computer programs. | Rewrite in the active voice and include a subject. |

## Pronouns

- Pronouns, which replace nouns, should clarify what they replace.
- The nouns that pronouns replace are called *antecedents*.
- Pronouns should agree with the replaced noun's (antecedent's) number and gender.

### A.1.17a. Clarify the Referents of Pronouns

| Incorrect | Correct | Note |
|---|---|---|
| I will use toys and pictures as stimuli, and give reinforcers for correct responses. *They* will be used continuously. | I will use toys and pictures as stimuli and give reinforcers for correct responses. *These reinforcers* will be used continuously. | *They* refers to what? Correct responses or reinforcers? |
| A lesion in Broca's area, in the left frontal cortex, causes Broca's aphasia. *It* may be diagnosed only after careful examination. | A lesion in Broca's area, in the left frontal cortex, may be diagnosed only after careful examination. *Such a lesion* causes Broca's aphasia. | *What* may be diagnosed? The corrected statement says it is the lesion. |
| Mark went with John because he did not know the address. | Mark did not know the address, so he went with John. | *Who* did not know the address? |
| The client told the clinician that she was happy. | The client told the clinician, "I am happy." | *Who* was happy? |

### A.1.18a. Let the Pronoun Agree in Number With Its Antecedent

See A.1.15a., Follow the Rules of Agreement, for related examples of correct and incorrect agreement.

| Incorrect | Correct | Note |
|---|---|---|
| A clinician may not recognize that their own limitations affect treatment outcomes. | A clinician may not recognize that his or her own limitations affect treatment outcomes. | The singular clinician did not agree with the plural pronoun (*their*). |
| Neither the child who stuttered nor the child who normally spoke fluently let their test performance suffer. | Neither the child who stuttered nor the child who normally spoke fluently let his or her test performance suffer. | Writing the initial nouns in plural will also correct the error. |

### A.1.19a. Use the Proper Case of Pronoun

| Incorrect | Correct | Note |
|---|---|---|
| Between *you* and *I*. | Between *you* and *me*. | |
| They have invited *you* and *myself*. | They have invited *you* and *me*. | Possessive pronouns *hers*, *theirs*, *ours*, and *its* do not take the apostrophe. |
| *Her's* is the big house. | *Hers* is the big house. | |

# Pronouns

### A.1.17b. Clarify the Referents of Pronouns

| Incorrect | Write Correctly |
|---|---|
| We use stimuli, modeling, and positive feedback. It will be used only when the child does not imitate, however. | |
| Many studies, conducted by several investigators, have confirmed this. They indicate that we should program maintenance. | |
| The clinician went with the supervisor because she did not know the practicum site. | |
| Jane told her female boss that she was upset. | |

### A.1.18b. Let the Pronoun Agree in Number With Its Antecedent

| Incorrect | Correct |
|---|---|
| Even if the clinician is pleased, a client may not be pleased with their own success in treatment. | |
| The patient who had aphasia knew well that they could not recall the names. | |
| Neither the clinician who treated the child nor the parent who sought help expressed their disappointment. | |

### A.1.19b. Use the Proper Case of Pronoun

| Incorrect | Write Correctly |
|---|---|
| You and myself should complete the assessment. | |
| He told Tom and I to finish the job. | |
| Ours' is an old house. | |

# Sentence Fragments

### A.1.20a. Do Not Break a Single Sentence Into Two Parts

| Incorrect | Correct |
|---|---|
| Upon subjective evaluation. The client's voice was judged normal. | Upon subjective evaluation, the client's voice was judged normal. |
| The client finally agreed to be tested. After much coaxing from his wife. | After much coaxing from his wife, the client finally agreed to be tested. |
| I work with 10 children. All with a severe articulation problem. | I work with 10 children, all with a severe articulation problem. |
| Children with hearing impairment have delayed oral language. And also may have voice problems. | Many children with hearing impairment have delayed oral language and also may have voice problems. |
| I will select 20 participants for the experiment. Based on the selection criteria. | Based on the selection criteria, I will select 20 participants. |
| My client with dysphagia is improving. Because of the treatment. | Because of the treatment, my client with dysphagia is improving. |

### A.1.21a. Do Not Write Sentence Fragments as a Series of Declarative Statements

| Incorrect | Correct |
|---|---|
| Graduate students have many problems. Lack of money. Family responsibilities. Job stress. | Graduate students have many problems, including lack of money, family responsibilities, and job stress. |
| Clinicians should consider several factors in planning therapy sessions. Like stimulus materials. Reinforcers to be given. Criteria for learning. | Clinicians should consider several factors in planning therapy sessions. For instance, stimulus materials to be used, reinforcers to be given, and criteria for learning should be determined before therapy. |

### A.1.22a. Do Not Punctuate Appositives

| Incorrect | Correct |
|---|---|
| Several authorities have advocated this type of therapy. For example, van Riper (1971) and Johnson (1958). | Several authorities have advocated this type of therapy, including van Riper (1971) and Johnson (1958). |
| Several theories have suggested that poor self-image causes language delay in children. For instance, the self-image-is-king theory and the sharper image theory. | Several theories—for example, the self-image-is-king theory and the sharper image theory—have suggested that poor self-image causes language delay in children. |

A.1  Basic Rules of Usage    37

# Sentence Fragments

### A.1.20b.  Do Not Break a Single Sentence Into Two Parts

| Incorrect | Write Correctly |
|---|---|
| I will treat twelve children with language disorders. Divided into two groups. | |
| The child finally began to cooperate. After two sessions of crying. | |
| I tested the hearing of all participants. In a sound-treated room. | |
| The client made excellent progress. In the final four sessions. | |
| Three phonological processes were eliminated. All during this semester. | |
| My advisor told me to register. Early in the semester. | |

### A.1.21b.  Do Not Write Sentence Fragments as a Series of Declarative Statements

| Incorrect | Correct |
|---|---|
| Cities offer many advantages. Green parks. Sports arenas. Music concerts. | |
| School clinicians face several challenges. Like uncooperative parents. Paperwork. Pressure from administrators. | |

### A.1.22b.  Do Not Punctuate Appositives

| Incorrect | Correct |
|---|---|
| Several studies have recommended this procedure. For example, those by Bloodstein (1971) and Thompson (2015). | |
| There are several genetic theory of stuttering. For instance, the multifactor theory and recessive gene theory. | |

## Nouns and Adjectives

### A.1.23a. Use Certain Terms Only in Their Adjectival Forms

| Incorrect | Correct | Note |
|---|---|---|
| The *paraplegic* also has aphasia. | The *patient with paraplegia* also has aphasia. | The incorrect versions put the disability first, not the person. The terms in italics within the incorrect constructions are used as nouns, which are preferably used only as adjectives. |
| The *aphasic* has naming problems. | The *person with aphasia* has naming problems. | |
| The *autistic* has echolalia. | The *child with autism* has echolalia. | |
| Ten stutterers will be selected. | Ten *persons with stuttering* will be selected. | |

### A.1.24a. Do Not Turn a Noun Into a Verb

Although many "verbized" nouns are popular and become established over time, a careful writer will be more cautious in using what seems to be acceptable.

| Incorrect | Correct | Note |
|---|---|---|
| We will *agendize* this matter for the next meeting. | We will place this matter on the next meeting's agenda. | The popular tendency to *ize* a noun has created many awkward verbs. |
| ASHA should not be *factionalized*. | ASHA should not be factious. | |
| The APA *Manual* has a *rigidized* format for empirical articles. | The APA *Manual* has a rigid format for empirical articles. | |
| The person who stutters was *therapized* by many clinicians. | The person who stutters had received therapy from many clinicians. | |
| The women and minority groups should never be *inferiorized*. | No one should think that women and minority groups are inferior. | |
| First, I *baselined* the target behaviors. | First, I established baselines of the target behaviors. *or,* First, I baserated the target behaviors. | Note that the word *baserate* may be used both as a noun and as a verb (e.g., *baserates* or *baserated*). |
| He finally *verbalized* his secret intentions. | He finally revealed his secret intentions. *or,* He finally spoke about his secret intentions. | Even though the term *verbalize* is often used, the alternatives are more direct and simple. |

# Nouns and Adjectives

### A.1.23b. Use Certain Terms Only in Their Adjectival Forms

| Incorrect | Write Correctly |
|---|---|
| The dysarthric has multiple communicative disorders. | |
| The retarded's language is delayed.<br>*Hint:* Intellectual disabilities | |
| The hemiplegic has motor speech disorders. | |
| Many apraxics exhibit articulatory groping problems. | |
| The autistic fails to develop emotional attachment. | |

### A.1.24b. Do Not Turn a Noun Into a Verb

| Incorrect | Write Correctly |
|---|---|
| She guested on a TV show. | |
| It is necessary to baseline behaviors before starting treatment. | |
| She thefted my textbooks. | |
| We partnershipped with the community. | |
| Our purpose is now collectivized. | |
| The heroes who died in the war will be funeralized in a state ceremony. | |

## Participial Phrase

### A.1.25a. Let a Participial Phrase at the Beginning of a Sentence Refer to the Grammatical Subject

A participle is a verbal phrase that can function as an adjective; for example, "*Dropped from the second floor*, the ball bounced around" contains the italicized participial phrase. This verbal phrase, acting as an adjective, refers to *the ball*, the subject of the sentence. When the participial phrase does not refer to the grammatical subject in the sentence, it may be described as *dangling* and sound ludicrous: "*Dropped from the second floor*, I saw the ball bounce around." In this dangling participial phrase, the person, not the ball, is dropped from the second floor!

| Incorrect | Correct | Note |
|---|---|---|
| A clinician of *great reputation*, I asked her to treat the client. | A clinician of great reputation, *she* was asked to treat the client. | Who was of great reputation? |
| *On discussing treatment options with the client's family*, they responded favorably to the clinician. | On discussing treatment options with the client's family, *the clinician* received favorable responses. | Who discussed and who responded favorably are not clear in the incorrect version. |
| *Being in a fixer-upper condition*, I found the house a good bargain. | Being in a fixer-upper condition, the house was a good bargain. | The house, not the speaker, was in a fixer-upper condition. |
| *Critically evaluating the evidence presented*, the article provides good insight into language acquisition. | *Critically evaluating the evidence presented*, I found the article to provide good insight into language acquisition. | The reader, not the article, critically evaluated the evidence presented. |

## Participial Phrase

### A.1.25b. Let a Participial Phrase at the Beginning of a Sentence Refer to the Grammatical Subject

| Incorrect | Write Correctly |
|---|---|
| Inexperienced in the treatment of dysphagia, the treatment goals were thought to be easy to establish.<br><br>*Hint:* Who was inexperienced? | |
| Without a friend to study with, the failure was inevitable.<br><br>*Hint:* Whose failure? | |
| Without help from parents, maintenance of target behaviors was difficult.<br><br>*Hint:* Whose maintenance? | |
| Studying carefully the data presented, the article makes a good contribution to treatment research.<br><br>*Hint:* Who studied the data carefully? | |

# A.2 Basic Rules of Composition

## Structure of Research Papers

### A.2.1a. Design a Broad Outline of Your Paper

- Before beginning to write a paper or an essay, make a broad outline of it.
- Write down the major topics you want to address in the paper.
- Type each major topic as a level 1 heading.
- Note that the example shows notes under each of the major topics to be addressed.

---

**Theories of Language Acquisition**

Brigitte Lopez

Brief Historical Introduction to the Study of Language (*untitled*)

(*The ancient and modern study of language, involvement of different disciplines, and so forth.*)

**Linguistic Theories of Language Acquisition**

(*Descriptive linguistics, transformational generative grammar, incidental learning explanations, and so forth*)

**Psychological Theories of Language Acquisition**

(*Behavioral explanations, cognitive explanations, interactive explanations*)

**Recent Developments in Theoretical Explanations**

(*Integration of different views, suggestions from cross-cultural studies*)

**Critical Evaluation of Theories**

(*Lack of experimental support for most theories*)

**Summary and Conclusions**

(*Need for additional research, future directions*)

---

*Note:* There is no one correct outline for a topic. The first outline usually is modified.

# Structure of Research Papers

### A.2.1b. Design a Broad Outline of Your Paper

Select a major academic or clinical topic and design an outline for it. Use the level 1 heading style shown in A.2.1a. Show your notes.

## A.2.2a. Design Headings and Subheadings of Your Paper

- Select levels of headings; see B.3.7 for examples.
- Use the major headings of your initial outline.
- Give technical headings.
- Prefer the shorter headings to the longer headings.
- Use those headings in your paper.
- Keep the number of subheadings under major headings roughly similar.
- Write at least two paragraphs under each heading or subheading.

---

**Theories of Language Acquisition**

Bridgette Lopez

Brief Historical Introduction to the Study of Language (*untitled*)

**Linguistic Theories of Language Acquisition**

*Descriptive Linguistic Theories*

*Transformational Generative Theories*

*Generative Semantic Theories*

*Recent Linguistic Developments*

**Psychological Theories of Language Acquisition**

*Behavioral Theories*

*Cognitive Theories*

*Interactional Theories*

**Recent Developments in Theoretical Explanations**

*Attempts at Integrating Different Views*

*Suggestions from Cross-Cultural Studies*

*Newer Theories*

**Critical Evaluation of Theories**

*Common Research Methods*

*Comparative Evaluation of Evidence*

*Suggestions for Future Research*

**Summary and Conclusions**

**References**

---

*Note:* The example contains only two levels of headings; you may need additional headings (see B.3.7.). In an actual paper, there will be text, at least two paragraphs (often more) under each heading.

## A.2.2b. Design Headings and Subheadings of Your Paper

For the outline you prepared under A.2.1b., design headings and subheadings. Revise your headings and subheadings until you can begin writing.

# Composing Paragraphs

### A.2.3a. Write Paragraphs That Express Related Ideas

- Express *related* ideas in a paragraph.
- Make each paragraph a conceptual unit.
- Do not mix different kinds of information in a paragraph.

| Incorrect | Correct | Note |
|---|---|---|
| The participants will be 25 children with hearing impairment. They will come from middle-class families. The children will be selected from a single school within the local school district. The school will be selected randomly. The parents of the children will have normal hearing. The intelligence of the children will be within normal limits. | The participants will be 25 children with hearing impairment. They will come from middle-class families. The parents of the children will have normal hearing. The intelligence of the children will be within normal limits.<br><br>The children will be selected from a single school within the local school district. The school will be selected randomly. | The first paragraph describes the *characteristics* of participants. The stricken sentence introduces a different idea (that of participant selection), which should be told in a separate paragraph. |
| The client will be seen two times a week in 30-minute sessions. The initial target behaviors will be the correct production of five phonemes. In the beginning, the client will be trained on discrete trials. Later, conversational speech will be used to stabilize the production of target phonemes. The parents will be trained to help maintain the production of target phonemes.<br><br>The initial training procedure will include discrete trials. A picture will be used to evoke the target phonemes in words. | The client will be seen two times a week in 30-minute sessions. The initial target behaviors will be the correct production of five phonemes.<br><br>The initial training procedure will include discrete trials. A picture will be used to evoke the target phonemes in words.<br><br>In the final stage of treatment, conversational speech will be used to stabilize the production of target phonemes. The parents will be trained to help maintain the production of target phonemes. | The first paragraph is about target behaviors. The stricken intrusive sentences about treatment are rephrased and placed in subsequent paragraphs.<br><br>The second paragraph is about the training procedure.<br><br>A separate paragraph is necessary to describe the final stage of treatment. |

# Composing Paragraphs

### A.2.3b. Write Paragraphs That Express Related Ideas

| Incorrect | Write Correctly |
|---|---|
| Mr. Garcia reported that he began to notice hearing problems some five months ago. His wife agreed that it was about that time that her husband began to turn up the volume of their television. He has always enjoyed good physical health. He has been socially active since his retirement two years ago. Around that time, he began to complain that his wife mumbles her speech. Mr. Garcia is a 65-year-old retired electrician. Reportedly, his hearing problem has worsened during the last three weeks. | |

| Write a Mixed Up Paragraph | Rewrite it Correctly |
|---|---|
| | |

## A.2.4a. Do Not Write Paragraphs That Are Too Long

- Break longer paragraphs into shorter ones.
- Make sure each paragraph is about related ideas.

| Too Long | About Right | Note |
|---|---|---|
| Assessment of Timmy's speech and language will include an orofacial examination, a hearing screening, and administration of the Thompson Vocabulary Test (Thompson, 2012), the Jenson Test of Articulatory Performance (Jenson, 2016), and the Shanks Test of Syntactic Constructions (Shanks, 2017). In addition, an extended conversational speech sample will be recorded. The results of this assessment will be integrated with information obtained through case history, reports from other specialists, and information gathered through an interview of Timmy's parents. The client's performance on the selected standardized tests will be analyzed according to the test manuals. The conversational speech samples will be analyzed to determine the accuracy of phoneme productions and language structures. The number of phonemes correctly produced, the number of syntactic structures correctly used, and the number of pragmatic rules appropriately followed also will be determined. Also, the mean length of utterance will be calculated using the Brown method. | Assessment of Timmy's speech and language behaviors will include an orofacial examination, a hearing screening, and administration of the Thompson Vocabulary Test (Thompson, 2012), the Jenson Test of Articulatory Performance (Jenson, 2016), and the Shanks Test of Syntactic Constructions (Shanks, 2017). In addition, an extended conversational speech sample will be recorded.<br><br>The results of this assessment will be integrated with information obtained through case history, reports from other specialists, and information gathered through an interview of Timmy's parents. The client's performance on the selected standardized tests will be analyzed according to the test manuals.<br><br>The conversational speech samples will be analyzed to determine the accuracy of phoneme productions and language structures. The number of phonemes correctly produced, the number of syntactic structures correctly used, and the number of pragmatic rules appropriately followed also will be determined. Also, the mean length of utterance will be calculated using the Brown method. | The long paragraph has been broken into smaller ones, each expressing a set of related ideas. |

*Note:* Standardized tests should be referenced; the examples given are fictitious.

## A.2.4b. Do Not Write Paragraphs That Are Too Long

| Too Long | Rewrite to Make it About Right |
|---|---|
| Aural rehabilitation is an extended process in which a person with hearing impairment is helped to make use of his or her residual hearing. The process begins with hearing testing, but it does not end with it. The process does not end even with a prescription for, or fitting of, a hearing aid. The purchase of a hearing aid is the beginning of aural rehabilitation. The client should be first familiarized with the workings of the hearing aid. The client should learn to change the battery, turn on the aid, adjust the volume, and so forth. The person who purchases a hearing aid should know how to take care of it, clean it periodically, and protect it from shock and other hazards. The person also should know when to take it for service. Even more important, the person with hearing impairment should know how to benefit from the aid. Initially, the hearing aid's amplification of sound and noise may irritate the person or cause discomfort. A person with hearing impairment may get headaches until getting used to the aid's amplified sound. The client should know how to handle the incoming, amplified signal. The audiologist should teach the client to recognize the meaning of sounds he or she can now hear. | |

## A.2.5a. Do Not Write One-Sentence Paragraphs

- This rule applies to scientific and academic writing.
- This rule does not apply to clinical report writing or popular writing.

| Inappropriate | Appropriate | Note |
|---|---|---|
| The effects of communication disorders are several. The disorders create many social and occupational difficulties. Some people with communicative disorders may withdraw from normal social interactions. Some employers may be unwilling to hire people with communicative problems.<br><br>People who have communicative problems may experience certain emotional problems. Such people may be frustrated in their attempts at communication.<br><br>*People who stutter or those who have aphasia experience frustration when they cannot express themselves promptly.* | The effects of communication disorders are several. The disorders create many social and occupational difficulties. Some people with communicative disorders may withdraw from normal social interactions. Some employers may be unwilling to hire people with communicative problems.<br><br>People who have communicative problems may experience certain emotional problems. For example, people who stutter or those who have aphasia experience frustration when they cannot express themselves promptly. | The one-sentence paragraph (the last one italicized in column one) stands alone with nothing to connect to.<br><br>Note that when the two paragraphs are combined, some change in the wording may be necessary to provide transition. |

### A.2.5b. Do Not Write One-Sentence Paragraphs

Choose an academic topic.

| Write Four One-Sentence Paragraphs | Integrate the Four One-Sentence Paragraphs into a Single Paragraph |
|---|---|
| | |

## A.2.6a. Begin and End Most Paragraphs With Transitionary Sentences

Lack of transition breaks the flow of thought and confuses the reader. To achieve smooth transition, **do** one or more of the following:

- End and begin adjacent paragraphs with a related idea.
- Suggest what will be said in the next paragraph.
- Make reference to what was said in the previous paragraph.

However, **do not** do the following:

- Introduce new topics abruptly.
- Randomly shift topics across paragraphs.

| Rough Transition | Smoother Transition | Note |
|---|---|---|
| 1. Methods of analysis of speech sound errors have undergone many changes. Traditionally, the clinicians have made the sound-by-sound analysis to judge the accuracy of individual sound productions.<br><br>2. In the place-voice-manner analysis, sounds are classified into patterns based on these phonetic features. Errors also are similarly classified.<br><br>3. Phonological processes are simplifications of speech sound productions that help classify multiple errors into groups or patterns. Another approach is that of distinctive feature analysis, which was suggested before the phonological process approach. | 1. Methods of analysis of speech sound errors have changed over the years. Traditionally, the clinicians have made the sound-by-sound analysis to judge the accuracy of individual sound productions. Therefore, *there is no attempt to see a pattern in the errors* based on an underlying principle.<br><br>2. The first approach to see a *pattern in the errors* was based on the place-voice-manner analysis. In this approach, sounds are classified into patterns based on the three phonetic features. Therefore, errors also are similarly classified. This classification resulted in somewhat *simplified patterns of errors*.<br><br>3. A method of classification resulting in more *complex patterns of errors* was suggested by the next approach: analysis of the distinctive features of speech sounds. Soon, however, a new approach based on *phonological theories* was proposed.<br><br>4. *Phonological theories* proposed that phonological processes, which are patterned simplifications of speech sound productions, explain errors of articulation. These processes help classify multiple errors into groups or patterns. | The first paragraph of the first column set the stage for a historical view. But with no transition and no historical sense, the second paragraph is isolated.<br><br>The first two paragraphs of the second column are related because of the common, italicized words. A theme flows from the first to the second paragraph.<br><br>The third paragraph of the first column abruptly introduces the phonological process approach. The rewriting achieves smoother transition as shown by a repeated theme (italicized words in the second and the third paragraphs).<br><br>The third paragraph in the first column confuses the historical sequence because of an abrupt shift to the phonological approach before mentioning the distinctive feature approach. |

## A.2.6b. Begin and End Most Paragraphs With Transitionary Sentences

| Rough Transition | Rewrite with Smoother Transition |
|---|---|
| College students face many problems. A basic problem all college students face is lack of money. In a technological society, everyone needs a college degree to make a decent living. Unfortunately, not everyone can afford the ever-escalating cost of higher education.<br><br>With limited resources, colleges are offering less financial aid to students. The rate at which the cost of higher education has escalated has outpaced that of inflation. This may be because of dwindling state support for higher education.<br><br>Reduced financial aid makes it especially difficult for students with families. Balancing the needs of a family and the demands of an academic program is difficult. The difficulty is aggravated when students are faced with financial problems. Limited financial aid makes it especially difficult for students with families.<br><br>*Hint:* Each paragraph contains a transitory sentence, but it is misplaced. | |

# Concise and Direct Writing

## A.2.7a. Prefer the Shorter to the Longer Sentences

- Maintain some variety.
- Alternate longer sentences with shorter ones.

| Longer Sentences | Preferred Shorter Sentences | Note |
|---|---|---|
| Many clinicians who employ the traditional method of articulation training tend to use nonsense syllables in the early stages of training, along with an emphasis on ear training with a view to promote auditory discrimination of speech sounds. | Many clinicians employ the traditional method of articulation training. In this method, the clinicians use nonsense syllables in the early stages of training. The training emphasis is on the auditory discrimination of speech sounds. | One sentence has been broken into three. These shorter sentences are easier to read and understand. |
| The many compounding problems of the child who is hearing impaired include social isolation, academic difficulties, problems in language learning, and many others that when unchecked by a well-designed management plan, can lead to additional problems later in life which are then very difficult to manage. | The many compounding problems of the child who is hearing impaired include social isolation, academic difficulties, and language learning problems. Unless checked by a well-designed management plan, these problems can lead to additional difficulties later in life. Such long-standing problems are difficult to manage. | The maze of long sentences obscures a chain of ideas or events.<br><br>Some long sentences contain unnecessary words that can be cut out to shorten them. |

# Concise and Direct Writing

### A.2.7b. Prefer the Shorter to the Longer Sentences

| Longer Sentences | Rewrite in Shorter Sentences |
|---|---|
| Many clinicians, who believe that auditory training is an important part of aural rehabilitation of hearing impaired children, nonetheless do not appreciate the need for such training in case of adult hearing impaired individuals, though it is well established that the recognition and discrimination of speech sounds is an integral part of any program of aural rehabilitation designed for individuals of all ages. | |
| While the psychoanalytic theory has stated that oral and anal regression during infancy causes stuttering, the behavioral view has asserted that faulty conditioning causes it, and the neurophysiological theories have implicated either the auditory system with defective feedback loops, the laryngeal mechanism with improper neural control, or the brain with its problems in language processing in the causation of stuttering. | |

### A.2.8a. Prefer the Active Voice

- In the active voice, the subject of a verb performs the action (e.g., *the boy hit the ball*).
- In the passive voice, the subject of a verb is acted upon or said to receive the action (e.g., *the ball was hit by the boy*). There is nothing wrong with the passive voice; it's just that the active voice is preferable.
- Passive sentences are long and indirect.
- Active sentences make writing brief, more direct, and easier to understand.

| Passive | Preferred Active |
| --- | --- |
| The supervisor was the person with whom I spoke. | I spoke to the supervisor. |
| The children were brought to the clinic by their mothers. | The mothers brought their children to the clinic. |
| The target responses will be modeled by the clinician. | The clinician will model the target responses. |
| When the target behaviors are selected, stimulus materials will be prepared. | After selecting the target behaviors, I will prepare the stimulus materials. |

### A.2.8b. Prefer the Active Voice

| Passive | Rewrite in Preferred Active Terms |
|---|---|
| Central auditory processing problems may be assessed by various tests. | |
| The client's behavior problems were not controlled by the clinician. | |
| There are many procedures that may be used in aural rehabilitation. | |
| The clinician was upset by the child's uncooperative behavior. | |

## A.2.9a. Say What It Is, Instead of What It Is Not

- It is more direct to say what something is.
- Say it directly, even when what is said is negative.

| What It Is Not | What It Is |
| --- | --- |
| The client often did not come to the treatment sessions at the appointed time. | The client often came late to treatment sessions. |
| These treatment procedures are not very effective. | These treatment procedures are ineffective. |
| The results of our tests do not suggest that the client does not have central auditory processing problems. | The results of our tests suggest that the client may have central auditory processing problems. |
| I do not believe that the client does not have a phonological disorder. | The client possibly has a phonological disorder. |
| I do not think that these procedures will not work with aphasia. | 1. I think that these procedures might work with aphasia.<br>2. These procedures will work with aphasia. |
| The man is not honest. | The man is dishonest. |
| The clinician did not pay any attention to the supervisor's suggestion. | The clinician ignored the supervisor's suggestion. |

## A.2.9b. Say What It Is, Instead of What It Is Not

| What It Is Not | What It Is |
|---|---|
| The instructor did not have much confidence in the student's explanation. | |
| The nativist theory does not do a great job of explaining language acquisition. | |
| Asking *yes/no* questions may not be an effective method of evoking continuous speech from a child. | |
| Some clinicians believe that phoneme auditory discrimination training may not be necessary in articulation treatment. | |
| Surgical procedures may not be very useful in the rehabilitation of certain types of hearing impairment. | |

### A.2.10a. Avoid Too Many Qualifications

Too many qualifications make your writing timid, weak, and uncertain. The reader will be unsure of what you say. Let your statements be as definite as the **observations or data warrant**.

| Overly Qualified and Weak | Stronger and Clearer |
| --- | --- |
| It is possible that some clinicians do not have a very strong belief in the validity of this theory. | 1. Some clinicians doubt the validity of this theory.<br>2. Some clinicians reject this theory. |
| The data may possibly suggest that in at least some cases, the technique may have some limited use. | The data suggest that the technique may be useful in some cases. |
| It would be beneficial to use this assessment procedure with children though it may or may not be just as effective with adults. | This assessment procedure may be more useful with children than with adults. |
| It may be possible to use the criterion of 90% correct response rate before dismissing the client. | The dismissal criterion will be 90% correct response rate. |

A.2 Basic Rules of Composition

## A.2.10b. Avoid Too Many Qualifications

| Overly Qualified and Weak | Stronger And Clearer |
|---|---|
| Theory may be of some value in explaining at least a small aspect of this complex phenomenon. | |
| I hope that with the help of this new procedure, I may be able to have some effect on the child's communication. | |
| I am favorably disposed to using the rate reduction procedure in the treatment of stuttering. | |
| I expect that I may be able to convince the parents that they may consider the possibility of holding informal treatment sessions at home. | |
| It is not unreasonable to expect that in all likelihood, the digital hearing aid may be of some use for this client. | |

## A.2.11a. Use Definite, Specific, and Concrete Language

- Avoid the overuse of generalized terms whose meanings are unclear.
- Be specific in describing symptoms of disorders, behaviors, procedures, effects, services, and so forth.

| Incorrect | Correct |
|---|---|
| *In all likelihood*, the treatment seems to have had some positive effect on the life of the client. | Possibly, treatment helped the client speak more fluently. |
| *Various* visual and auditory stimulus input methods will be used in treatment. | Pictures, objects, action figures, and tape-recorded models of speech sound productions will be used in treatment. |
| I will *make sure that* the parents support Johnny's production of target behaviors at home. | I will ask the parents to praise Johnny at home for his correct production of speech sounds. |
| *A variety of* grammatical morphemes will be the treatment targets. | Many grammatical morphemes, including regular plurals, possessives, articles, and prepositions will be the treatment targets. |
| The child was not *very cooperative* during assessment. | Often crying or whining, the child refused to name the pictures shown. |
| The clinician *indicated* that the client has aphasia. | The clinician said that the client has aphasia. |
| Children with cleft palate and their families need *numerous* services from an array of different specialists. | Children with cleft palate and their families need services from many specialists, including pediatricians, dentists, orthodontists, plastic surgeons, otologists, audiologists, speech-language pathologists, psychologists, and others. |
| Lack of treatment progress had some *negative effect* on the client's emotionality. | The client was disappointed because of lack of progress in treatment. |
| A child's improved language skills may produce many *desirable effects*. | A child's improved language skills may produce better academic performance, enriched peer interactions, and generally more efficient social communication. |
| I have a behavioral *issue* with the child. | The child tends to leave the chair during treatment. |
| | The child does not separate from the mother before the treatment session. |

*Note:* In each of the correct examples, general terms such as *a variety of, various, numerous, several, many, some, positive effect, issues,* and so forth are replaced by specific terms.

## A.2.11b. Use Definite, Specific, and Concrete Language

| Incorrect | Write Correctly |
|---|---|
| The man with aphasia did not seem very happy during the treatment sessions.<br><br>Describe behaviors that suggest unhappiness. | |
| Voice therapy seems to have changed the life of Mr. Shreik.<br><br>Describe one or two observable changes in life. | |
| I will use any and all means of promoting response maintenance at home.<br><br>Specify two or three techniques. | |
| The child did not want to be assessed.<br><br>What did the child do? | |
| I will use many different procedures to assess the child's articulation.<br><br>Specify two or three procedures. | |
| Stuttering has many kinds of effects on most aspects of life.<br><br>Describe a few effects. | |
| A child with hearing impairment who has an active ear pathology needs a variety of professional services from many different specialists.<br><br>Name a few services and professionals. | |
| The client was unfavorably disposed to continuing treatment next semester.<br><br>What did the client say? | |
| I have issues with writing my clinical reports.<br><br>Specify the problems you have in writing reports. | |

## A.2.12a. Eliminate or Replace Unnecessary Phrases

| Unnecessary Words | Recommendation |
|---|---|
| abilities or capabilities (unless distinguished from action) | describe actions |
| along the lines of | eliminate |
| as a matter of fact | eliminate |
| as far as . . . is (are) concerned | eliminate |
| at the present time | now |
| at this point in time | now |
| by means of | eliminate |
| call your attention to the fact that | remind you or notify you |
| due to the fact that | eliminate |
| experienced an inability | describe actions |
| experienced great difficulty | describe actions |
| for all intents and purposes | eliminate |
| hands-on experience | experience |
| I was unaware of the fact that | I did not know |
| in all honesty | eliminate |
| in any shape or form | eliminate |
| in order to | to |
| in spite of the fact that | eliminate |
| in the time frame | in about |
| in the area of | just name the area, topic, discipline |
| in the event that | if |
| is considered to be | eliminate |
| on account of the fact that | eliminate |
| owing to the fact that | eliminate |
| question as to whether | whether |
| the fact of the matter is | eliminate |
| the field of | name the discipline |
| the type of (unless you describe different types) | eliminate |
| there is no doubt that | no doubt, doubtless, undoubtedly |
| this is a subject that | this subject |
| to tell the truth | just say what you want to say |
| unable to (in most cases) | describe actions |
| until such time as | until |
| used for the purpose of | used for (to) |
| with regards to, with regard to, in regard to | eliminate |
| with respect to | eliminate |
| with reference to | eliminate |

## A.2.12b. Eliminate or Replace Unnecessary Phrases

Find at least five unnecessary phrases that people use:

1.

2.

3.

4.

5.

Write sentences containing unnecessary phrases in the first column and their revised forms in the second column.

| Imprecise | Precise |
|---|---|
|  |  |
|  |  |
|  |  |
|  |  |
|  |  |

A.2.12a., eliminate or replace unnecessary phrases *(continued)*

| Imprecise | Precise |
|---|---|
| *In the time frame* of an hour, assessment may be completed. | In about an hour, assessment may be completed. |
| Aphasia *is considered to be* a language disorder. | Aphasia is a language disorder. |
| We have much controversy *in the area of* language treatment. | We have much controversy in language treatment. |
| Reading, writing, and speaking *abilities* were affected. | Reading, writing, and speaking were affected. |
| The patient *experienced an inability* to produce speech. | The patient could not produce speech. |
| The tongue demonstrated weakness *with regards to* lateral strength. | The tongue demonstrated lateral weakness. |
| A mixed probe will be *the type of* probe administered. | A mixed probe will be administered. |
| If the client *is unable to* produce the word, the clinician will model it. | If the client fails to produce a word, the clinician will model it. |
| She *experienced great difficulty* speaking as demonstrated by slow, labored, and effortful speech. | Her speech was slow, labored, and effortful. |
| For *all intents and purposes*, assessment and diagnostics mean the same. | Assessment and diagnostics mean the same. |
| Treatment goals were not achieved *due to the fact that* the client missed several sessions. | Treatment goals were not achieved because the client missed several sessions. |
| *On account of the fact that* she was unemployed, she could not afford treatment. | Because she was unemployed, she could not afford treatment. |
| John won, *in spite of the fact* that he was injured. | John won, though he was injured. |
| We cannot offer any monetary rewards *at this point in time*. | We cannot offer any monetary rewards now. |
| *At the present time*, my case load is full. | Now my caseload is full. |

## A.2.12b., eliminate or replace unnecessary phrases *(continued)*

| Imprecise | Write Precisely |
|---|---|
| Modeling may be considered to be an effective stimulus control procedure. | |
| In the area of phonological disorders, we have many assessment procedures. | |
| Respiration, phonation, and articulation abilities were disordered. | |
| The patient who has a laryngectomy experiences an inability to phonate normally. | |
| With regard to long-term effects, loud noise is detrimental to normal hearing. | |
| A single-subject design will be the type of design to be used in this study. | |
| When the client is unable to imitate a target response, I will use the shaping procedure. | |
| He experienced great difficulty in producing phonemes in sequence as demonstrated by his trial-and-error movement of the articulators. | |

A.2.12a., eliminate or replace unnecessary phrases *(continued)*

| Imprecise | Precise |
|---|---|
| *The question as to whether* all children with speech sound disorders also have phonological disorders has been debated. | Whether all children with speech sound disorders also have phonological disorders has been debated. |
| *In the field of* communicative disorders | In communicative disorders |
| He has *the ability to* lead the team. | He can lead the team. |
| It is good to get some *hands-on* experience in the workplace. | It is good to get some experience in the workplace. |
| During treatment, improvement *in terms of* the response rates was good. | During treatment, the response rates improved. |
| *As far as* the child's correct production of phonemes at home was concerned, the results were disappointing. | At home, the child did not (does not) correctly produce the phonemes. |
| *In the event that* Hector cannot complete the task, Sheila will take over. | If Hector cannot complete the task, Sheila will take over. |
| We will win *by means of* working harder. | We will win by working harder. |
| *He is a man who (she is a woman who)* knows about religion. | He (She) knows about religion. |
| The clinician spoke *along the lines of* normal language development. | The clinician spoke about normal language development. |
| *With reference to* mild conductive hearing loss in infancy, it may cause language delay. | Mild conductive hearing loss in infancy may cause language delay. |
| *With respect to* our earlier conversation, I will see you tomorrow. | As we talked earlier, I will see you tomorrow. |
| *To tell you the truth*, I will not be able to attend your party. | I am sorry that I cannot attend your party. |
| *There is no doubt that* he will come to the party. | He undoubtedly will come to the party. |
| *I was unaware of the fact that* she was going to bring her child. | I did not know that she was going to bring her child. |
| *Owing to the fact that* early treatment of language disorders is effective, we recommend immediate treatment for your child. | Because early treatment of language disorders is effective, we recommend immediate treatment for your child. |

A.2.12b., eliminate or replace unnecessary phrases *(continued)*

| Imprecise | Write Precisely |
|---|---|
| Morphologic training was not initiated this semester due to the fact that the client did not meet the other targets. | |
| On account of the fact that they did not attend the IEP meetings, the parents could not be informed about the treatment targets. | |
| The client made excellent progress in spite of the fact that she had a severe speech sound problem. | |
| The fact of the matter is that many untested theories confuse the clinician. | |
| Our waiting list is long at this point in time. | |
| At the present time, all the treatment targets have been achieved. | |
| Until such time as the interfering behaviors are controlled, language targets cannot be trained. | |
| Tokens may be used for the purposes of reinforcement. | |
| In order to assess the client's syntactic structures, a language sample was recorded. | |
| The researchers have investigated the question as to whether mild conductive hearing impairment in young children causes language delay. | |

A.2.12a., eliminate or replace unnecessary phrases *(continued)*

| Imprecise | Precise |
|---|---|
| I am very busy *until such time as* the holidays are over. | I am very busy until the holidays are over. |
| Our office is *used for the purposes* of distribution. | Our office is used for distribution. |
| *In order to* teach the morphologic features, I will model the correct responses. | To teach the morphologic features, I will model the correct responses. |
| *I wish to call your attention to the fact* that aphasia treatment is effective. | Please note that aphasia treatment is effective. |
| *This is a subject that* interests me. | This subject interests me. |

A.2.12b., eliminate or replace unnecessary phrases *(continued)*

| Imprecise | Write Precisely |
|---|---|
| The client has the ability to speak fluently. | |
| You can get some hands-on experience in word processing at our computer lab. | |
| In terms of making a complete assessment, language samples are excellent. | |
| As far as the client's motivation for treatment is concerned, you should make a good judgment. | |
| In the time frame of 20 minutes, you should administer a probe. | |
| In the event that the treatment sessions cannot be held twice a week, a once-a-week schedule might be tried. | |
| Articulation was assessed by means of the *Goldman–Fristoe Test of Articulation* (Goldman & Fristoe, 1986). | |
| She is a clinician who can treat patients with aphasia. | |
| The clinician worked along the lines of response maintenance. | |
| The field of audiological practice is challenging and stimulating. | |
| I was unaware of the fact that the client had prior therapy. | |
| Owing to the fact that the child has a hearing loss, there may be language delay. | |
| I wish to call your attention to the fact that the patient may have suffered head injury. | |
| This is a subject that I am interested in doing a thesis on. | |

## A.2.13a. Avoid Redundant Phrases

Most redundant phrases contain two or more words that mean the same. Such phrases should be shortened, often to only one or the other word.

| Redundant | Essential |
|---|---|
| future prospects | Prospects |
| advance planning | Planning |
| absolutely incomplete | incomplete |
| exactly identical | Identical |
| repeat again | Again |
| each and every | each *or* every |
| totally unique | Unique |
| uniquely one of a kind | one of a kind *or* unique |
| reality as it is | Reality |
| actual facts | Facts |
| solid facts | |
| true facts | |
| famous and well known | famous *or* well known |
| goals and objectives (when the two are not distinguished) | goals *or* objectives; *or,* distinguish the two |
| three different kinds | three kinds |
| seven different varieties | seven varieties |
| four different types | four types |
| as of yet | Yet |
| prison facilities | prison, church, hospital |
| church facilities | |
| hospital facilities | |
| crisis situation | Crisis |
| problem situation | Problem |
| prepay first | prepay *or* pay first |
| free gift | gift *or* free |
| positive growth | Growth |
| bad weather conditions | bad weather |
| deteriorating economic conditions | deteriorating economy |
| deteriorating client response conditions | client's deteriorating responses |
| positive affirmative action | affirmative action |
| actively involved, actively looking | involved, looking |
| preconditions | conditions |
| unexpected surprise | surprise |
| successfully completed | completed |
| successfully avoided | avoided |
| make an effort to try | make an effort *or* try |
| advice and counsel | advice *or* counsel |
| necessary and essential | necessary *or* essential |
| fair and equitable | fair *or* equitable |

## A.2.13b. Avoid Redundant Phrases

Find five redundant phrases used in everyday language. Suggest the essential terms.

| Redundant Phrases | Essential |
|---|---|
|  |  |
|  |  |
|  |  |
|  |  |
|  |  |

A.2.13a., avoid redundant phrases *(continued)*

| **Redundant Phrases** | **Essential** |
|---|---|
| The *future prospects* of speech–language pathology are excellent. | The future of speech–language pathology is excellent. |
| NSSLHA held an *advanced planning* meeting for fund raising. | NSSLHA held a planning meeting for fund raising. |
| The story was *absolutely incomplete*. | The story was incomplete. |
| The plagiarized paper the student submitted was *exactly identical* to the author's. | The plagiarized paper the student submitted was identical to the author's. |
| Can you *repeat* that *again*? | Can you repeat that? |
| *Each and every* student was required to write a paper. | Each (*or*, Every) student was required to write a paper. |
| Each client is *totally unique*. | Each client is unique. |
| This new test on traumatic brain injury is *uniquely one of a kind*. | This new test on traumatic brain injury is one of a kind (*or*, unique). |
| Outside the world of academia, *reality as it is* is different from what the professors imagine. | Outside the world of academia, reality is different from what the professors imagine. |
| Overgeneralization of certain words is a *true fact* of early language development. | Overgeneralization of certain words is a fact of early language development. |
| She is a *famous and well-known* lecturer. | She is a famous (*or*, well-known) lecturer. |
| We should write some *goals and objectives*. *Note:* This is fine when goals are distinguished from objectives. When they are not, the phrase is redundant. | We should write some goals (*or*, objectives). |
| We have *three different kinds of* language tests. | We have three kinds of language tests. |
| It is not done *as of yet*. | It is not done yet. |
| We will visit the *prison facilities*. | We will visit the prison. |
| We have a *crisis situation* on hand. | We have a crisis on hand. |
| Deteriorating client *response conditions* were distressing. | Deteriorating client responses were distressing. |
| There were some *pre*conditions for negotiation. | There were some conditions for negotiation. |

A.2.13b., avoid redundant phrases *(continued)*

| Redundant Phrases | Essential |
|---|---|
| The future prospects of maintenance of fluency are excellent. | |
| The officers held an advanced planning meeting. | |
| The treatment report was absolutely incomplete. | |
| The two stimuli used on treatment and probe trials were exactly identical. | |
| The clinician will repeat modeling again. | |
| Each and every client's family members should be trained in response maintenance. | |
| For each client, we do not need totally unique treatment procedures. | |
| I found uniquely one-of-a-kind software for surfing the Internet. | |
| Reality as it is may be more disappointing than we imagine it to be. | |
| An actual fact of clinical practice is some degree of apprehension. | |
| He is a famous and well-known author. | |
| My treatment goals and objectives were not clear. | |

A.2.13a., avoid redundant phrases *(continued)*

| **Redundant Phrases** | **Essential** |
|---|---|
| She is *actively looking* for a job. | She is looking for a job. |
| We had an *unexpected surprise* in therapy session. | We had a surprise in therapy session. |
| She *successfully completed* our graduate program. | She completed our graduate program. |
| The person who stutters *successfully avoids* certain words. | The person who stutters avoids certain words. |
| I will make an *effort to try* to train parents in response maintenance. | I will try to train parents in response maintenance. |
| A *necessary and essential* element of treatment is positive reinforcement. | A necessary (*or*, essential) element of treatment is positive reinforcement. |
| The grading was *fair and equitable*. | The grading was fair (*or*, equitable). |

A.2.13b., avoid redundant phrases *(continued)*

| Redundant Phrases | Essential |
|---|---|
| We have three different types of assignments in the class. | |
| We offer 11 different varieties of language treatment. | |
| The treatment program is not complete as of yet. | |
| We will visit the hospital facilities. | |
| The problem situation is getting worse. | |
| The bad weather conditions were getting worse. | |
| I did not accept their preconditions for employment. | |
| My client is actively involved in the treatment process. | |
| The child's sudden temper tantrum was an unexpected surprise to me. | |
| The client successfully completed all steps in the treatment. | |
| She made an effort to try to keep the appointment. | |
| Paperwork is a necessary and essential element of professional practice. | |
| The pay raise offered to us was fair and equitable. | |

## A.2.14a. Avoid Wordiness

Wordiness is the use of many kinds of words that makes the writing vague, timid, and unnecessarily long.

| Wordy | Precise | Note |
|---|---|---|
| It seems to me that it certainly is very important to consider many factors in selecting treatment procedures. | I should consider many factors in selecting treatment procedures. | It is assumed that you will soon specify at least a few factors. |
| It became evident from my conversation with the parents of the child that they had a very difficult time to do what they were told to do because of their busy lifestyle. | The parents of the child told me that they did not have time to conduct treatment sessions at home. | |
| Although the client was certainly not negatively disposed to continuing the treatment for a reasonable amount of time, she finally decided to discontinue it. | The client discontinued the treatment, though she said she wanted to continue it. | The overused word *certainly* often suggests no certainty. |
| There were several crucial factors that led me to select these assessment procedures. | These assessment procedures were selected because of their known reliability, validity, and simplicity. | Often, the word *crucial* is an overstatement. |
| A variety of procedures will be used. | Many procedures will be used. | Procedures may be specified in subsequent sentences. |
| A number of clients were treated. | Several clients were treated. | It is assumed that the exact number is unimportant. |
| Certain limitations of standardized tests make it imperative to carefully reconsider the whole issue of reliability and validity of assessment procedures. | Because of the limitations of standardized tests, we should reconsider the reliability and validity of assessment procedures. | Limitations will have been specified. |
| It is not in the least inappropriate to offer the suggestion that cochlear implant may be a reasonably attractive method of aural rehabilitation that should not be rejected out of hand. | The option of cochlear implant should be considered. | The more precise statement says it positively as well. |

## A.2.14b. Avoid Wordiness

| Wordy | Rewrite Precisely |
|---|---|
| In my judgment, it is reasonable to conclude that there are different types of aphasia though many symptoms are common to the different types. | |
| I personally think that it is not totally inappropriate to suggest that children with multiple misarticulations have a phonological disorder. | |
| I used two tests that were known to have a reasonable degree of reliability. | |
| It certainly seems to me that we need more treatment efficacy research. | |
| A variety of investigators have found it appropriate to suggest that both genetic and environmental factors play a causative role in stuttering. | |
| It is not unreasonable to suggest that we carefully consider all minimally attractive alternatives available to us as at this important juncture. | |
| It is certainly apparent to most competent clinicians that it is reasonably worthwhile to offer voice therapy to certain clients who may wish to consider it as an attractive alternative to surgical procedures. | |
| If one were to infer from these assessment data that the client has Broca's aphasia, the inference would certainly not seem totally inappropriate. | |

## A.2.15a. Avoid Jargon

- *Jargon* is a technical or specialized term, often unavoidable in scientific, professional, and technical writing.
- Do not overuse jargon.
- When necessary, describe what jargon means in everyday language.
- When you write to people without technical knowledge, describe everything in nontechnical terms; if necessary, introduce the technical terms accompanied by nontechnical descriptions.
- When writing to technical audiences, retain the technical terms but define them.

| Jargon | Plain | Note |
|---|---|---|
| The child's *linguistic competence* is limited. | The child's *language* is limited. | In some cases, there may not be a need to introduce the technical terms at all. |
| Use an *FR2 schedule* to reinforce correct responses at home. | Reinforce *every other correct response* at home. | |
| In using your hearing aid, you should learn to control the *intensity of the signal*. | In using your hearing aid, you should learn to control the *volume*. | |
| The child's *MLU* is limited. | The child speaks in short *phrases or sentences*. | |
| The woman has *anomia*. | The woman has naming difficulties. We call them anomia. | Examples in which technical terms also are introduced. |
| A patient with a stroke may have dysphagia. | A patient with a stroke may have difficulty swallowing. It is called dysphagia. | |
| The child has a phonological disorder. | The child has difficulty producing certain speech sounds correctly. This difficulty is known as a phonological disorder. | |
| The child should be praised for correct morphologic use. | The child should be praised for correct use of such grammatical words as plurals or past tense inflections. | The clinician should then go on to give examples. |

## A.2.15b. Avoid Jargon

| Jargon | Write in Plain Language |
|---|---|
| The boy has a severe problem in correctly positioning his articulators. *Hint:* Difficulty producing speech sounds. | |
| The child has telegraphic speech. *Hint:* Omits certain grammatical features. | Introduce the technical term. |
| The woman has aphonia. | Introduce the technical term. |
| The child has a final consonant deletion process. | Introduce the technical term. |
| The man has Wernicke's aphasia. *Hint:* Fluent speech but poor understanding of spoken language. | Introduce the technical term. |
| The woman has apraxia of speech. *Hint:* Difficulty producing speech sounds in proper sequence. | Introduce the technical term. |
| The child has a specific language impairment. *Hint:* Only a language problem, no other problems. | |

## A.2.16a. Avoid Euphemism

- Euphemistic expressions disguise negative meanings.
- Such expressions falsely suggest neutral or positive meanings.
- Euphemistic writing can be dishonest.

| Euphemistic | Direct |
|---|---|
| Because of poor progress, the family will be *counseled out* of our services. | 1. Because of poor progress, the family will be dismissed from our services.<br>2. Because of poor progress, we recommended to the family that our services be discontinued. |
| The client is *communicatively challenged*. | 1. The client has a communicative disorder.<br>2. The client stutters. |
| The child comes from an *economically deprived* background. | The child comes from a poor family. |
| The clinic reported *negative profits* for the third quarter. | 1. The clinic reported a loss of revenue for the third quarter.<br>2. The clinic lost money during the third quarter. |
| The child is *developmentally other-abled*. | 1. The child has intellectual disabilities.<br>2. The child has a developmental disability.<br>*Note*: The term *intellectual disabilities* is preferred. |
| He is a *residentially challenged* person. | He is a homeless person. |
| The stuttering treatment had *negative outcomes*. | 1. The stuttering treatment was ineffective.<br>2. The stuttering treatment was harmful to the clients. |
| The army reported *collateral damage* from the bombings. | 1. The army reported civilian casualties resulting from the bombings.<br>2. The bombs killed civilians and destroyed their homes. |
| The government announced new *revenue enhancement measures*. | The government increased taxes. |
| Children with *special needs* require special services. | 1. Children with disabilities need special services.<br>2. Gifted children need special services. |
| The parents were *less than cooperative* in maintaining their child's fluency at home. | The parents did little or no work at home to maintain their child's fluency. |

A.2 Basic Rules of Composition

## A.2.16b. Avoid Euphemism

| Euphemistic | Write More Directly |
|---|---|
| The student was counseled out of the major. | |
| The child comes from an underprivileged family. | |
| The man is physically challenged. | |
| Today, the garbologist did not collect the trash. | |
| I bought a previously owned car. | |
| Evaluating your performance in the comprehensive examination, we have decided to give you another opportunity to take the examination. | |
| The surgical treatment had a negative outcome for the patient. | |
| The arbor technician pruned the fruit trees. | |
| I made negative profits from my home-based business. | |
| I found the parents less than helpful in helping the child complete home assignments. | |

## A.2.17a. Keep Related Words Together

- Do not split related words by introducing intervening words.
- Keep the conceptually related words adjacent to each other.

| Incorrect | Correct | Note |
|---|---|---|
| He ate seven hot dogs for lunch last Friday, and three more for dinner. | Last Friday, he ate seven hot dogs for lunch and three more for dinner. | |
| An unruly behavior of a child, if you do not control it, will prevent rapid progress in treatment. | Unless controlled, a child's unruly behavior will prevent rapid progress in treatment. | What prevents rapid progress? |
| Treatment of cluttering, because of limited research, is not well established. | Because of limited research, treatment of cluttering is not well established. | What is not well established? |
| Some clinicians, though they are keenly interested in it, are not well trained in the assessment of dysphagia. | Although they are keenly interested in dysphagia, some clinicians are not well trained in its assessment. | In what are the clinicians not well trained? |
| The supervisor asked clinicians to write a treatment plan for each client at the meeting on Wednesday. | At the meeting on Wednesday, the supervisor asked clinicians to write a treatment plan for each client. | Did not write a treatment plan at the meeting! |
| This is an assessment report on Mr. Davis, referred to us by Dr. Benson, seen last week in our facility. | This is an assessment report on Mr. Davis, seen last week in our facility. He was referred to us by Dr. Benson. | Dr. Benson was not seen last week! |
| Women who are pregnant, but unaware of its bad effects, may continue to drink alcohol. | Women who are pregnant, but unaware of the bad effects of alcohol on the fetus, may continue to drink. | Bad effects of drinking or pregnancy? |
| The human fertility clinic extracted multiple ova from women, then froze them. | The human fertility clinic extracted multiple ova from women. The clinic then froze the ova. | Ova, not women, were frozen! |

*Note:* See also A.1.16a and A.2.21a about the correct use of modifiers.

## A.2.17b. Keep Related Words Together

| Incorrect | Write Correctly |
|---|---|
| Maintenance of target behaviors, if not carefully programmed, will not be achieved. | |
| In assessing phonological disorders, though many procedures may be appropriate, conversational speech is the most productive. | |
| Meeting the IEP goals within three months, even if I work hard and the child is regular for sessions, will be difficult. | |
| The selected target behaviors may be taught, assuming that the client will be regular for treatment sessions, in about 10 sessions. | |
| The final target of treatment, it has been suggested, is maintenance. | |
| The treatment procedure will include generalized reinforcers, to make it more effective. | |
| Clinicians who are inexperienced, but do not know how hazardous it is, may cause serious problems by using wrong methods of dysphagia treatment. | |
| I wrote this treatment plan for Mrs. Jones, after careful consideration of her strengths and weaknesses. | |

# Parallelism

## A.2.18a. Write in Parallel Terms

- Parallelism is the expression of a series of ideas in the same grammatical form.
- Parallelism is broken when some ideas in a series are expressed in one form and the others in the same series are expressed in different forms.

| Incorrect | Correct | Note |
|---|---|---|
| Children with language disorders tend to be deficient in their use of grammatical morphemes, syntactic structures, and *they also may have a limited vocabulary.* | Children with language disorders tend to be deficient in their use of grammatical morphemes, syntactic structures, and complex words. | The incorrect versions have a *nonparallel final clause.* The correct versions restore parallelism to the final clause. |
| The hearing impaired child has difficulty speaking, reading, and *self-confidence.* | The hearing impaired child has difficulty speaking, reading, and in maintaining self-confidence. | |
| Disadvantages of primary reinforcers include satiation, dietary restriction, and *they also are difficult to administer to groups.* | Disadvantages of primary reinforcers include satiation, dietary restriction, and problematic group administration. | |
| Parental reinforcement of target behaviors helps maintenance by *not* allowing extinction, strengthening the behaviors, and increasing their use in natural environments. | Parental reinforcement of target behaviors helps maintenance by *not* allowing extinction, by strengthening the behaviors, and by increasing their use in natural environments. | The incorrect version is nonparallel because the word *not* applies only to the first in the series. In the correct version, the repetition of *by* restores parallelism. |
| The targets, the stimuli, and reinforcers, should all be specified. | The targets, the stimuli, and the reinforcers should all be specified. | An article is either repeated before all parallel terms, or is used only before the first term. (The targets, stimuli, and reinforcers . . . ) |

# Parallelism

## A.2.18b. Write in Parallel Terms

| Incorrect | Write Correctly |
|---|---|
| Many persons who stutter have been frustrated in the past because the therapists lacked adequate training, supervised experience, and the therapists' scientific knowledge of stuttering has been limited. | |
| Persons with communicative problems have difficulty talking, reading, and self-confidence. | |
| Some of the side effects of saying "no" to a client include aggression, reticence, and the client may also feel resentment toward the clinician. | |
| To promote response maintenance, I will select stimuli from the client's home, train self-monitoring skills, teach target behavior charting, and parent training will also be included. | |
| Patients with aphasia may be treated with auditory stimulation and verbal expression also may be taught. | |
| The theory may be criticized for three reasons: first, it is illogical; second, it is nonempirical; third, it is also difficult to apply. | |
| The client may receive treatment in fall, spring, or in summer terms.<br><br>*Hint:* The preposition is either repeated before all terms or used before the first term only. | |

## A.2.19a. Maintain Parallelism in Numbered or Bulleted Lists

| Incorrect | Correct | Note |
|---|---|---|
| Today's treatment objectives will include<br>• training the /s/ in the word final positions<br>• working on naming skills<br>• oral–motor exercises | Today's treatment objectives include<br>• training the /s/ in the word final positions<br>• working on naming skills<br>• providing oral–motor exercises. | Incorrect mixing of verb phrases with noun phrases in a list is corrected; this is a common mistake in numbered or bulleted lists. |
| Assessment will include the following steps:<br>1. hearing screening<br>2. orofacial examination<br>3. language sampling<br>4. any special tests that need to be administered should also be considered | Assessment will include the following steps:<br>1. hearing screening<br>2. orofacial examination<br>3. language sampling<br>4. special test administration (if any) | |
| In treating children, specialists recommend that you:<br>• speak in simple terms<br>• choose client-specific stimuli<br>• select reinforcers<br>• parent training also should be considered | In treating children, specialists recommend that you:<br>• speak in simple terms<br>• choose client-specific stimuli<br>• select reinforcers<br>• train parents | |
| Characteristics of motherese include:<br>• slower rate of speech<br>• greater pitch variations<br>• simpler words<br>• higher speech fluency<br>• articulation may be clear | Characteristics of motherese include:<br>• slower rate of speech<br>• greater pitch variations<br>• simpler words<br>• higher speech fluency<br>• clearer articulation | |

# A.2.19b. Maintain Parallelism in Numbered or Bulleted Lists

| Incorrect | Write Correctly |
|---|---|
| Children with language disorders show the following four major problems:<br>1. poor listening skills<br>2. limited understanding of word meanings<br>3. limited verbal expressions<br>4. narrative skills also may be impaired | |
| Research on speech sound acquisition has shown that:<br>• vowels are acquired before consonants<br>• stops are mastered earlier than fricatives<br>• nasals are mastered before affricates<br>• consonant clusters may take the longest to be acquired | |
| To promote response maintenance, I will:<br>• select stimuli from the client's home<br>• train self-monitoring skills<br>• teach target behavior charting<br>• parent training will be included | |
| The problems associated with cleft palate in children include:<br>• feeding problems<br>• middle ear infections<br>• dental problems<br>• parents may have negative emotional reactions | |

# Misplaced or Dangling Modifiers

## A.2.20a. Avoid Dangling Modifiers

- Dangling modifiers often do not seem to modify anything in a sentence.
- A phrase that is better placed at the beginning of a sentence may be left dangling at the end.

| Incorrect | Correct | Note |
|---|---|---|
| The clinician selected children for treatment, *taking into consideration the eligibility criteria*. | *Taking into consideration the eligibility criteria*, the clinician selected children for treatment. | In most cases, dangling phrases can be fixed by moving them to an earlier position in the sentence. |
| Many undesirable effects of amplification have been eliminated, *with the use of digital hearing aids*. | 1. *With the use of digital hearing aids*, audiologists have eliminated many undesirable effects of amplification.<br><br>2. Audiologists have shown that *digital hearing aids* eliminate many undesirable effects of amplification. | |
| I will teach the client self-monitoring skills, *to promote maintenance*. | *To promote maintenance*, I will teach the client self-monitoring skills. | |
| Children's language problems should not be ignored, *because they can lead to academic failure*. | *Because they can lead to academic failure*, we should not ignore children's language problems. | |

# Misplaced or Dangling Modifiers

## A.2.20b. Avoid Dangling Modifiers

| Incorrect | Write Correctly |
|---|---|
| I selected assessment procedures, giving much thought to reliability and validity. | |
| The problems of response maintenance may be handled, using parent training programs. | |
| Hearing will be tested, with an appropriately calibrated audiometer. *Hint*: Indicate who will test the hearing. | |
| Ten children will be selected for the study, all with cochlear implants. *Hint*: Indicate who will select the children. | |
| I will teach the client several phonemes this semester, to eliminate his articulation disorder. | |
| Alzheimer's disease profoundly affects everyone involved, because it changes everything for the patient and the family. | |

## A.2.21a. Avoid Misplaced Modifiers

- Misplaced modifiers seem to modify the wrong word in a sentence.
- Move the modifier closer to the word it correctly modifies.

| Incorrect | Correct | Note |
|---|---|---|
| Based on this hypothesis, Erickson developed his theory. | The theory that Erickson developed was based on this hypothesis. | Erickson was not based on the hypothesis. |
| In the study, these assumptions were only tested partially in the study. | In the study, these assumptions were tested only partially. | The misplaced word *only* is moved closer to the word it is supposed to modify. |
| The experimental group scored 10, but the control group only scored 5. | The experimental group scored 10, but the control group scored only 5. | |

### A.2.21b. Avoid Misplaced Modifiers

| Incorrect | Correct |
|---|---|
| Based on this evidence, I developed a treatment. | |
| Only the evidence partially supported the theory. | |
| The adults gained 10 points whereas the children only gained 4 points. | |

# Shifts Within and Between Sentences

## A.2.22a. Avoid Shifts Within and Between Sentences

- Unless justified, do not shift tense, voice, and mood within or between sentences.
- Do not shift number within or between sentences.

| Incorrect | Correct | Note |
|---|---|---|
| The clinician *was* well trained. She *knows* how to treat a variety of disorders. Nevertheless, she *had* difficulty treating this client. | The clinician *was* well trained. She *knew* how to treat a variety of disorders. Nevertheless, she *had* difficulty treating this client. | A shift in tense (in a group of sentences or in a single sentence) is corrected by maintaining the same past or present tense. |
| The story *talks* about a man and woman who *fell* in love. | The story *talks* about a man and woman who *fall* in love. | |
| Van Riper first *developed* an eclectic theory and later a more integrative theory was also *proposed*. | Van Riper first *developed* an eclectic theory and later *proposed* a more integrative theory. | A shift from active to passive voice is corrected by maintaining the active voice. |
| When *one* is reviewing the literature, *you* find that few studies exist. | When *one* is reviewing the literature, *one* finds that few studies exist. | A shift from second to third person is corrected by maintaining the same pronoun form. |
| If a *student* studies hard, *you* will impress teachers. | If a *student* studies hard, *he* or *she* will impress teachers. | A shift from third to second person is corrected by maintaining the third. |
| If a *client* misses many treatment sessions, *they* will not show improvement.  *Note:* This is an agreement problem as well. | If a *client* misses many treatment sessions, *he* or *she* will not show significant improvement. | A shift from singular to plural is corrected by maintaining the singular. |
| All *hospitals* have *a* physician. | All hospitals have physicians. | A shift from plural to singular is corrected by maintaining the plural. |
| It is important that an author *buy* a computer and *uses* it regularly. | It is important that an author *buy* a computer and *use* it regularly. | A shift in mood is corrected by maintaining the same imperative mood. |

A.2  Basic Rules of Composition  95

# Shifts Within and Between Sentences

## A.2.22b. Avoid Shifts Within and Between Sentences

| Incorrect | Write Correctly |
|---|---|
| The client was highly motivated for treatment. Therefore, the progress is good. | |
| I will first train grammatical morphemes. Later, syntactic features also will be trained. | |
| When one considers treatment options, you find many alternatives. | |
| A clinician who does not program maintenance will soon find that they have not completed the treatment. | |
| A review shows that this type of experiment has not been conducted. The review also has shown that it is difficult to control all the variables. | |
| The data suggested that the method was effective. The response rates indicates that maintenance also is enhanced. | |
| All public schools have a speech–language pathologist. | |
| If a clinician is exceptional, you are likely to get promoted. | |
| It is important that a clinician buy recent books and studied them carefully. | |
| The supervisor observed the client, and then talks to the parent. | |

# Quotations

### A.2.23a. Make Quotations Count

- Select only effective and memorable phrases to quote.
- Do not quote descriptive and ordinary statements.

| Descriptive And Ordinary | Rewritten Without Quotations | Note |
|---|---|---|
| Not all communicative disorders are related to environmental variables. Research has shown that "many genetic syndromes are associated with communicative disorders" (Brightly, 2015, p. 25). | Not all communicative disorders are related to environmental variables. Research has shown that several genetic syndromes may be related to communicative disorders (Brightly, 2015). | These quotations do not say anything worth quoting; they are rephrased. |
| According to Qotme, "aphasia is a common communicative disorder found in the elderly" (2012, p. 9). | Among older people, aphasia is a common communicative disorder (Qotme, 2012). | Give reference to specific source of information. |
| Quotman stated that "many neurological conditions can be associated with communicative disorders" (2014, p. 589). | Communicative disorders may be correlated with many neurological diseases or problems (Quotman, 2014). | Although common-knowledge or general statements do not need a reference, it may be prudent to give one in scientific writing. |
| Communicative disorders have a significant effect on the "social, occupational, and personal life of an individual" (Wisdon, 2013, p. 28). | Communicative disorders negatively affect an individual's personal, occupational, and social life (Wisdon, 2013). | Note that even common knowledge or general statements found in a source should be rephrased to avoid plagiaristic writing. |
| According to Surveyor, "roughly 10% of the population may have a communicative disorder" (2016, p. 18). | It is believed that one or more communicative disorders may be found in 10% of the population (Surveyor, 2016). | |

# Quotations

### A.2.23b. Make Quotations Count

In rewriting the passages, do not just remove the quotation marks from the statements; rewrite them in your words. If you simply remove the quotation marks, the writing will be plagiaristic.

| Descriptive and Ordinary | Rewrite Without Quotations |
|---|---|
| According to Linguistron, "many school-age children have language disorders that go undetected" (2017, p. 50). | |
| Many researchers have studied "the relation between mild conductive hearing loss and language development" (Otiss, 2015, p. 19). | |
| During hearing testing, "the clinician should mask the better ear" (Noisley, 2015, p. 567). | |
| According to Effecton, "some treatment procedures are effective while others are not" (2016, p. 20). | |
| Brimm has stated that "language acquisition is a complex process" (2005, p. 23). | |
| "speech sound disorders are common among school-age children" (Soundman, 2012, p. 20). | |

### A.2.24a. Do Not Overuse Quotations

- Do not use quotations to reduce the amount of your writing.
- Unless a quote is memorable, paraphrase it and give credit.
- Limit the number of quotations to no more than just a few in any paper you write.
- Minimize the use of long (block) quotations.

| Overuse | Judicious Use | Note |
|---|---|---|
| The study of language has shown "many rapid changes over the years" (Thomas, 2010, p. 90). In the 1940s "descriptive linguistics dominated the study of language" (TeNiel, 2005, p. 13). According to Thomas (2010), the focus shifted to "transformational generative grammar in the late 1950s and early 1960s" (p. 118). Then again in the 1970s, the focus was shifted to "the essence of language: meaning" (Revolutionary, 2015, p. 50). Soon, however, this approach was abandoned in favor of a "new pragmatic approach" (Bomber, 2016, p. 120). | During the past few decades, the study of language has changed many times. In the 1940s, descriptive linguistics was the main approach to the study of language. Dissatisfied with a purely descriptive study, Chomsky (1957) and others in the late 1950s proposed a new transformational generative grammar approach. In the 1970s, those who disagreed with the purely theoretical grammar approach proposed a new semantic view that focused on "the essence of language: meaning" (Revolutionary, 2015, p. 50). Soon, this, too, was replaced by the newer pragmatic approach (Bomber, 2016). | Overuse of quotations tends to include unremarkable statements as well. Writing littered with ineffective quotes is difficult to read. |
| Some question whether "apraxia of speech exists in children at all" (Smoothly, 2014, p. 27). In adults, apraxia is "associated with observable signs of neurological disease or trauma" (Brain, 2016, p. 25). Head (1929) has stated that when there is no evidence of neurological involvement, "apraxia of speech in children is a doubtful diagnostic classification" (p. 19). | Some question the existence of apraxia of speech in children. In adults who have apraxia of speech, symptoms of neurological diseases or trauma are documented. Therefore, in the absence of neurological involvement, diagnosis of apraxia in children is questionable (Brain, 2016; Head, 1929; Smoothly, 2014). | |

## A.2.24b. Do Not Overuse Quotations

In rewriting the passages, do not just eliminate the quotation marks. Rephrase the quotations.

| Overuse | Rewrite With Fewer Quotations |
|---|---|
| Inappropriate behavior causes several forms of voice disorders. According to Scream, "how you use your voice will determine whether you will have a healthy voice or not" (2008, p. 90). Loud (2013) also stated that "certain occupations pose high risk for voice disorders" (p. 13). Shout said a prudent person avoids "noisy places" (2009, p. 118). | |
| Either the right or the left ear may be tested first because "the selection is purely arbitrary" (Horton, 2014, p. 32). Research has not shown that it is "better to test one or the other ear first" (McClauey, 2015, p. 67). Most audiologists "begin testing at 1000 Hz, though the order in which the frequencies are tested may not be important" (Soundson, 2016, p. 45). Some audiologists "do not test at 125 Hz at all, while others do" (Southern, 2007, p. 22). | |

### A.2.25a. Do Not Include Islands of Quotations

- Do not let quotations stand alone in your writing.
- Blend quotations smoothly into your expressions.
- Write phrases that lead to the quotation.
- On occasion, write your own words after the quotation.

| Incorrect | Correct | Note |
|---|---|---|
| Autism is a serious childhood disorder. It starts in early childhood. "Children who are autistic do not live in the world of their families, but in their own world of distorted fantasy" (Scitzmoore, 2015, p. 10). The disorder affects thought and language. "Children who are autistic are unable to form emotional bonds with their loved ones" (Sentiment, 2013, p. 15). This can cause serious interpersonal problems. | Autism is a serious childhood disorder. It starts in early childhood. Children who are autistic are not in touch with their surroundings as they seem to live "in their own world of distorted fantasy" (Scitzmoore, 2015, p. 10). The disorder affects thought, language, and emotional experience. According to Sentiment (2013), the children who are autistic are "unable to form emotional bonds with their loved ones" (p. 15), resulting in serious interpersonal problems. | You quote fewer words when you integrate quotations with your writing. In the correct version, no quotation stands alone. Phrases such as *according to*, *as stated by*, *as written by*, and *the author stated that* lead the reader to the quotation and help blend a quotation with the main writing. |

## A.2.25b. Do Not Include Islands of Quotations

| Incorrect | Write Correctly |
|---|---|
| Multiple misarticulations suggest a need for a phonological pattern analysis. "A pattern analysis helps the clinician see order in what might appear to be a collection of random errors" (Godsen, 2015, p. 45). Several methods of phonological analysis are available. "The clinician should select the one that is simple to use and comprehensive in its analysis" (Nixon, 2017, p. 10). | |

### A.2.26a. Do Not Begin a Sentence With a Quotation

- Begin sentences with your words.
- Insert quotations within or at the end of your sentence.

| Incorrect | Correct |
| --- | --- |
| "Cleft palate speech is most readily recognized" (Milton, 2015, p. 20) because of its unique characteristics. | Because of its unique characteristics, "cleft palate speech is most readily recognized" (Milton, 2015, p. 20). |
| "In recent years, computerized audiometers have been developed to automatically control all aspects of pure tone air- and bone-conduction testing" (Robotson, 2005, p. 98); however, this does not mean that we "do not need audiologists who have a good clinical sense" (Robotson, 2005, p. 99). | In recent years, the administration of hearing tests has been computerized. However, as pointed out by Robotson (2005), we still need audiologists "who have a good clinical sense" (p. 99). |

### A.2.26b. Do Not Begin a Sentence With a Quotation

| Incorrect | Write Correctly |
|---|---|
| "Audiometers alone, no matter how advanced, will not diagnose hearing impairment" (Torkin, 2016, p. 32). It is the clinician's expert interpretation of results that leads to a clinical diagnosis. "No mechanical device is a substitute for good clinical sense" (Barkin, 2017, p. 551). | |
| "Specific language disorder often is not associated with an identifiable cause" (Barney, 2014, p. 40). The child may be normal in every respect except for delayed language. "It is hypothesized that specific language delay may have a genetic basis" (Tomokin, 2013, p. 22). | |

### A.2.27a. Use Quotation and Punctuation Marks Correctly

- Enclose all direct quotations within two double quotations marks ("and").
- Use single quotation marks ('and') to enclose a quotation within a quotation.
- In most cases, place the punctuation mark *within* the quotation mark; take note of an exception in the last example.
- Double-check for missing quotation marks at the beginning or the ending of quotations.

| Incorrect | Correct | Note |
|---|---|---|
| The clinician said, "Good job". | The clinician said, "Good job." | The first two incorrect versions have the punctuation marks outside the quotation marks. |
| I will say "wrong", and then mark the incorrect response on the sheet. | I will say "wrong," and then mark the incorrect response on the sheet. | The last two have missing quotation marks. |
| He said that he was "sorry for what happened. | He said that he was "sorry for what happened." | The last example also shows an exception to the punctuation rule. |
| According to Soundson, hearing impairment costs billions of dollars to the nation's health care system." (2010, p. 9). | According to Soundson, "hearing impairment costs billions of dollars to the nation's health care system" (2010, p. 9). | When a reference citation follows a quotation, the period is placed after the closing parenthesis. |

## A.2.27b. Use Quotation and Punctuation Marks Correctly

| Incorrect | Write Correctly |
|---|---|
| Mrs. Aktsungfoong added that her husband is "stubborn" and "difficult to manage". | |
| The parents said that their son is "delighted", "very pleased", and "impressed" with the services. | |
| One expert stated that "remediating pragmatic language disorders is the most important treatment target". | |

## A.2.28a. Do Not Misuse Quotation Marks

Do not enclose book and journal titles, technical terms, terms of special emphasis, and linguistic examples within quotation marks; use italics as shown.

| Incorrect | Correct | Note |
|---|---|---|
| "Aphasia: A clinical approach." | *Aphasia: A clinical approach.* | A book title or a journal name is italicized. |
| "Journal of Audiology" | *Journal of Audiology* | |
| "Dysphonia" means disordered voice. | *Dysphonia* means disordered voice.<br><br>**Dysphonia** means disordered voice. | When it is defined, a technical term is shown in italics or bold face. |
| You may not always substitute the conjunction "and" for the ampersand "&." | You may not always substitute the conjunction *and* for the ampersand *&*. | Linguistic examples are italicized (not bolded). |

*Exception:* The titles of articles and research papers are neither enclosed within quotation marks nor italicized. However, titles of theses and dissertations (published or unpublished) are italicized.

## A.2.28b. Do Not Misuse Quotation Marks

| Incorrect | Write Correctly |
|---|---|
| "Introduction to Audiology" by Matson | |
| "Journal of Speech, Language, and Hearing Research" | |
| "Congenital disorder" is a disorder noticed at the time of birth or soon thereafter. | |
| The child does not produce the possessive "s" and the present progressive "ing." | |

### A.2.29a. Give References for All Direct Quotations

In scientific writing, all direct quotations should include the following:

- the last name of the author or authors
- the year of publication
- the number of the page or pages on which the quotation is found

| Incorrect | Correct | Note |
|---|---|---|
| According to Confusius, "a terrible confusion between who you are and what you want to be" causes stuttering. | According to Confusius (2002), "a terrible confusion between who you are and what you want to be" (p. 37) causes stuttering. | The incorrect version includes neither the year of publication nor the page number. |
| Mixtupton recommended that "children with phonological disorders should be separated from those with a mere articulation disorder" (2015). | Mixtupton recommended that "children with phonological disorders should be separated from those with a mere articulation disorder" (2015, p. 23). | The incorrect version includes the year of publication, but omits the page number. |
| It has been stated that "chronic and excessively loud speech is detrimental to healthy voice." | It has been stated that "chronic and excessively loud speech is detrimental to healthy voice" (Louden, 2012, p. 10). | The worst of the three, this incorrect version omits the author's name, year of publication, and the page number. |
| Although persons who stutter may show some excessive anxiety, it is "often associated with speech, and, therefore, there is no evidence for a "trait anxiety" in most stutterers" (Angst, 2011, p. 67). | Although persons who stutter may show some excessive anxiety, it is "often associated with speech, and, therefore, there is no evidence for a 'trait anxiety' in most stutterers" (Angst, 2011, p. 67). | A phrase with double quotation marks within a quotation is enclosed within single quotation marks. |
| Although found in all societies, "the incidence of cleft palate varies across different racial groups, suggesting the importance of genetic factors in its etiology" (Geneson, 2013, p. 10–11). | Although found in all societies, "the incidence of cleft palate varies across different racial groups, suggesting the importance of genetic factors in its etiology" (Geneson, 2013, pp. 10–11). | The correct version shows the page on which the quotation begins and the page on which it ends. Use p. for one page and pp. for two or more pages, both in lowercase. |

*Note:* There are different methods of placing the name, the year, and the page number. The period is placed only after the parenthetical closure, not before or after the quotation marks.

## A.2.29b. Give References for All Direct Quotations

Invent the information that is needed to correct the statements.

| Incorrect | Write Correctly |
|---|---|
| According to Loveson, many factors cause language delay, "but none can be directly traced to lack of parental love for the child." | |
| Boontenthorpe has written that "adults who have strokes and aphasia show remarkable spontaneous recovery within 3 to 6 months of onset" (2014). | |
| It has been stated that "a single, loud scream can damage the vocal folds." | |
| A neglected cause of hearing impairment is "the types of food we eat; it is possible that "pesticide-laced grains and fruits" are a source of cochlear damage in some cases" (Peston, 2011, p. 67). | |
| Recent developments in cochlear implants have "made it possible for many deaf children to begin their aural rehabilitation early in life" (Coplant, 2015, p. 15–16). | |

### A.2.30a. Reproduce Quotations Exactly

- Make quotations identical to the original in words, spelling, and punctuation.
- Reproduce errors as they are in the original with the insertion of the word [*sic*], italicized, and placed within brackets.

| A Quotation With an Error in it | Note |
|---|---|
| Numbasa's description of language as a mental phenomenon "that can be studied only by some powerfil [*sic*] intuitive procedures" was especially appealing to clinicians who had based their treatment procedures on intuition. | In the quotation, the italicized word [*sic*] suggests that in the original, the word *powerful* is misspelled. |

### A.2.31a. Integrate Quotations of Fewer Than 40 Words With the Text

| Incorrect (Unintegrated) | Correct | Note |
|---|---|---|
| Mentalis defined language as:<br><br>"A cognitive ability to synthesize and symbolize mental experience and to represent this experience in patterns of sounds, words, and sentences following linguistic rules that are innately given" (2014, p. 95).<br><br>Mentalis's definition has been widely cited by cognitive psychologists and linguists who think that language is not action, but a mental process. | Mentalis defined language as "a cognitive ability to synthesize and symbolize mental experience and to represent this experience in patterns of sounds, words, and sentences following linguistic rules that are innately given" (2014, p. 95). Mentalis's definition has been widely cited by cognitive psychologists and linguists who think that language is not action, but a mental process. | Only quotations of 40 words or more are set off from the rest of the text as *block* quotations. See A.2.32. |

## A.2.30b. Reproduce Quotations Exactly

| Quotation With an Error in it | Quote it Appropriately |
|---|---|
| Softhead (2015) said that "language is not to be confused with what people say, because language is a metal tool of imagination" (p. 40).<br><br>*Hint:* *metal* or *mental*? | |

## A.2.31b. Integrate Quotations of Fewer Than 40 Words With the Text

| Incorrectly Arranged Quotation | Integrate the Quote With Text |
|---|---|
| Nullbrain (2015) stated that:<br><br>   Every child who learns to speak his or her language is a scientist who tests alternative hypotheses about the nature of language. The utterances the child hears are the data for hypothesis testing. (p. 23)<br><br>Critics have contended that such statements betray a theoretical fantasy. | <br><br><br><br><br><br><br><br><br><br><br><br><br>*Hint:* Write a single paragraph containing the quotation. |

## A.2.32a. Arrange Quotations as a *Block* When They Have 40 Words or More

- A quotation set apart from the text is a *block quotation*.
- Set quotations of 40 words or more as block quotations.
- Indent the entire quotation by five spaces from the left margin, as for a new paragraph.
- Indent the first line of the second (and subsequent) paragraphs of the quoted material five more spaces.
- Do not use quotation marks.
- However, place within *double quotation marks* a quotation within a block quotation.
- After the quotation, type the page number of the quotation within parentheses.
- Do not type a period after the closing parenthesis.
- Begin your text with a new paragraph.

| Block Quotation | Note |
|---|---|
| In his powerful explanation of language intervention, Numbskull (2015) has stated the following:<br><br>    Language intervention is a process of unleashing powerful but painfully hidden but unconsciously active communicative potential. The goals of language intervention include transcendental self- actualization, cognitive reorganization, and reconstruction of perceptual–emotive reality.<br>        The process of language intervention is mysterious. A successful clinician has an innate ability to solve this mystery. (p. 19)<br><br>Numbskull's explanation is now a basis for many language treatment programs. Clinicians who despise tiresome objectivity in language treatment have gladly adopted this view. | Alternatively, you may end the quotation with the author name, year, and the page number or numbers as shown:<br><br>    Several experts believe that language intervention is the unleashing of communicative potential. For instance:<br><br>    Language intervention is a process of unleashing powerful but painfully hidden but unconsciously active communicative potential . . .<br>        The process of language intervention is mysterious. A successful clinician has an innate ability to solve this mystery. (Numbskull, 2015, p. 19) |

## A.2.32b. Arrange Quotations as a *Block* When They Have 40 Words or More

| Quotation of More Than 40 Words | Arrange it Properly |
|---|---|
| Dumdum (1992) has stated that "the root cause of stuttering is lack of a shining self-image. That fluent speech is a function of self-image that throws bright light into the eyes of the listener is well established. Therefore, to make stuttering persons speak fluently, we must find ways of polishing their self-image so it begins to shine again" (pp. 35–36). All clinicians should consider this powerful explanation of stuttering in planning treatment for their clients. Treatment based on this explanation will undoubtedly solve the nagging problem of maintenance of fluency. | |

### A.2.33a. Show Correctly the Changes in Quotations

- When you omit words from a sentence within a quotation, insert three ellipsis marks with a space before and after each mark (e.g., mark . . . ).
- When you omit words between sentences, insert four ellipsis marks; the first of these four is a period, hence no space before it; the three other marks are separated by a space; there is a space after the third mark (e.g., mark. . . . ).
- Do not insert ellipsis marks at the beginning and end of a quotation even when it begins or ends in midsentence.
- If you insert words into a quotation, enclose them within brackets.
- Italicize the words *you* emphasize in the quotation that were not emphasized in the original; next to the italicized word, type the words [italics added] within brackets.
- Add quotation marks, author name, year of publication, and the page number as shown in the examples.

| Changed Quotation | Note |
| --- | --- |
| Bluff has stated that "stuttering cannot be measured by . . . merely counting dysfluencies" (1993, p. 58). | Omitted words within a sentence indicated: *by . . . merely* (three ellipsis with space in between) |
| "Stuttering and dysfluencies are not to be confused. . . . Stuttering is more than mere dysfluencies" (Bluff, 1993, p. 59). | Omitted words between sentences indicated by a period and three dots: *confused. . . . Stuttering* (the dots after the period are each separated by one space) |
| According to Bluff, "stuttering is not a speech problem. There is no need to treat it as a communication disorder. It [stuttering] is a problem of cognitive dissonance" (1993, p. 67). | A word may be inserted into a quotation to make the reference clear. Inserted word or words are bracketed: *It* [stuttering] *is* . . . in this example. |
| Bluff's extraordinary claim is that "stuttering treatment should involve *cognitive rehabilitation*" [italics added] (1993, p. 68). | One or more words in the quotation may be italicized to add emphasis. Note that all quotations need the author's name, year of publication, and the page number with p. as its abbreviation. |

### A.2.33b. Show Correctly the Changes in Quotations

| Changed Quotation | Rewrite Correctly |
|---|---|
| Snuff has stated that "Voice disorders are not only a product of various medical pathologies (words omitted) but also a product of certain life styles. Therefore, clinicians should take a careful and detailed history of the client (words omitted at the end of the sentence). Information obtained through history is invaluable in planning treatment for voice clients (the last three words added). They (the clinicians: *added words*) should not hesitate to probe the *client's life style*" (the last three words italicized to add emphasis; not in the original) (2002, p. 50).<br><br>*Hint:* More than 40 words! | |

## A.2.34a. Quote Correctly the Sources on the Internet

- Quoting Internet sources with no print editions can be challenging partly because the sources tend to change in both accessibility and content.
- The author, the date, and the page numbers of materials published online may be unclear.
- Reliability and validity of the materials posted may be difficult to assess.
- It is prudent to limit quotes to those taken from established scientific and professional organizations and electronic versions of peer-reviewed journals and to avoid quotes from blogs, wikis, and other such unstable sources on the Internet unless such sources are a topic of research or discussion.

| Quote Correctly | Note |
| --- | --- |
| Johns (2015) stated that "the frequency of dysfluencies is more important than their type" (para. 7). | When the page numbers are not available, give the paragraph number if possible (para., abbreviated). |
| In his study, Williams (2008) claimed that "a genetic basis for child language will soon be discovered" (Introductory section, para. 4). | If no continuous paragraph or page numbers are available for the entire article, specify the section heading and the paragraph number (manually counted) under the heading. |
| The authors suggested that "early intervention for language disorders is the best means of promoting later academic success" (Boss & Best, 2016, "Promoting Academic Success," para. 2). | When no page or paragraph numbers for the entire article are available, and the heading is too long, abbreviate the heading. In this example, the heading was "Promoting Academic Success Through Early Language Intervention in Children From Low Socioeconomic Backgrounds in Urban Settings." You will have to omit the paragraph number if it is not possible to determine. |

### A.2.34b. Quote Correctly the Sources on the Internet

| Quote | Write Correctly |
|---|---|
| Thomas wrote that "the voice disorders need a more valid system of classification"<br><br>Year: 2014; no page numbers<br>Paragraph, 3 | |
| In his study, James concluded that "autism is not caused by vaccinations of any kind"<br><br>Year: 2011<br>No page number<br>Section heading: Discussion<br>Paragraph, 7 under the section. | |
| The authors suggested that "nodules are better treated with vocal behavior modification"<br><br>Year: 2003<br>Authors: Ram and Jam<br>No page number<br>Paragraph 2<br>Full title: Treating vocal nodules and the attending voice disorders in professional singers and teachers a large urban setting. | |

# Precision in the Use of Scientific Terms

## A.2.35a. Use the Terms Ending in *-ology* Correctly

A few terms that end with *ology* are frequently misused even in scholarly and clinical writing. *Ology* is a study of something or a branch of learning. Therefore, *phonology group*, *phonology disorder*, and *impaired morphology* imply that the writer or speaker is careless in using technical terms.

| Incorrect | Correct | Note |
|---|---|---|
| The child had a disordered morphology. | The child's morphologic productions were impaired. The child does not produce certain morphologic features. | *Disordered morphology* means chaotic study of morphologic aspects of language! |
| His morphology needs attention. | His morphological skills need attention. | Does his study of morphologic aspects of language need attention? |
| The disordered phonology was a major clinical concern. | The phonologic disorder was a major concern. | Is the study of phonologic aspects of language disordered? |
| She described the child's phonology. | She described the child's phonological performance. | Did the child produce a branch of learning called phonology? |
| We had two groups in the study: A phonology disorder group and a normal group. | We had two groups in the study: a group of children with phonological disorders and a group of children who spoke normally. | *Disordered phonology* is a frequent mistake in the writings of speech-language pathologists. |
| Because of his cancer, his physiology is disordered. | Because of his cancer, his physiological system is upset. | These less common mistakes highlight the inappropriateness of *disordered phonology* and *impaired morphology*. |
| A brain tumor implies disordered neurology. | A brain tumor implies a neurological disorder (disease). | |
| Her psychology is off. | Her emotional state is disturbed. | State precisely what is observed to be wrong or impaired. |

## Precision in the Use of Scientific Terms

### A.2.35b. Use the Terms Ending in *-ology* Correctly

| Incorrect | Write Correctly |
|---|---|
| The client has a disturbed morphology. | |
| The child's morphology should be targeted for treatment. | |
| The assessment results show that the child's phonology is disordered. | |
| A good description of a client's phonology is essential before starting phonologic treatment. | |
| Her biology is impaired. *Hint:* Specify a biological system. | |
| His psychology is disturbed. *Hint:* Specify a psychological disturbance. | |
| The patient with aphasia has impaired neurology. | |

## A.2.36a. Use Certain Terms Ending in *-ics* Correctly

Certain terms that end with *ics* mean the study of something. Such terms should be used to refer only to a study of something, body of knowledge, discipline, or a branch of learning. Such terms as *impaired semantics* or *disordered pragmatics* are examples of careless usage of technical terms, and imply ironically that the study itself is impaired or disordered.

| Incorrect | Correct | Note |
| --- | --- | --- |
| His semantics is impaired. | His understanding of meaning (semantic features) is impaired.<br><br>His productions suggest impaired semantic skills. | Semantics is the study of meaning in language; it cannot be impaired. |
| The training should concentrate on her semantics. | The training should concentrate on her semantic features. | Should the training concentrate on (her) study of meaning? |
| The client's pragmatics needs help. | The client's pragmatic skills need treatment. | Does the client's study of language use need help? |
| The impaired pragmatics requires advanced training. | The impaired pragmatic language skills require advanced training. | Does the study of pragmatic aspects of language require advanced training? |
| The child's linguistics is impaired. | The child's language performance is impaired. | These are less common mistakes; nonetheless, they point out the inappropriateness of such terms as *impaired semantics* and *disordered pragmatics*. |
| Studies have shown that disordered genetics may partly be responsible for stuttering that runs in families. | Studies have shown that genetic factors may partly be responsible for stuttering that runs in families. | |

## A.2.36b. Use Certain Terms Ending in *-ics* Correctly

| Incorrect | Write Correctly |
|---|---|
| Her semantics is difficult to analyze. | |
| Semantics was one of the treatment goals. | |
| His use of pragmatics is questionable. | |
| Her pragmatics should be a treatment target. | |
| The child's linguistics is impaired. | |
| The man's genetics is faulty. | |

# Use of Fresh Language

## A.2.37a. Avoid Clichés

- Clichés are overused, dull, and stale expressions; they include most idioms.
- Replace clichés and idioms with direct and fresh expressions.

| Cliché | Simple and Direct | Note |
|---|---|---|
| We do not have many *tried-and-true* treatment techniques. | We do not have many proven treatment techniques. | The word *proven* is more acceptable for this kind of writing. |
| Though he recently had a stroke, the patient was *fit as a fiddle*. | Though he recently had a stroke, the patient was in good health. | An everyday term is more appropriate than the cliché. |
| Treating patients with laryngectomy is not her *cup of tea*. | 1. She does not enjoy treating patients with laryngectomy. <br> 2. She does not know how to treat patients who have had laryngectomy. | Some clichés mask multiple meanings. |
| In *this day and age*, the clinician needs to have computer skills. | The clinician needs to have computer skills. | |

## A.2.38a. Avoid Colloquial or Informal Expressions

- Avoid such expressions in scientific and professional writing.
- Use your judgment in including them in informal and general writing.

| Informal | Formal | Note |
|---|---|---|
| If the client *can't* imitate, I will use the shaping method. | If the client *cannot* imitate, I will use the shaping method. | Avoid informal contractions. |
| Continuous reinforcement *won't* be used. | Continuous reinforcement *will not* be used. | |
| The researcher *felt* that the procedure was effective. | The researcher *thought* that the procedure was effective. | Avoid such subjective terms as *felt* unless the reference is to feelings. |
| The clinician should *get across* the idea that maintenance treatment is important. | The clinician should *point out* that maintenance treatment is important. | Such colloquial expressions are not appropriate in scientific writing. |
| The clinician *came up* with a dysphagia assessment procedure. | The clinician *developed* a dysphagia assessment procedure. | |

# Use of Fresh Language

### A.2.37b. Avoid Clichés

| Cliché | Write In Simple And Direct Words |
|---|---|
| The child is bored to tears with therapy. | |
| The initial progress gave the client a shot in the arm. | |
| The child who stutters is sick and tired of teasing from her friends. | |
| In promoting maintenance, I will leave no stone unturned. | |
| My treatment plan was off track. | |

### A.2.38b. Avoid Colloquial or Informal Expressions

| Informal | Formal |
|---|---|
| The client just wouldn't imitate the modeled stimulus. | |
| The clinician hadn't prepared the stimulus materials. | |
| I feel that the client's hoarseness of voice is due to vocal nodules. | |
| During counseling the clients, you should get across the idea that early intervention is important. | |
| The clinician cooked up a novel method of evoking the /r/. | |

# A.3. Commonly Misused Words and Phrases

Avoid the common mistakes of misusing words that sound similar, but have different meanings.

## A.3.1a. Accept and Except

The two do not share meaning, but a phonetic similarity may cause confusion. *Accept* means to receive something offered; *except* means with the exclusion of (something or someone). Erroneous substitution of *except* for *accept* is a common mistake.

| Incorrect | Correct | Note |
|---|---|---|
| I *except* your kind offer. | I *accept* your kind offer. | The incorrect expressions do not make sense. |
| She *excepted* our gift. | She *accepted* our gift. | |
| I was the only one *accepted* from the regulation. | I was the only one *excepted* from the regulation. | |
| All were admitted into the bar, *accept* me. | All were admitted into the bar, *except* me. | |
| I will *except* all conditions *accept* the first. | I will *accept* all conditions *except* the first. | The incorrect expression may be interpreted to mean the opposite of what is intended. |
| Scientists have *excepted* these hypotheses, accept perhaps the last two. | Scientists have *accepted* these hypotheses, except perhaps the last two. | |

## A.3.2a. Affect and Effect

Generally, use *affect* as a verb and *effect* as a noun. **Exceptions:** Use *effect* (or the term *to effect*) always as a verb or verb phrase when the meaning is *to cause a change* or *create an effect* (e.g., *Education is intended to effect changes in thinking*); use *affect* as a noun when it refers to an emotional state (e.g., *When he lost the bet, his affect changed*).

| Incorrect | Correct |
|---|---|
| Many researchers have studied the masking noise *affect* on stuttering. | Many researchers have studied the masking noise *effect* on stuttering. |
| She studied the treatment *affects*. | She studied the treatment *effects*. |
| The treatment *effected* the behavior. | The treatment *affected* the behavior. |
| How did the variable *effect* the outcome? | How did the variable *affect* the outcome? |
| The clinician's goal is *to affect* changes in the client's communicative behaviors. | The clinician's goal is to *effect* changes in the client's communicative behaviors. |
| The clinician could not *affect* changes in the patient's naming skills. | The clinician could not *effect* changes in the patient's naming skills. |

### A.3.1b. Accept and Except

| Incorrect | Write Correctly |
|---|---|
| I am pleased to except your job offer. | |
| He did not except our offer of assistance. | |
| Everyone got in, accept John. | |
| The faculty excepted all applicants, accept one. | |
| Scientists have excepted these theories, accept perhaps the first. | |

### A.3.2b. Affect and Effect

| Incorrect | Write Correctly |
|---|---|
| The affect of environmental deprivation on language acquisition is significant. | |
| This study on the affect of aphasia treatment was poorly designed. | |
| Modeling effected the target response. | |
| To affect changes in clients' behaviors, the clinician needs strong treatment programs. | |
| How does the parental dysfluency rate effect the child's stuttering? | |
| In spite of her excellent efforts, the clinician could not affect changes in the patient's cognitive skills. | *Hint*: *to cause changes* (the exceptional case). |

### A.3.3a. Alternate and Alternative

*Alternate* means different events occurring or succeeding by turns; to alternate is to shift from one to the other. *Alternative* suggests a choice between two possibilities.

| Incorrect | Correct | Note |
|---|---|---|
| We will use the two *alternative* treatments to see if one is more effective than the other. | We will *alternate* the two treatments to see if one is better than the other. | Clinician shifts from one treatment to the other; both are offered in different sessions. |
| The appliance uses *alternative* current. | The appliance uses *alternating* current. | Current reverses its direction at regular intervals. |
| I will take the *alternate* route. | I will take the *alternative* route. | The person chose the other route. |
| The only *alternate* to treatment is continued stuttering. | The only *alternative* to treatment is continued stuttering. | The statement says there is only one choice. |

### A.3.4a. Allusion and Illusion

Use *illusion* to refer to an unreal image and *allusion* to suggest an indirect reference.

| Incorrect | Correct |
|---|---|
| She made an *illusion* to the new theory of voice production. | She made an *allusion* to the new theory of voice production. |
| The ghost he thought he saw was merely an *allusion*. | The ghost he thought he saw was merely an *illusion*. |

### A.3.5a. And/Or

Do not write *and/or*. Rewrite the sentence.

| Incorrect | Correct |
|---|---|
| Pictures *and/or* objects will be used to evoke the target behaviors. | Pictures, objects, *or both* will be used to evoke the target behaviors. |
| Speech-language pathologists *and/or* psychologists may assess persons with dementia. | Speech-language pathologists, psychologists, *or both* may assess persons with dementia. |

### A.3.3b. *Alternate* and *Alternative*

| Incorrect | Write Correctly |
|---|---|
| It leaves me with no alternate. | |
| You can alternative the two probe procedures. | |
| We will alternatively use auditory comprehension and speech production to see which one is more effective. | |
| The alternate to a college education is a low-paying job. | |

### A.3.4b. *Allusion* and *Illusion*

| Incorrect | Write Correctly |
|---|---|
| He made an illusion to an emerging trend in the treatment of dysarthria. | |
| The treatment effects reported in the study were merely an allusion. | |

### A.3.5b. *And/Or*

| Incorrect | Write Correctly |
|---|---|
| The father and/or the mother of the client will be trained in response maintenance. | |
| Language disorders and/or phonological disorders may coexist with stuttering. | |

### A.3.6a. *Baseline* and *Baserate*

- Use *baseline* only as a noun.
- Use *baserate* as a verb or as a noun.
- Note that the words *baserate* and *baseline* are single words (not written as *base rate* or *base line*).

| Incorrect | Correct | Note |
|---|---|---|
| Before starting treatment, the clinician should *baseline* target behaviors. | Before starting treatment, the clinician should establish *baselines* of target behaviors. | *Baselines* incorrectly used as a verb and correctly used as a noun. |
| I *baselined* the target responses. | I will establish *baselines* of target responses. | |
| I will *baseline* phoneme productions. | I will *baserate* phoneme productions. I will measure the *baserate* of phoneme productions. | *Baseline* incorrectly used as a verb and correctly substituted with *baserate*. *Baserate* correctly used as a noun. |

### A.3.7a. *Effect* and *Impact*

- In scientific writing, prefer the term *effect* to currently popular *impact*; it makes little sense to say "treatment made an impact" unless you mean that the treatment collided the client and got stuck on him or her.
- Note that the original meaning of *impact* is *striking of one body against the other* (as in the expression, *the man who jumped from the fifth floor died of injuries caused by the impact*).
- Note that the term *impact* also means *to pack firmly*, as in the expression *the audiologist found impacted wax in the client's ear*.

| Inaccurate | Accurate | Note |
|---|---|---|
| Modeling has an *impact* on the client's productions. | Modeling has an *effect* on the client's productions. | Modeling does not strike or firmly pack the client's productions. |
| This treatment is known to have an *impact*. | This treatment is known to have an *effect*. | The traditional word does fine. |
| The *impact* of poverty on language acquisition needs additional research. | The *effect* of poverty on language acquisition needs additional research. | |

### A.3.6b. *Baseline* and *Baserate*

| Incorrect | Write Correctly |
|---|---|
| All target behaviors should be baselined before starting treatment. | |
| I first baselined turn taking in conversation. | |
| I will baseline morphologic productions. | 1. Correct noun form:<br><br>2. Correct verb form: |

### A.3.7b. *Effect* and *Impact*

| Inaccurate | Write More Accurately |
|---|---|
| Slow rate of speech has a profound impact on stuttering. | |
| Several investigators have analyzed the impact of noise on speech. | |
| The impact of treatment was negligible. | |

### A.3.8a. *Elicit* and *Evoke*

- Note that a stimulus (e.g., a tap on the knee) *elicits* a reflexive response (e.g., a knee-jerk reflex) and a different stimulus (e.g., a picture) *evokes* a voluntary response (e.g., a name from a person with aphasia).
- In natural settings or in treatment sessions, speech-language responses, being voluntary, are not *elicited*, but *evoked*.
- Prefer the word *evoke* to imply the action of stimulating speech and language responses in assessment or treatment sessions.

| Less Accurate | More Accurate | Note |
|---|---|---|
| I will *elicit* a language sample from the child with the help of toys. | I will *evoke* a language sample from the child. | Technically, reflexive responses are *elicited* and voluntary responses are *evoked*. Speech and language production is not reflexive. |
| I will *evoke* dilation of the pupil by a flash of light. | I will *elicit* dilation of the pupil. | |
| Pavlov *evoked* the salivary reflex by placing meat powder in the dog's mouth. | Pavlov *elicited* the salivary reflex by placing meat powder in the dog's mouth. | |
| By reinforcing them, Skinner *elicited* and increased the bar pressing responses in rats. | By reinforcing them, Skinner *evoked* and increased the bar pressing responses in rats. | |

### A.3.9a. *Elicit* and *Illicit*

- Because of an especially troublesome confusion, some students try to *illicit target responses*.
- Note that *illicit* is not a verb, it is an adjective (but a supervisor with no sense of humor may pull out handcuffs!)

| Incorrect | Correct | Note |
|---|---|---|
| Pictures will be used to *illicit* the phoneme. | Pictures will be used to *evoke* the phoneme. | The less accurate *elicit* is preferable to the illegal *illicit*. |
| I will teach the mother to *illicit* the target behaviors at home. | I will teach the mother to *evoke* the target behaviors at home. | |

A.3  Commonly Misused Words and Phrases            131

### A.3.8b.  *Elicit* and *Evoke*

| Less Accurate | Write More Accurately |
|---|---|
| Pavlov evoked the salivary reflex. | |
| Skinner elicited the bar press response. | |
| There are many procedures to elicit the production of /s/. | |
| I will evoke the psychogalvanic reflex. | |
| I know a few methods of evoking the swallow reflex. | |

### A.3.9b.  *Elicit* and *Illicit*

| Incorrect | Write Correctly |
|---|---|
| She illicited single-word responses from her client. | |
| I will demonstrate in front of a mirror to illicit /k/. | |
| I will use pictures to illicit naming responses from my patient with aphasia. | |

*Note:* There is no such word as *illicited*.

## A.3.10a. *Farther* and *Further*

Use *farther* to refer to distance. Use *further* to refer to time or quantity.

| Incorrect | Correct |
|---|---|
| She walked *further* than any person. | She walked *farther* than any person. |
| I sent the parents a *farther* notice of an IEP meeting. | I sent the parents a *further* notice of an IEP meeting. |
| *Farthermore*, the client was often late. | *Furthermore*, the client was often late. |

## A.3.11a. *Focus* and *Analysis (Study)*

- Note that *focus* is another fancy term whose popularity is ever escalating.
- In scientific writing, substitute this term with more appropriate terms, including *study* or *analysis*.

| Vague | More Precise | Note |
|---|---|---|
| In her lecture, she *focused* on the principles of aerobic dancing. | In her lecture, she *elaborated* the principles of aerobic dancing. | The inaccurate statement does not say what the lecturer did. |
| To prevent heart diseases, scientists are *focusing* on people's dietary habits. | To prevent heart diseases, scientists are *studying* people's dietary habits. | Just *focusing* on a problem may not help analyze it or solve it. |
| In solving the crime problem, investigators have *focused* on family dynamics. | In solving the crime problem, investigators have *analyzed* family dynamics. | |

## A.3.10b. *Farther* and *Further*

| Incorrect | Write Correctly |
|---|---|
| New York is further than you think. | |
| After establishing the target behaviors, the clinician should do farther work on maintenance. | |
| I will study the subject farther. | |

## A.3.11b. *Focus* and *Analysis (Study)*

| Vague | Write More Precisely |
|---|---|
| Because I am getting poor grades, I need to focus on my study skills. | |
| The instructor focused on some difficult theories. | |
| The researchers now focus on the genetic bases of hearing impairment. | |

### A.3.12a. *Incidence* and *Prevalence*

- Incidence refers to the future occurrence of an event in a population. (*How many normally speaking children will begin to stutter in a twelve month period?*)
- Prevalence refers to the current existence; you take a head count. (*How many children in the school district currently have a hearing impairment?*)

| Incorrect | Correct | Note |
|---|---|---|
| The *incidence* of stuttering in the U.S. population is about 2 million. | The *incidence* of stuttering in the U.S. population is about 1%.<br><br>The prevalence of stuttering in the country is about 2 million. | Incidence of stuttering refers to the number of people who are expected to stutter. |
| The *prevalence* of hearing impairment is about 10%. | The *prevalence* of hearing impairment in Fresno is about 1,100 children.<br><br>The *incidence* of hearing impairment is about 10%. | Prevalence refers to the total number of persons who already have a characteristic or a disorder. |

### A.3.13a. *Inter-* and *Intra-*

*Inter-* means *between* or *among*. *Intra-* means *within*.

| Incorrect | Correct | Note |
|---|---|---|
| The *intraobserver* reliability index is based on the observations of two graduate students. | The *intraobserver* reliability index is based on two observations of the same graduate student. | To determine *intraobserver* reliability, the same person should repeat observations. |
| The *interobserver* reliability index is based on the experimenter's two observations. | The *interobserver* reliability index is based on the observations of the experimenter and an outside expert. | To determine *interobserver* reliability, two or more persons should observe the same event. |
| I will take an *intrastate* highway to cross the state boundary. | I will take an *interstate* highway to cross the state boundary. | An *interstate* highway runs across states. |
| Motivation is an *interpersonal* variable. | Motivation is an *intrapersonal* variable. | Motivation is a within-person factor. |

### A.3.12b. *Incidence* and *Prevalence*

| Incorrect | Write Correctly |
|---|---|
| The incidence of strokes in the country is about 500,000. | |
| The prevalence of language disorders in the school-age children in the city is 10%. | |

### A.3.13b. *Inter-* and *Intra-*

| Incorrect | Correct |
|---|---|
| I will establish the intraobserver reliability by correlating my observations with those of another observer. | |
| The experimenter established an interobserver reliability index by correlating two of her observations. | |
| At least two observers are needed to calculate an intraobserver reliability index. | |
| The same observer has to make at least two observations to calculate an interobserver reliability index. | |

### A.3.14a. *Latter* and *Later*

- *Latter* means the second of the two things just mentioned; contrasts with *former*, which means the first of the two things just mentioned.
- *Later* refers to time: it refers to something done after another activity or time period.

| Incorrect | Correct | Note |
|---|---|---|
| Teach the skills first and work on maintenance *latter*. | Teach the skills first and work on maintenance *later*. | Your work on maintenance comes later in time. |
| Your training criterion may be 80% or 90% correct; the *later* requires more training. | Your training criterion may be 80% or 90% correct; the *latter* requires more training. | The latter refers to the second of the two criteria mentioned (90%). The term helps avoid repetition of an element. |

### A.3.15a. *Proof* and *Support*

- The terms *proof*, *proved*, or *disproved* are overstatements in science.
- Prefer the words *support*, *evidence*, *confirm*, and so forth as shown in the examples.

| Less Accurate | More Accurate | Note |
|---|---|---|
| My data *prove* that there is a gene for grammar. | My data *support* the hypothesis that there is a gene for grammar. | Besides *support*, several other words are good substitutes for *proof*. |
| These observations *prove* that the treatment was effective. | These observations *suggest* that the treatment was effective. | |
| Johnson *proved* that the Native Americans do not stutter. | Johnson *claimed* that the Native Americans do not stutter. | The word *claimed* suggests that the author is skeptical of the hypothesis. |
| More recent studies have *disproved* Johnson's claim. | More recent studies have *contradicted* Johnson's claim. | |
| The data prove the stated hypotheses. | The data confirm the stated hypotheses. | A hypothesis is *confirmed*, not proven. |

### A.3.14.b. *Latter* and *Later*

| Incorrect | Correct |
|---|---|
| I am busy now; will do it latter. | |
| First, I will teach; latter I will probe. | |
| Both treatment and counseling are essential; the later requires additional clinical skills. | |
| I took courses on biology and physics; I liked the former, but hated the later. | |

### A.3.15b. *Proof* and *Support*

| Less Accurate | Write More Accurately |
|---|---|
| The linguists have proved that there is an innate language acquisition device. | |
| My data prove that the hypothesis is invalid. | |
| Chimpsky proved that all children are born with universal grammar. | |
| Recent research disproves Chimpsky's claim. | |

### A.3.16a. Secondly and Thirdly

- Avoid this usage.
- Write: *First, Second, Third,* and so forth.

| Not Preferred | Preferred | Note |
|---|---|---|
| *First*, I will assess the client. *Secondly*, I will select the target behaviors. *Thirdly*, I will prepare the stimulus materials. | *First*, I will assess the client. *Second*, I will select the target behaviors. *Third*, I will prepare the stimulus materials. | Some write *firstly*, but it is worse than *secondly* and *thirdly*. |

### A.3.17a. Since and Because

- The word *since* often is misused.
- Use *since* to suggest a temporal (time) sequence, as in *Since the introduction of in-the-ear hearing aids, social acceptability of hearing aid usage has increased.*
- Use *because* to suggest causation, as in *Because the man stuttered, he felt self-conscious.*

| Incorrect | Correct | Note |
|---|---|---|
| *Since* the stimulus pictures are ambiguous, the responses are not certain. | *Because* the stimulus pictures are ambiguous, the responses are not certain. | Ambiguous pictures cause uncertain responses. |

### A.3.18a. There and Their

Use *there* to suggest location and *their* to suggest group possession.

| Incorrect | Correct | Note |
|---|---|---|
| This is *there* house. | This is *their* house. | A common mistake. |
| *Their* is the book you wanted. | *There* is the book you wanted. | |
| Was *their* a party tonight? | Was *there* a party tonight? | |
| How is *there* health? | How is *their* health? | |

### A.3.16b. *Secondly* and *Thirdly*

| Not Preferred | Preferred |
|---|---|
| First, I will instruct the client. Secondly, I will place the headphones on the client. Thirdly, I will begin hearing testing. | |

### A.3.17b. *Since* and *Because*

| Incorrect | Write Correctly |
|---|---|
| Since the auditory discrimination procedure was not effective, I shifted to production training. | |
| Since the child is not cooperative, automatic audiologic assessment procedures are necessary. | |

### A.3.18b. *There* and *Their*

| Incorrect | Write Correctly |
|---|---|
| That was once there haunt. | |
| Their is what you need. | |
| I thought their was going to be a quiz today. | |
| How is there new baby? | |

## Note to Student Writers

Examples on the previous pages represent only a small number of commonly misused words and phrases. Use this page to write down additional examples of such words and phrases. Practice correct usage of those words and phrases.

| Misused Words | Correct Usage |
|---|---|
| | |
| | |
| | |
| | |
| | |
| | |
| | |
| | |
| | |
| | |

*Note:* Many books on writing contain sections on word usage.

# B.1. Introduction to Scientific Writing

Scientific writing is
- related to data, research, or theory;
- direct;
- precise;
- objective; and
- organized according to an accepted format.

Scientific papers have somewhat rigid formats. Different scientific journals have their specific formats.

Journals like those the American Speech-Language-Hearing Association (ASHA) publishes use a format that is based on the *Publication Manual of the American Psychological Association* (6th ed., 2010) (APA *Manual*).

However, please take note that ASHA journals do not strictly follow the APA *Manual* in all respects. Certain aspects of article design including heading styles and reference citations of ASHA may vary from the APA style.

All writing is designed for an audience. In addition, scientific and professional writing is designed for an agency or a source of publication. For example, a research paper may be designed according to the format prescribed by a journal to which it is submitted. A grant proposal, on the other hand, may be designed according to the guidelines of a government agency or a private foundation.

Undergraduate and graduate students write term papers. Advanced graduate students may write research papers, theses, and dissertations. In completing their writing projects, students should follow a prescribed format. The instructor of a course, the graduate school, or a departmental policy may dictate the format.

Students should find out the accepted or prescribed format and write accordingly. Throughout this part on scientific writing, the APA style is used for illustration.

**Printed Notes**

**Class Notes**

There always are reasons to deviate from a particular style. You should ascertain from your instructor the acceptable deviations from the prescribed style. Potential or recommended deviations from the APA *Manual* guidelines are specified in this section.

Please note that most books do not fully conform to the APA style in its headings, paragraph indentations, margins, the use of italics and underlining, and so forth. A *coursebook*, such as this one, has a unique format as you can see. General design features that are appropriate for an article or a term paper may not be appropriate for a book. Each publishing company uses its own style in designing books. For esthetic reasons, headings, paragraph styles, and so forth often are uniquely designed for each book. Therefore, students should not look at book designs, including the design of this book, to understand the APA style.

## B.2. Writing Without Bias

**Printed Notes**

An important skill to acquire is *writing without bias*. All kinds of writing, not just scientific writing, should be free from racial, cultural, ethnic, social, personal, economic, and gender-related biases. Negative connotations about disabilities, unless such connotations are a matter of scientific study, also should be avoided. Scientific writing avoids stereotypic language about gender, gender identity, and ethnicity.

Scientific writing makes reference to ethnic, racial, gender, and other cultural factors only when

- those factors themselves are the subject of a study; and
- the knowledge of such factors is necessary to understand the results of a study or issues on hand.

Necessary references to gender, culture, ethnicity, and race are made in

- nonevaluative and nonoffensive language; and
- terms that groups use to refer to themselves.

Gender bias is the most frequent problem. Implied or direct negative reference to disabilities also is a frequent problem.

Note that biases are not just a problem in scientific writing. They are a problem in

- all writing;
- conversational speech; and
- media reports.

In the popular press discussions, the term *politically correct* is often heard with a negative connotation. It should be clear to the scientific writers, however, that writing without bias and prejudice is not *politically* correct, it is just *correct*.

The sections that follow illustrate principles of scientific writing and offer examples and exercises.

**Class Notes**

## B.2.1a. Write Without Gender Bias

| Terms That Suggest Bias | Appropriate Use | Note |
|---|---|---|
| *Man* (when used indiscriminately) | Use only when you refer to a *male* person. | Take note of the different ways of avoiding gender bias in writing. |
| *He* (when the gender is not specific); *His* (when the gender is not specific) | he or she [but not *he/she*, nor *(s)he*] *his or her* | |
| Animals share only a part of *man's* capacity for communication. | Animals share only a part of *humans'* capacity for communication. | |
| Scientific achievements of *mankind* are extraordinary. | 1. Scientific achievements of *men and women* are extraordinary.<br>2. Scientific achievements of *humans* are extraordinary. | |
| The *child* is not alone in learning *his* language. *He* gets significant help from *his* caregivers. | 1. *Children* are not alone in learning their language. *They* get significant help from their caregivers.<br>2. The *child* is not alone in learning his or her language. *He or she* gets significant help from caregivers. | The excessive use of *he or she* makes the writing cumbersome to read. Prefer the plural pronouns and consider other strategies shown here. |
| The child may be referred to a *pediatrician* with the expectation that *he* will follow up on the recommendations. | The child may be referred to a *pediatrician* with the expectation that *she or he* will follow up on the recommendations. | Alternate the order in which you write *he or she (she or he)* and *woman or man (man or woman)*. |
| Busy judges tend to neglect their *wives*. | Busy judges tend to neglect their *spouses*. | Replace a gender-specific term with a common term. |
| A child with intellectual disabilities will be slow in *his* acquisition of language. | A child with intellectual disabilities will be slow in *the* acquisition of language. | Replace the pronoun with an article. |
| A scientist investigates funding sources available for *his* research. | A scientist investigates funding sources available for research. | Drop the pronoun altogether. |
| A child with speech disorders will be deficient in *his* academic performance. | A child *who* has speech disorders will be deficient in academic performance. | Recast the sentence with *who* and eliminate the pronoun. |

## B.2.1b. Write Without Gender Bias

- Do not overuse the term *he or she*.
- Use all the different strategies shown in the previous exemplars.

| Incorrect | Write Correctly |
|---|---|
| The client who stutters is frustrated with his speech. | |
| Mankind has known about aphasia for a long time. | |
| Refer the client to a biotechnician. He will fashion a prosthetic device. | |
| Hearing loss in old age affects a man's social behavior. | |
| Giving accurate information to a client is a clinician's ethical responsibility. He should never evade it. | |
| The child should be treated as a total person. He should not be thought of merely as a client. | |
| Refer the client to a laryngologist. He will evaluate. | |
| Engineers tend to marry women who are artists. *Hint:* Eliminate the word *women* in your revision. | |
| The company's manpower is limited. *Hint:* Use an alternative (e.g., *workforce* or *personnel*). | |
| A child with stuttering may be slow in responding to questions. *Hint:* Recast the sentence by using *who* and by avoiding the use of *his*. | |

## B.2.2a. Write Without Prejudicial Reference to Disabilities

- Describe disabilities objectively.
- Avoid sentimental, evaluative, or euphemistic terms.
- Put people first, not their disability.
- Do not use disabilities to suggest metaphoric meanings.
- Avoid "normal" versus "abnormal" evaluations.

| Incorrect | Correct | Note |
|---|---|---|
| The man was a *victim* of laryngectomy. | The man had a laryngectomy. | Avoid such terms as *victim*, *suffers from*, and *crippled* because they suggest negative evaluations. |
| The child *suffers* from severe articulation problems. | The child has a severe articulation disorder. | |
| The man with aphasia is *crippled*. | The man with aphasia has hemiplegia. | |
| The *stutterer* could not order in restaurants. | 1. Mr. Jones, who stutters, could not order in restaurants. <br> 2. A person who stutters has difficulty ordering in restaurants. | The correct versions put the persons first, not their disabilities. |
| The child *stutterer* did not ask questions. | 1. The child, because of her stuttering, did not ask questions. <br> 2. The child, who stutters, did not ask questions. | |
| The *aphasic* did not recall the names. | 1. The woman with aphasia did not recall the names. <br> 2. The person who is aphasic did not recall the names. | The term *aphasic* is not a noun; it is an adjective. |
| The *wheelchaired* need access to our clinics. | People in wheelchairs need access to our clinics. | The term *confined to wheelchair* also is unacceptable. |
| Supervisors are *blind* to our day-to-day problems. | Supervisors do not appreciate our day-to-day problems. | Metaphoric use of a disability. |
| Dysfluency rates of children who stutter were compared with those of normal children. | Dysfluency rates of children who stutter were compared with those of non-stuttering children. | The revision avoids the implication that children who stutter are *abnormal*. *Normally speaking children* (or *adults*) is acceptable. |

## B.2.2b. Write Without Prejudicial Reference to Disabilities

| Incorrect | Write Correctly |
|---|---|
| The child was a victim of bilateral clefts of the hard palate. | |
| The woman, afflicted with a laryngeal infection, has a voice disorder. | |
| The disabled person is crippled. | |
| Blind and deaf children need special methods to learn communication. | |
| The teachers' plea for more computers fell on deaf ears. | |
| This aphasic has lost her speech. | |
| The stutterer agreed to come for treatment. | |
| The dysarthric had prosodic problems. | |
| The paraplegics need appropriate access to buildings. | |
| Disabled people have rights, too. | |
| The scores of children with articulation disorders were compared with those of normal children. | |
| | *Hint:* Use the acceptable term, *normally speaking*. |

### B.2.3a. Write Without Prejudicial Reference to Ethnic or Racial Background

- Use the terms that ethnic or racial groups prefer to describe themselves.
- When appropriate, use the more specific terms to general terms (e.g., the more specific *Chinese Americans* rather than the more general *Asian Americans*).
- Be alert to changes in the usage of racial and ethnic terms as the preferences do change over time. Because they are personal nouns, racial and ethnic terms are capitalized (e.g., *White* and *Black*, not *white* and *black*).

| Incorrect | Correct | Note |
| --- | --- | --- |
| Seven Afro-American children participated in the study. | Seven African American children participated in the study. | The term *African American* typically is not hyphenated. |
| A majority of *black* and *white* Americans agree. | A majority of Black and White Americans agree. | *Black Americans* is acceptable although *African Americans* is more widely used. |
| The study included 25 *Hispanic* children. | The study included 25 Mexican American children. | Although the term *Hispanic* may be correct in many contexts, such terms as *Cuban American* or *Puerto Rican American* add specificity when needed. |
| Only a small number of *Native Americans* could be sampled. | Only a small number of Navaho Indians could be sampled. | Although the term *Native Americans* is acceptable, it is preferable to specify the group as there are about 450 groups of Native Americans. |
| A majority of subjects were *Orientals*. | A majority of subjects were Vietnamese. | The term *Oriental* is now prejudicial and nonspecific. Prefer the more specific term. |

### B.2.3b. Write Without Prejudicial Reference to Ethnic or Racial Background

| Incorrect | Write Correctly |
|---|---|
| The prevalence of high blood pressure is high among Afro-American adults. | |
| We will select an equal number of white and black students for evaluation. | |
| Hispanic adults with a history of heart disease will be recruited for the study. | *Hint:* Select a more specific group among Hispanics. |
| Native Americans participants did as well as any other ethnic group. | *Hint:* Select a more specific group among Native Americans. |
| The oriental clients did not exhibit the same characteristics as the White clients. | *Hint:* Select a more specific group among Asian Americans. |

### B.2.4a. Write Without Prejudicial Reference to People With Varied Sexual Orientation

- Use the term *sexual orientation*, not *sexual preference*.
- Use the terms *lesbians* or *gay men* instead of *homosexuals*.
- *Bisexual men* and *bisexual women* are appropriate terms.

| Incorrect | Correct | Note |
| --- | --- | --- |
| Twenty male and 20 female *homosexuals* participated in the study. | Twenty *gay males* and 20 *lesbians* participated in the study. | Although correct in many contexts, the term *homosexual* is better avoided when specificity is needed. |
| The language skills of 20 lesbians were compared with those of 20 *normal* women. | The language skills of 20 lesbians were compared with those of 20 *heterosexual* women. | Avoid the implications of normality or abnormality. |
| Sexual orientation of the participants was not significant, although the *sex* of the participant was. | Sexual orientation of the participants was not significant, although the *gender* of the participants was. | The revised version avoids a potential confusion between gender and sexual orientation. |
| The family values of lesbians were compared with *acceptable traditional* values. | The family values of lesbians were compared with those of *heterosexual* women. | The revision avoids the implication of *unacceptable* values of lesbians. |
| The speech of lesbian mothers directed to their children was compared with those of the *standard* group. | The speech of lesbian mothers directed to their children was compared with the speech of women who were *heterosexual*. | The revision avoids the notion of standard set by one or the other group. |

### B.2.4b. Write Without Prejudicial Reference to People With Varied Sexual Orientation

| Incorrect | Write Correctly |
|---|---|
| *Homosexual* men and women were recruited for the study. | |
| Voice characteristics of 50 lesbians were compared with those of a group of *normal* women. | |
| Computer skills of men with *normal sexual orientation* were assessed along with those of gay men. | *Hint:* Use the term *heterosexual*. |
| A client's sex, not sexual orientation, may be a significant factor. | *Hint:* Use the term gender instead of sex. |
| The religious values of gay men were compared with *acceptable traditional values*. | |

## B.2.5a. Use the Appropriate Gender Identity Terms

- Use the current gender identity term of the individual.
- Use the appropriate pronoun for the current gender identity.

| Inappropriate | Appropriate | Note |
| --- | --- | --- |
| John Doe is a transgender man. He is now Jane Doe. | John Doe is a transgender person. She is now Jane Doe. | The noun or the pronoun should match the new (current) gender identity. |
| Jane is a transgender. | Jane is a transgender person. | *Transgender* is an adjective, not a *noun*. However, the term *transsexual* may be a noun or an adjective. |
| He is transgendered. | He is a transgender person. | |
| He is a transvestite. | The person is a cross-dresser. | The term *cross-dresser* is preferred to *transvestite*. |
| Male-to-female transformed person. | Male-to-female transgender person. | Correct use of the term *transgender* and the current gender identity term. |
| Male-to-female transformed man. | She is a male-to-female transgender person. | |
| Female-to-male transformed person. | Female-to-male transgender person. | |
| Female-to-male transformed woman. | Female-to-male transgender man. | |

### B.2.5b. Use the Appropriate Gender Identity Terms

| Inappropriate | Write Correctly |
|---|---|
| She transgendered to male. She now calls herself John. | |
| Tom is a transgender. | |
| Rachel is transgendered. | |
| She is a transvestite. | |
| Male-to-female transformed individual. Male-to-female transformed man. | |
| She is female-to-male transformed. Female-to-male transformed person. | |

## B.3. Format of Scientific Writing

### Margins

#### B.3.1. Leave Correct Margins

Margins should be 1 inch (2.54 cm) on the top, bottom, right, and left of every page. Use the specified margins on all papers you submit.

```
+------------------------------------------------+
|                    Top 1"                      |
+------+----------------------------------+------+
|      |                                  |      |
|      |                                  |      |
|Left 1"|                                 |Right 1"|
|      |                                  |      |
|      |                                  |      |
+------+----------------------------------+------+
|                   Bottom 1"                    |
+------------------------------------------------+
```

# Title Page

### B.3.2. Type Correctly the Title Page of a Paper for Publication

- Titles should be succinct.
- APA guideline limits the titles of journal articles to a maximum of 12 words.

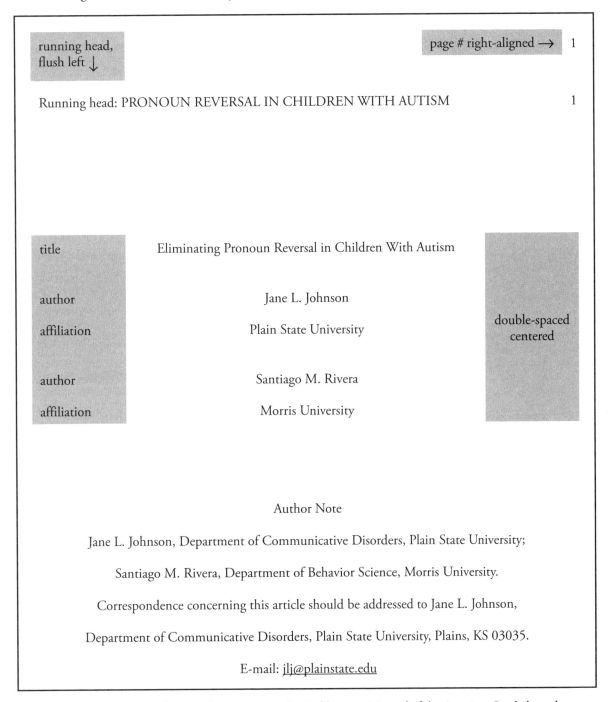

*Note:* For other elements of the Author Note, see the *Publication Manual of the American Psychological Association,* 6th Edition (2010).

### B.3.3. Type Correctly the Title Page of a Class (Term) Paper

- All lines are double-spaced and centered.

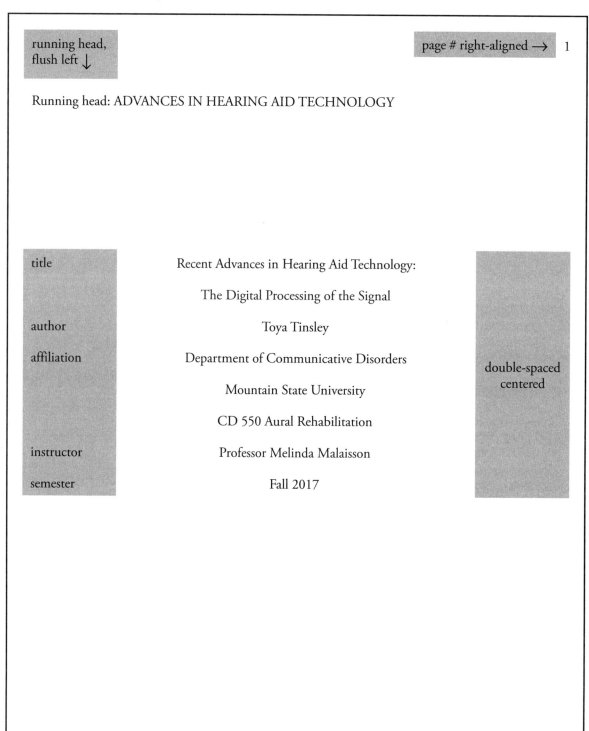

# Running Head

### B.3.4. Type the Manuscript Running Head Correctly

- Type a **running head**—a shorter version of the title—at the top-left corner of **each page** (including the title page), except pages that contain figures.
- Insert the appropriate page number, right-justified.
- The running head is printed on the right- or the left-hand page of published articles or books.

---

Running head: TREATING STUTTERING IN CHILDREN                                              1




Treating Stuttering in Children:  A review of research


Indira M. Gonzalez

Mountain State University





Author Note

Indira M. Gonzalez, Department of Speech and Hearing Sciences, Mountain State University.

Correspondence concerning this article should be addressed to Indira M. Gonzalez,

Department of Speech and Hearing Sciences, Mountain State University,

Mountain, LS 76765. E-mail: indirag@mountainstate.edu

## Abstract Page

### B.3.5. Write an Abstract on the Second Page

- Type an abstract on the second page.
- Type the word Abstract at the top, center portion of the page.
- Do not indent the first line; write the entire abstract in a single paragraph.
- Type the running head on the top-left corner and the page number on the top-right corner.
- Double-space the abstract.
- Do not exceed 150 words (APA's range is 150 to 250 words; for the precise number, check the guideline of the journal to which you plan to submit your paper).
- Do not quote, but cite authors if necessary.
- Use abbreviations, but spell them out on their first use.
- Type all numbers as digits (except those that begin a sentence).
- See B.5.1 for more on *Abstracts*.

---

PRONOUN REVERSAL IN CHILDREN WITH AUTISM　　　　　　　　　　　2

Abstract

Pronoun reversal, a persistent language problem of children with autism, has been difficult to eliminate. It has been suggested that echolalia, which is frequently observed in children with autism, may contribute to pronoun reversal. I tested this possibility by reducing echolalia with a time-out contingency and by measuring the frequency of pronoun reversal. Four children between 5 and 7 years of age, diagnosed with autism, were the subjects. I used the multiple baseline design across the four subjects. As the experimental contingency of time-out decreased the frequency of echolalia, the frequency of pronoun reversal also decreased.

---

*Note:* This boxed display does not show the required margins. The term *running head* does not precede the actual running head from this page on.

# Beginning of Text

## B.3.6. Begin the Text With an Untitled Introductory Section on Page Three

- Type the title of the paper and center it. Do not type the author's name.
- Indent each paragraph by five to seven spaces; use the word processor's default setting.

---

PRONOUN REVERSAL IN CHILDREN WITH AUTISM      3


Eliminating Pronoun Reversal in Children With Autism:

An Experimental Analysis


Among the many language characteristics of children with autism, echolalia and pronoun reversal occur frequently. **Echolalia** is the seemingly meaningless repetition of what is heard. **Pronoun reversal** refers to the frequent substitution of an appropriate personal pronoun with an inappropriate pronoun. For example, a child with autism may substitute *you* for *me,* and vice versa (Weathermeir, 2016).

[text continues]

---

*Note:* Defined terms may be italicized or printed in bold type. Also note that this boxed display does not show the required margins.

# Heading Levels

## B.3.7. Use the Headings Within the Text Consistently

- Design headings thoughtfully so they can help organize your writing.
- Use the word processor's *Style* menu to create headings that will repeat automatically in a paper or book chapter.
- Headings help readers understand the material better.
- Headings help the writer better organize a paper.
- In empirical reports (a study done with human participants or animal subjects), use standard headings (e.g., Method, Results, Discussion, References).
- In a term paper written to fulfill a class requirement, create headings and subheadings in the APA style that fit the content of the paper.
- Make headings brief and direct.
- Write headings that concentrate on the topic or discussion that follows.
- Note that headings in books use more appealing styles than journal articles and may not conform to the APA style.
- APA style includes up to five levels of heading.
- Capitalize the first letter of only the major words of a heading and the first letter of all words that contain four letters or more (i.e., in a heading or title, the *a* in *and* will not be capitalized, but the *w* in *With* will be).
- Use the selected heading style consistently.
- Note that an introduction is **untitled**; do not type *Introduction* at the beginning of a paper.
- Note that journals that purport to use the APA style are not entirely faithful to all aspects of that style, especially to the levels of heading.
- Note that the *headings* appear within the text of an article and the *title* is essentially the name of the article.
- Write more than one paragraph of text under a heading.

# Two Levels of Heading

**Results**

The study will be presented descriptively as well as statistically . . .

(Level 1; centered, boldface, uppercase and lowercase heading)

**Treatment Effects**

Effects of the two treatments are presented in Figure 1 and two . . .

(Level 2; flush left, boldface, uppercase and lowercase side heading)

## Three Levels of Heading

**Method**

(Level 1; centered, boldface, uppercase and lowercase heading)

**Stimulus Selection**

We selected objects as well as colorful pictures for training stimuli . . .

(Level 2; flush left, boldface, uppercase and lowercase side heading)

    **Baseline procedure.** We established the baselines with 20 stimulus items . . .

(Level 3; indented, boldface, lowercase paragraph heading ending with a period. After one space, the text begins on the same line.)

# Four Levels of Heading

> **Method**
>
> (Level 1; centered, boldface, uppercase and lowercase heading)
>
> **Assessment Materials**
>
> We used both standardized assessment instruments and client-specific procedures prepared for each client . . .
>
> (Level 2; flush left, boldface, uppercase and lowercase side heading; the text begins on the next indented line.)
>
>     **Stimulus pictures.** We selected colorful pictures from various magazines . . .
>
> (Level 3; indented, boldface, lowercase paragraph heading ending with a period. After one space, the text begins on the same line.)
>
>     ***Dependent variables.***  We used several instruments to measure the dependent variables . . .
>
> (Level 4; indented, boldface, italicized, lowercase paragraph heading ending with a period. After one space, the text begins on the same line.)

## Five Levels of Heading

**Experiment 1: Morphologic Training**

(Level 1; centered, boldface, uppercase and lowercase heading)

**Participant Selection Procedure**

We selected participants from the list of clients seeking services . . .

(Level 2; flush left, boldface, uppercase and lowercase heading; the text begins on the next indented line.)

    **Stimulus materials.** We selected artist-drawn pictures to evoke the target responses . . .

(Level 3; indented, boldface, lowercase paragraph heading ending in a period; the text begins after the period, on the same line.)

    ***Training procedure.*** We used the discrete trial training procedure . . .

(Level 4; indented, boldface, italicized, lowercase paragraph heading ending in a period; the text begins after the period, on the same line.)

    *Probe procedure.* We used both the intermixed probe and pure probe methods . . .

(Level 5; Indented, italicized, lowercase paragraph heading ending in a period; the text begins after the period, on the same line.)

## Note to Student Writers

The APA heading styles are required for research papers to be submitted to a journal that uses that style. Those heading styles also may be required for theses and dissertations. It is better to use the same style in term papers. Always using one style format, such as that of the APA, will make it easier to organize any kind of writing. Nonetheless, make sure to follow the guidelines provided by your instructor in each class.

Also, as noted in *B.1. Introduction to Scientific Writing*, books, including this one, do not fully conform to all aspects of the APA style. Books are uniquely designed to conform to the style of the publishing house and for esthetic purposes. Therefore, APA style examples are not to be selected by looking at the stylistic aspects of this or any other book. Unfortunately, and as pointed out earlier, such examples cannot be selected by looking at many journals (especially the ASHA journals) that purport to use the APA style.

# Typefaces

## B.3.8. Use Acceptable Typefaces and Size

- Select a *serif* typeface. The serif typefaces have fine-line strokes that finish off the main strokes of letters (as the two small horizontal lines on N).
- A *san serif* typeface lacks the finer strokes (e.g., **N**, a sans serif).
- Type in the International Phonetic Symbols as needed. They are available online.

| Recommended Typeface And Size | Unacceptable | Note |
|---|---|---|
| Times New Roman<br><br>Use a sans serif for labels and legends within figures.<br><br>12-point font size | Exotic and ornamental typefaces<br><br>Cursive typefaces<br><br>Condensed type<br><br>Very large or very small sizes | See how the printed page looks and then make a judgment. |

## B.3.9. Use Boldface Correctly

| Use Bold For | Examples | Note |
|---|---|---|
| Terms when they are defined | **Semantics** is the study of meaning. | Do not use bold for subsequent use of the term. |
| L1 through L4 headings | **Bilingualism** (level 1)<br>**Sequential Bilingualism** (level 2) | Do not bold the level 5 italicized paragraph heading. |

# Page Numbers

### B.3.10. Number the Pages Correctly

| Do | Do Not | Note |
|---|---|---|
| Place the page number on the top-right corner, five spaces to the right of the running head. | Number the pages that contain figures and figure captions. | Use the *Header* command of the word processor to automatically insert page numbers and the running heads.<br><br>Format page numbers as a right-aligned paragraph to print them at the end of the right margin. |
| Number all pages of the paper consecutively, including the title page, tables, and other end materials. | | |
| Insert unnumbered pages (e.g., figures) at the end of the paper following all numbered material. | | |
| Renumber or repaginate the entire paper when you delete or add pages. | Give a new identity to the inserted pages (e.g., 32A, 59B). | |

### B.3.11. Reprint the Corrected Pages

| Do | Do Not | Note |
|---|---|---|
| Reprint or retype the corrected pages. | Use handwritten corrections on your paper.<br><br>Use correction paper or liquid. | Final submission should be free from distracting corrections. |

# Line Spacing and Line Length

### B.3.12. Use Appropriate Line Spacing

| Double Space | Triple Space | Single Space |
|---|---|---|
| title page<br>entire paper<br>all headings<br>all text<br>quotations<br>tables (single-spacing is acceptable)<br>figure legends<br>reference lists<br>initial drafts of clinical reports | Triple space before starting a major heading (optional). | Single space no portion of a research or term paper, except for the tables, which may be single- or double-spaced (an APA *Manual*, 6th edition ambivalence).<br><br>**Exception:** The final versions of clinical reports and all forms of correspondence. These are always single-spaced. |

### B.3.13. Use Appropriate Line Length

| Limit Each Line To | Do Not | Note |
|---|---|---|
| 6.5 in.<br>Use the flush-left style (text at the right margin will be uneven).<br>Do not break words at the end of a line by using a hyphen. | Right-justify the lines. | Justified text will have uneven spaces between words. |

### B.3.14. Correct the Spelling Errors

| Do | Do Not | Note |
|---|---|---|
| Keep the word processor's spell-checker turned on to make online corrections.<br>Manually double-check the spelling yourself, preferably on printed pages. | Depend entirely on the word processor's spell-checker.<br>Depend entirely on the spell-checker's auto-correction feature. | If you typed *he* for *the*, the spell-checker will not highlight it because *he* is a word in the dictionary.<br>The auto-correction feature may insert a wrong word. |

## B.4. Selected Matters of Scientific Style

## Capitalization

### B.4.1. Capitalize the First Words

| Capitalize | Examples | Note |
|---|---|---|
| the first letter of the first word in a sentence | This does not concern you. | |
| the first letter of the first word after a colon that begins a complete sentence | Only one thing is certain: No one has made a perfect study. | |
| the first letter of the first word and the first letter of the first word after a colon when referencing a book or an article in the reference list | Bowen, J. (1998). *Joy of journalism: One woman's journey.* Fresno, CA: Premier Press.<br><br>Tan, K. (2001). Ecstasy of scientific writing: A tutorial. *Journal of Scientific Writing, 55,* 23–45. | Note the italics used for book titles, journal titles, and journal volume numbers. |

### B.4.2. Capitalize the First and the Major Words

| Capitalize | Examples | Note |
|---|---|---|
| book and article titles specified in the text | Although the article, "Neuroscience: A Tutorial" is good, the book *Neuroscience of Communication* is more comprehensive. | The article title is enclosed within quotation marks; the book title is italicized. However, in the *Reference* list, only the first word of a book title and the first word after a colon is capitalized. |
| names of specific university departments | Department of English, California State University—Fresno | However, *a department of English* |
| titles of specific university courses | CSD 200 Introduction to Research Methods | However, *a course on research methods* |
| specific test titles | Test of Early Language Development | However, *a test on language development* |

## B.4.3. Capitalize the Words Correctly in Headings

| Capitalize | Examples | Note |
|---|---|---|
| major words in heading levels 1 and 2, including grammatical words with four or more letters | **Method** (L1)<br><br>**Dependent Variables** (L2)<br><br>**Persons With Aphasia** (L2) | Grammatical terms like the conjunction *and* and articles *a* and *the* will not be capitalized in the headings.<br><br>See the section, *Headings*, B.3.7. |
| only the first word in level 3, 4, and 5 (indented paragraph) headings in which the text begins after the heading | **Baseline procedures.** (L3)<br><br>*Probe procedures.* (L4)<br><br>*Group A Results.* (L5) | There is no heading with all capital letters. |

## B.4.4. Capitalize Proper Nouns and Trade Names

| Capitalize | Examples | Note |
|---|---|---|
| all proper nouns and trade names in the text, the headings, and the reference list | Skinnerian conditioning<br>Pavlovian experiments<br>The Lombard effect<br>Microsoft Word<br>The Adobe Acrobat | Note that in the first two examples, the second word is not capitalized.<br><br>But *eustachian tube* and *cesarean section* are not capitalized. |

## B.4.5. Capitalize the Chapters and Sections the Reader Is Referred To

| Capitalize | Examples | Note |
|---|---|---|
| section titles or book chapters in the same article or book the reader is referred to | As pointed out in the Discussion section . . .<br><br>See Chapter 4 for details. | However, *the discussion section in a paper*<br><br>However, *the various chapters of a book* |

## B.4.6. Capitalize Nouns That Are Followed by a Number or Letter

| Capitalize | Examples | Note |
|---|---|---|
| nouns followed by a numeral or a letter | As shown in Table 7 . . .<br>As described in Document QZ<br>As specified in Section 9(b)<br>During Trial 9 | However, *the article did not contain any tables, documents, sections, and trials . . .* |

## B.4.7. Capitalize Both Words in Otherwise Capitalized Hyphenated Compound

| Capitalize | Examples | Note |
|---|---|---|
| the first letter of both words in the case of a hyphenated compound word that needs to be capitalized | An excellent book, *Education of Hearing-Impaired Children* . . .<br>The HIV-AIDS risk factors . . .<br>The client is of Anglo-Irish background. | The rule applies only if the term is otherwise capitalized; this is generally the case within the text; see B.4.8. for exceptions. |

## B.4.8. Do Not Capitalize the Second Word of a Hyphenated Compound in Reference Lists

| Do Not Capitalize | Examples | Note |
|---|---|---|
| the first letter of the second word of a hyphenated compound word in reference lists | Barr, B. (2002). Long-term effects of stuttering therapy. *Journal of Stuttering Therapy, 55,* 28–38.<br><br>Kang, U. (2001). *Accident-prone adults and traumatic brain injury.* Los Angeles, CA: Academic Publication. | The rule applies to entries in a reference list; see also, B4.7. However, *HIV-AIDS* in the reference list as well |

## Italicization

### B.4.9. Use Italics Correctly Within the Body of Text

Underline if you cannot italicize (as in handwriting and typing on an old typewriter).

| Use Italics For | Examples | Note |
|---|---|---|
| specific book titles in text citations | Allport's classic book, *Introduction to Psychology*, is excellent. | All major words of book and journal titles are capitalized in the text, but only the first letter of the first word in the reference list is capitalized; see B.4.10. |
| names of journals | *Journal of Mind*, is good for the new mentalists. | |
| an undefined new, technical, or key term when first introduced | The term *phonology* does not refer to a skill.<br><br>*Cognition* is a surrogate for observable behaviors. | Do not italicize the following:<br><br>a posteriori<br><br>a priori<br><br>et al.<br><br>per se |
| terms or morphemes that denote linguistic examples | The present progressive *ing* and the pronouns *he* and *she* were taught.<br><br>The plural *s* cannot stand alone. | |
| letters used as statistical symbols or algebraic variables | *t* test<br>trial *c* | |
| category names in a rating scale | A rating of 1 means *excellent* and 2 means *good*. | |
| words that could be misread | The *big* group did not do as well as the *small* group (referring to a group name, not to its size). | |

### B.4.10. Use Italics Correctly in the Reference List

Underline if you cannot italicize.

| Use Italics For | Examples | Note |
|---|---|---|
| book titles | *Introduction to communicative disorders* | Only the first word is capitalized. |
| names of journals and their volume numbers | *Journal of Human Communication, 52* | All major words are capitalized. |
| titles of unpublished papers presented at conventions, meetings, and symposia | Crosslin, J. (2002, April). *Noun phrase training*. Paper presented at the Tennessee Conference on Language Disorders, Memphis, TN. | See the section *Reference List*. |

# Hyphenation

## B.4.11. Use the Hyphen Correctly

- Follow the guidelines given in *Merriam-Webster's Collegiate Dictionary*, as recommended by the APA *Manual*.
- Note, however, that other dictionaries may or may not agree with Webster.
- Always check the current usage, because many terms that start out as hyphenated eventually lose the hyphen to become solid words.

| Incorrect | Correct | Note |
|---|---|---|
| Three follow up assessments were scheduled. | Three follow-up assessments were scheduled. | *Follow-up* as a noun (or adjective) is hyphenated. |
| It is necessary to follow-up all clients. | It is necessary to follow up all clients. | *Follow up* as a verb is not hyphenated. |
| I sent an email message. | I sent an e-mail message. | The usage of *E-mail* has declined in favor of *e-mail*. |
| The role playing method is good for language sampling. | The role-playing method is good for language sampling. | Hyphenate a compound with a participle when it precedes the term it modifies. |
| Stuttering increases in anxiety arousing situations. | Stuttering increases in anxiety-arousing situations. | |
| The use of food deprived participants is unethical. | The use of food-deprived participants is unethical. | |
| Trial by trial analysis | Trial-by-trial analysis | Hyphenate an adjectival phrase when it precedes the term it modifies. |
| Minute by minute method of scoring stuttering | Minute-by-minute method of scoring stuttering | |
| To be probed stimulus items | To-be-probed stimulus items | |
| The high achievement group | The high-achievement group | Hyphenate an adjective-and-noun compound when it precedes the term it modifies. |
| The middle class families | The middle-class families | |
| Low frequency stuttering | Low-frequency stuttering | |
| A six item test | A six-item test | Hyphenate a compound that begins with a number and the compound precedes the term it modifies. |
| Two way analysis of variance | Two-way analysis of variance | |
| A 5 s duration between trials | A 5-s duration between trials | |
| Teaching 5th grade children | Teaching 5th-grade children | |
| pro Freudian | pro-Freudian | Compounds in which the base word is capitalized |
| post Skinnerian | post-Skinnerian | |
| pre 1990 | pre-1990 | Compounds in which the base word is a number |
| post 2000 | post-2000 | |

Use the Hyphen Correctly *(continued)*

| Incorrect | Correct | Note |
|---|---|---|
| post FR change<br>pre ASHA era | post-FR (for *fixed ratio*) change<br>pre-ASHA era | Compounds in which the base word is an abbreviation |
| self concept | self-concept | All *self*-compounds used as nouns or adjectives |
| self scored quiz | self-scored quiz | |
| self examination | self-examination | |
| recount (meaning, *count again*)<br>recover (meaning *cover again*)<br>recreation (meaning, *creating again*)<br>resend | re-count (versus *recount*)<br>re-cover (versus *recover*)<br>re-creation (versus recreation)<br>re-send (versus *resend*) | Words that could be mistaken without a hyphen |
| a follow up (*used as a noun*) | a follow-up (*used as a noun*) | However, it is *follow up* when used as a verb. |
| metaanalysis | meta-analysis | Hyphen separates the same vowel or consonant in the compound word. *Exception*: prefixes *re* and *pre*; see B4.13. |
| antiintellectual | anti-intellectual | |
| cooccurrence | co-occurrence | |
| sworddance | sword-dance | |
| client centered counseling | client-centered counseling (*However*, The counseling was client centered.) | Use the hyphen when a compound adjective precedes the word it modifies.<br><br>Do not use the hyphen when the compound adjective follows the word it modifies, as shown in parenthetical examples. |
| same sex children | same-sex children (*However*, The children were of the same sex.) | |
| user friendly program | user-friendly program (*However*, The program was user friendly.) | |
| student oriented exam | student-oriented exam (*However*, The exam was student oriented.) | |
| the low, moderate, and high anxiety clients | the low-, moderate-, and high-anxiety groups | When the base word (*anxiety* in the first example) is used only with the last modifier in a series of compound modifiers (*low*, *moderate*, and *high* in the same example), use the hyphen as shown. |
| 5 and 10 sec time-out durations | 5- and 10-sec time-out durations | |
| teacher and student centered techniques | teacher- and student-centered techniques | |
| long and short term treatment goals | long- and short-term treatment goals | |

### B.4.12. Do Not Overuse the Hyphen

| Incorrect | Correct | Note |
|---|---|---|
| Health-care programs are complex. | Health care programs are complex. | Do not use hyphens if the term is well established and the meaning is clear without it. |
| Dysfluency-rates were measured. | Dysfluency rates were measured. | |
| Sex-role differences were not clear. | Sex role differences were not clear. | |
| We calculated rank-order correlation. | We calculated rank order correlation. | |

### B.4.13. Do Not Misuse the Hyphen

Note, however, usage varies. Certain terms that do start out as separate or hyphenated words eventually become solid words; consult *Webster's* for correct usage.

| Incorrect | Correct | Note |
|---|---|---|
| life-style changes | lifestyle changes | Once hyphenated or written separately, these are now solid words. |
| I searched a data-base. | I searched a database. | |
| bi-lingual child | bilingual child | These prefixes are not followed by a hyphen. See *Webster's* for additional examples. However, *meta-analysis* |
| co-operate | Cooperate | |
| counter-balanced design | counterbalanced design | |
| extra-sensory | Extrasensory | |
| infra-structure | Infrastructure | |
| inter-dental | Interdental | |
| intra-observer reliability | intraobserver reliability | |
| macro-cephaly | Macrocephaly | |
| mega-byte | Megabyte | |
| meta-cognition | Metacognition | |
| micro-computer | microcomputer | |
| mid-section | Midsection | |
| mini-series | Miniseries | See *Webster's* for many more examples. |
| multi-lingual | Multilingual | |
| non-clinical | Nonclinical | *Exception*: All capitalized nouns preceded by *non*-(e.g., non-Christian, non-Chinese). |
| over-qualified | Overqualified | More prefixes that are not followed by a hyphen |
| post-test | Posttest | |
| pre-test | Pretest | |

**Do Not Misuse the Hyphen** *(continued)*

| Incorrect | Correct | Note |
|---|---|---|
| pre-experimental | preexperimental | Exceptions to the general rule that prefixes that end and the base words that begin with the same vowel are hyphenated |
| re-engineer | Reengineer | |
| pro-revolutionary<br>pro-war | prorevolutionary<br>prowar | However, *pro-Darwinian* |
| pseudo-science<br>pseudo-logic | pseudoscience<br>pseudologic | |
| re-evaluate<br>re-examine | reevaluate<br>reexamine | An exception to the general rule stated in 4.11. |
| semi-annual<br>semi-literate | semiannual<br>semiliterate | These prefixes are not followed by a hyphen.<br><br>See *Webster's* for many such examples. |
| socio-economic<br>psycho-linguistics | socioeconomic<br>psycholinguistics | |
| sub-test<br>sub-division | subtest<br>subdivision | |
| super-script<br>super-ordinate | superscript<br>superordinate | |
| supra-glottal<br>supra-orbital | supraglottal<br>supraorbital | |
| ultra-sensitive<br>ultra-liberal | ultrasensitive<br>ultraliberal | |
| un-conditioned<br>un-defined | unconditioned<br>undefined | |
| under-funded<br>over-emphasize | underfunded<br>overemphasize | |

# Indentation

## B.4.14. Use Correct Indentation

| Indent | Do Not Indent | Note |
|---|---|---|
| **five to seven** spaces:<br><br>the first line of each paragraph of the text<br><br>level 3, 4, and 5 headings<br><br>the second and subsequent paragraphs of block quotations | abstracts<br><br>titles and most headings<br><br>titles of tables and notes<br><br>legends of figure captions<br><br>the first paragraph of block quotations<br><br>the first line of each reference entry | Heading levels 1 and titles are **centered**.<br><br>Unindented lines are typed *flush left*.<br><br>To indent paragraphs uniformly, use the word processor's default setting (typically five spaces) or set your own tab settings, or use the *style* feature on your word processor. |

B.4  Selected Matters of Scientific Style

# Space After Punctuation

## B.4.15. Give Correct Space or No Space After Punctuation

| Correct | Number of Spaces |
|---|---|
| | **One space after** |
| Speech, language, and hearing | Commas |
| The clinician said: "Stop!" | Colons |
| These rules may be vague; nonetheless, you are expected to follow them! | Semicolons |
| Penn, P. Z. (1993).<br>Q. X. Zenkin | each period that separates initials in names |
| | **One space between** |
| Penn, P. Z. (1999). *Nation of children.* New York: Infancy Press. | each element in a reference list |
| | **One space on either side of** |
| 10 – 5 is 5. (A hyphen serves as a minus sign.) | a minus sign preceded and followed by a number |
| | **One space before, but no space after** |
| The negative value was –70. | a minus sign followed by a number |
| | **One *or* two spaces after** |
| The data were valid. But no one cared.<br>He said, "Let us go!" She asked, "Go where?" | After a period or any other kind of punctuation (e.g., ! or ?) at the end of a sentence (An ambivalence of the APA *Manual,* 6th ed. It used to be one space.) |
| | **No space after** |
| p.m.; i.e.; U.S. | internal periods in abbreviations |
| The ratio is 4:1. | around colons in ratios |
| | **No space before or after** |
| The yet-to-be published book | two single hyphens |
| The client—a professional singer—came to the clinic with a hoarse voice. (dashes) (According to the APA *Manual,* two typed hyphens with no space on either side become —.) | double hyphens (*em dash*)<br><br>Most word processors automatically convert two typed hyphens into one long hyphen (em dash) if no space is placed on either side of the hyphens. |
| I completed my studies during the 2016–2017 academic year. | An *en dash* is longer than a hyphen but shorter than an em dash. Select an en dash from the Insert Symbol menu. |

## Abbreviations

### B.4.16a. Write Out Abbreviations the First Time You Use the Term and Enclose the Abbreviations in Parentheses

- Use only generally known abbreviations (e.g., HTL in audiologic writing).
- Abbreviate only to save space while retaining clarity of writing.
- Once selected, use the abbreviation consistently.
- APA *Manual* recommends the use of certain abbreviations as words (e.g., IQ) that are accepted as words in *Webster's Dictionary*. Nonetheless, if the readers are not likely to know the abbreviation (e.g., IPA for International Phonetic Alphabet, accepted as word), spell it out the first time.

| First Correct Citation | Subsequent Correct Citation | Note |
|---|---|---|
| The hearing threshold level (HTL) was measured . . . | The HTL was . . . | |
| A value of 100 Hertz (Hz) means that . . . | A tone of 200 Hz was presented. | |
| A decibel (dB) is one tenth of a | In 5 dB increments . . . | |
| The temporomandibular joint (TMJ) is an important joint . . . | The TMJ is important for . . . | These audiological abbreviations need not be spelled out even the first time if an audiogram that spells them out accompanies the report. |
| We measured the mean length of utterance (MLU) in syllables. | The obtained MLU values are shown in Table 1. | |
| The tone—a conditioned stimulus (CS)—may be presented . . . | The intensity of the CS was increased. | |
| You must obtain your Certificate of Clinical Competence (CCC). | The American Speech-Language-Hearing Association issues the CCC in . . . | |
| Our professional organization is the American Speech-Language-Hearing Association (ASHA). | The president of ASHA spoke at the convention. | |

### B.4.17a. Do Not Start a Sentence With a Lowercase Abbreviation

| Incorrect | Correct | Note |
|---|---|---|
| dB is one tenth of a Bel. | The dB is one tenth of a Bel. | |
| ppb* is useful in measuring the amount of pesticides in water. | The amount of the residual pesticide in water is measured in ppb. | The correct examples show the subsequent citations of the abbreviated words, which were spelled out earlier. |
| m, being a measure of micrometer . . . | Being a measure of micrometer, m is . . . | |
| ns is a very brief time period. | One needs special equipment to measure the ns. | |

*ppb: parts per billion; ns: nanosecond.

### B.4 Selected Matters of Scientific Style

## Abbreviations

### B.4.16b. Write Out Abbreviations the First Time You Use the Term and Enclose the Abbreviations in Parentheses

| Incorrect First Citation | Rewrite Correctly |
|---|---|
| The ASHA *Code of Ethics* is an important document. The members of ASHA should adhere to the code. | |
| In hearing evaluation, the SDT should be obtained. The (SDT) is the hearing level at which a person is just aware of speech. | |
| A loud noise is a UCS for startle response. The presentation of a UCS results in a UCR. | |
| The LAD is the mechanism by which children derive the grammar of their language. Without the LAD, the child would be lost in confusion. | |
| In DRO, you specify the behavior that will not be reinforced. The effectiveness of DRO is well established. | |
| The child has a PE tube. Surgically implanted PE tubes allow for middle ear ventilation. | |

ASHA: American Speech-Language-Hearing Association; SDT: speech-detection threshold; UCS: unconditioned stimulus; UCR: unconditioned response; LAD: language acquisition device; DRO: differential reinforcement of other behavior; PE tube: pressure-equalizing tube

### B.4.17b. Do Not Start a Sentence With a Lowercase Abbreviation

| Incorrect | Write Correctly |
|---|---|
| cc, being a metric measure . . . | |
| lb is a popular measure in the U.S. | |
| min is an abbreviation for minutes. | |
| ms is longer than ns. | |

cc: cubic centimeter; lb: pound; ms: millisecond

## B.4.18a. Use Latin Abbreviations Only in Parenthetical Constructions

In non-parenthetical written sentences, use their English equivalents; do not use Latin abbreviations in conversational speech.

| Abbreviation | English Equivalent |
|---|---|
| etc. | and so forth |
| e.g., | for example |
| i.e., | that is |
| viz., | namely |
| cf. | compare |
| vs. | versus, against |

**Exceptions:**
1. Use the abbreviation v. for versus when referring to court cases: The historic *Brown v. Board of Education* ruling has been upheld.
2. Use the Latin abbreviation et al., which means "and others" in both the parenthetical and non-parenthetical constructions. See B.4.31. and B.4.32. for examples.

| Incorrect | Correct |
|---|---|
| Pictures, objects, line drawings, etc. will be used as stimuli. | Pictures, objects, line drawings, and so forth will be used as stimuli. |
| | A variety of stimuli (pictures, objects, line drawings, etc.) will be used. |
| Various reinforcers, e.g., tokens, stickers, and points, will be used as reinforcers. | Various reinforcers, for example, tokens, stickers, and points, will be used as reinforcers. |
| | Various reinforcers (e.g., tokens, stickers, and points) will be used. |
| The basic continuous reinforcement schedule, i.e., the fixed ratio 1 (FR1), may be used. | The basic continuous reinforcement schedule, that is, the fixed ratio 1 (FR1), may be used. |
| | The basic reinforcement schedule (i.e., the fixed ratio 1) may be used. |
| Certain variables, viz., motivation, severity of the disorder, and intelligence are known to influence the treatment outcome. | Certain variables, namely, motivation, severity of the disorder, and intelligence are known to influence the treatment outcome. |
| | Certain variables (viz., motivation, severity of the disorder, and intelligence) are known to influence the treatment outcome. |
| Nativism vs. empiricism is a historical topic of discussion. | Nativism versus empiricism is a historical topic of discussion. |
| | The two opposing views (nativism vs. empiricism) are a historical topic of discussion. |

### B.4 Selected Matters of Scientific Style

## B.4.18b. Use Latin Abbreviations Only in Parenthetical Constructions

Take note of an exception, however.

| Incorrect | Write Correctly |
|---|---|
| The various types of dysfluency including interjections, prolongations, repetitions, etc. characterize stuttered speech. | |
| Certain types of newer hearing aids, e.g., the digital aids, can reduce background noise. | |
| Neural hearing loss, i.e., the type of loss with nerve damage, is difficult to treat surgically. | |
| Many variables, viz., heredity, environmental toxicity, and maternal alcoholism can cause mental retardation. | |
| Behaviorism vs. cognitivism is a good topic for debate. | |
| The Brown versus the Board of Education ruling forced racial integration in public schools. | |

### B.4.19a. Add the Lowercase Plural Morpheme *s* to Plural Abbreviations Without an Apostrophe

| Incorrect | Correct | Note |
|---|---|---|
| ABR's, ECG's, EEG's, IQ's, Ed's., vol's. | ABRs, ECGs, EEGs, IQs, Eds. (for *Editors*), vols. (for volumes) | A common mistake is to add an apostrophe. |

### B.4.20a. With Abbreviations, Use the Period Correctly

| Add Periods To | Do Not Add Periods To |
|---|---|
| Initials of names (Z. Q. Xompompin) | Capital letter abbreviations and acronyms: ASHA, APA, UNESCO, IQ |
| Degree abbreviations: Ph.D., M.D., D.D.S., J.D., M.A., M.S., B.A., B.S. (*Note*: Practice varies with these degrees; some omit the period.) | |
| | Abbreviations of state names: CA, NY |
| Geographic names (U.S. Military) | Measurement abbreviations: hr (for hour), min (for minutes), s (for seconds), kg (for kilogram), ft (for foot), lb (for pound) |
| U.S. as an adjective (U.S. Department of Health and Human Services) | |
| Latin abbreviations: *i.e., vs., a.m., e.g.* | *Exception:* Add a period to in. (for inch) as it could be misread without the period. |
| Reference abbreviations: *vol. 2nd ed. p.* 10. | |

### B.4.21a. Abbreviate Units of Measurement When a Number Is Specified

| Incorrect | Correct | Note |
|---|---|---|
| 20 seconds, 2 hours, 20 kilograms, 5 centimeters, 29 percent | 20 sec, 2 hr, 20 kg, 5 cm, 29% | In scientific papers, units of time and other measures are abbreviated. The units are always singular (e.g., kg, *not* kgs). Unless they are at the end of a sentence, there is no period at the end of these abbreviations. *Exception*: in. (for inch; a period is always added). |

*Note:* In the noun phrase, no hyphen is used between the number and the abbreviation (20 sec); a hyphen is used in an adjectival phrase (as in *a 20-sec interval will be used*).

### B.4.19b. Add the Lowercase Plural Morpheme *s* to Plural Abbreviations Without an Apostrophe

| Incorrect | Write Correctly |
|---|---|
| HTL's | |
| MLU's | |
| SRT's | |
| FR's (for Fixed Ratio of Reinforcement) | |

### B.4.20b. With Abbreviations, Use the Period Correctly

| Incorrect | Write Correctly |
|---|---|
| US Park Service | |
| Secretary, US Department of Labor | |
| viz | |
| etc | |
| ASHA. | |

### B.4.21b. Abbreviate Units of Measurement When a Number Is Specified

| Incorrect | Write Correctly |
|---|---|
| 10 minutes | |
| 10 feet | |
| 5 pounds | |
| 5 seconds | |
| 15 centimeters | |
| 2 hours | |

## Numbers in Words or Numerals

### B.4.22a. Write Out Units of Measurement When a Number Is Not Specified

| Incorrect | Correct | Note |
|---|---|---|
| The weight was specified in kg.<br><br>The specified weight was 10 kilograms. | The weight was specified in kilograms.<br>The specified weight was 10 kg. | A specified number is always followed by an abbreviated unit of measure.<br><br>An unspecified unit of measure is always followed by a word, not an abbreviation. |
| measured in cm . . .<br><br>It was 10 centimeters long. | measured in centimeters . . .<br><br>It was 10 cm long. | |
| several lb of sugar . . .<br><br>You have 10 pounds of sugar. | several pounds of sugar . . .<br><br>You have 10 lb of sugar. | |
| calculated the % of dysfluencies . . .<br><br>The client had a 10 percent dysfluency rate. | calculated the percentage of dysfluencies . . .<br><br>The client had a 10% dysfluency rate. | |

### B.4.23a. Use Roman Numerals Only When It Is an Established Practice

| Incorrect | Correct |
|---|---|
| Cranial nerve 4 | Cranial nerve IV |
| Type 2 error | Type II error |
| King George 3rd | King George III |

### B.4.24a. Use Arabic Numerals for Numbers 10 and Above

However, see exceptions under B.4.25.

| Incorrect | Correct | Note |
|---|---|---|
| I selected eleven participants. | I selected 11 participants. | Numbers 10 and above are not written in words unless they start a sentence. |
| The client is seventy-five years old. | The client is 75 years old. | |
| The client met the training criterion on the fifteenth trial. | The client met the training criterion on the 15th trial. | |
| The client was twenty percent dysfluent. | The client was 20% dysfluent. | |

# Numbers in Words or Numerals

### B.4.22b. Write Out Units of Measurement When a Number Is Not Specified

| Incorrect | Write Correctly |
|---|---|
| You can take several mg without side effects. | |
| The voice onset time of persons who stutter was slower by several ms. | |
| This task may take many hr. | |

mg: milligrams; ms: milliseconds

### B.4.23b. Use Roman Numerals Only When It Is an Established Practice

| Incorrect | Write Correctly |
|---|---|
| Cranial nerve 8 | |
| Type one error | |
| Pope Paul 6th | |

### B.4.24b. Use Arabic Numerals for Numbers 10 and Above

| Incorrect | Write Correctly |
|---|---|
| A caseload of fifty-five is large. | |
| The client met the training criterion in only twelve trials. | |
| The client's baserate production was fifteen percent. | |
| There are ten clients on the waiting list. | |
| Her age is twenty five years. | |

## B.4.25a. Use Numerals for Numbers Below 10 in Specified Contexts

Generally, numerals below 10 are written out in words. There are exceptions, however. Numbers below 10 are written in numerals when they

- are grouped for comparison with numbers 10 or above;
- precede a unit of measurement;
- represent statistical or mathematical functions; and
- represent time, dates, ages, sample, number of subjects in a study, scores on a scale, exact amounts of money, and items in a quantitative series.

| Incorrect | Correct | Note |
|---|---|---|
| I answered only nine out of 12 questions. | I answered only 9 out of 12 questions. | In each of these examples, a number below 10 is compared with a number 10 or above. Therefore, even the numbers below 10 are written in numerals. |
| Stimuli include five pictures, three toys, and 12 objects. | Stimuli include 5 pictures, 3 toys, and 12 objects. | |
| The ninth graders did better than the 12th graders. | The 9th graders did better than the 12th graders. | |
| The fourth and 15th participants did not do well. | The 4th and the 15th subjects did not do well. | |
| Of the 15 clients, four dropped out of therapy. | Of the 15 clients, 4 dropped out of therapy. | |
| Only seven of the 20 probe responses were correct. | Only 7 of the 20 probe responses were correct. | |
| I used three lb of sugar. | I used 3 lb of sugar. | Numbers precede units of measurement. |
| I took a five-mg tablet. | I took a 5-mg tablet. | |
| I divided it by seven. | I divided it by 7. | Numbers with statistical or mathematical functions. |
| A dysfluency rate of five % is high. | A dysfluency rate of 5% is high. | |
| The third quartile. | The 3rd quartile. | |
| The experiment took two weeks. | The experiment took 2 weeks. | Numbers that represent time, date, age, and so forth. Number in a series (of tables and pages, in this case). |
| I completed the degree in four years. | I completed the degree in 4 years. | |
| The participants were four-year olds. | The subjects were 4-year-olds. | |
| She scored six on a 7-point scale. | She scored 6 on a 7-point scale. | |
| Please see Table Five for details. | Please see Table 5 for details. | |
| You can find this on page seven. | You can find this on page 7. | |

## B.4.25b. Use Numerals for Numbers Below 10 in Specified Contexts

| Incorrect | Write Correctly |
|---|---|
| I scored only six out of 12 answers. | |
| The seventh graders did better than the 11th graders. | |
| The third and 12th participants did not do well. | |
| Of the 17 clients, six needed booster treatment. | |
| The client's responses were correct on the seventh and 11th trials. | |
| I bought five kg of pesticide. | |
| The normal dosage is three mg. | |
| Multiply this number by four. | |
| An error rate of seven % is unacceptable. | |
| I completed the study in four weeks. | |
| I had seven-year-olds as participants. | |
| He scored five on a 7-point scale. | |
| Please see page nine. | |
| These data are presented in Figure four. | |
| Find the details in Chapter two. | |

## B.4.26a. Write Out in Words Numbers Below 10 in Specified Contexts

Use this general rule, but take note of exceptions to this rule in B.4.25. Use words instead of numerals to write numbers that are

- not precisely measured values;
- not set in comparison with numbers 10 and above;
- the numbers zero and one in most (but not all) cases;
- common fractions; and
- traditionally expressed only in words.

| Incorrect | Correct | Note |
|---|---|---|
| Such instances are few; perhaps 3 or 4. | Such instances are few; perhaps three or four. | Precise measurement is not implied. |
| The client repeated it 3 times. | The client repeated it three times. | |
| These are 4 concepts that mean the same. | These are four concepts that mean the same. | |
| She is the only 1 who is well prepared. | She is the only one who is well prepared. | |
| The client has missed 2 or 3 sessions this semester. | The client has missed two or three sessions this semester. | |
| After 5 imitated responses, I will fade modeling. | After five imitated responses, I will fade modeling. | *Five* or *eight* is not in comparison with number 10 or above. |
| I will use 8 items for training. | I will use eight items for training. | |
| He got a 0 on the test. | He got a zero on the test. | the numbers *zero* and *one* in most (but not all) cases |
| Still, 1 response was wrong. | Still, one response was wrong. (*but*, Only 1 out of 15 was wrong). | |
| Do not write a 1- sentence paragraph. | Do not write a one-sentence paragraph. | |
| One 5th of the class was absent today. 1/5th of the class was absent today. | One fifth of the class was absent today. | common fractions<br>*Note:* The second wrong example also starts the sentence with a number, another violation. |
| You need a 2/3 majority. | You need a two-thirds majority. | |
| The 4th of July was a hot day. | The Fourth of July was a hot day. | traditionally expressed only in words |
| The 10 Commandments are well known. | The Ten Commandments are well known. | |

## B.4.26b. Write Out in Words Numbers Below 10 in Specified Contexts

| Incorrect | Write Correctly |
|---|---|
| At any one time, 4 to 5 students can observe the sessions. | |
| The instructor repeated it 4 times. | |
| These 5 terms have similar meanings. | |
| He is the only 1 who can be trusted. | |
| I will use 6 stimuli on my probe list. | |
| It is no fun having 0-degree temperature. | |
| Today, 1/4th of the class is absent. | |
| *The 12th Night* is a play by Shakespeare. | |
| The original 12 Apostles were the disciples of Jesus. | |

## B.4.27a. Write Out in Words Any Number That Begins a Sentence

- Do not begin a sentence with a numeral.
- Apply this rule to titles and headings as well.

| Incorrect | Correct | Note |
|---|---|---|
| 5 children were tested. | Five children were tested. | No sentence starts with a number written in numerals. |
| 75 clinicians attended the workshop. | Seventy-five clinicians attended the workshop. | |
| 15% of the schoolchildren have some form of communicative disorders. | Fifteen percent of the schoolchildren have some form of communicative disorders. | |
| 99 Ways to Get A Grades | Ninety-nine Ways to Get A Grades | article title |

## B.4.28a. Combine Words and Numerals in Specified Contexts

Combine words and numerals to express
- large numbers (million and more); and
- back-to-back modifiers.

| Incorrect | Correct | Note |
|---|---|---|
| Special education needs five billion dollars. | Special education needs $5.0 billion. | large numbers |
| The population is at least five million. | The population is at least 5 million. | |
| We have two two-way mirrors. We have 2 2-way mirrors. | We have 2 two-way mirrors. or, We have two 2-way mirrors. | back-to-back numerical modifiers |
| We selected 6 9-year-olds for the study. | We selected six 9-year-olds for the study. | |
| I had the speech rated on 2 5 point scales. | I had the speech rated on two 5-point scales. | |
| Check the 1st 12 entries in the index. | Check the first 12 entries in the index. | |

### B.4 Selected Matters of Scientific Style

### B.4.27b. Write Out in Words Any Number That Begins a Sentence

| Incorrect | Write Correctly |
|---|---|
| 9 phonemes will be trained. | |
| 39th percentile is not too impressive. | |
| 37 children will be screened. | |
| 80% probe response rate did not meet the criterion. | |
| 29 Methods of Stuttering Treatment [A paper] | |

### B.4.28b. Combine Words and Numerals in Specified Contexts

| Incorrect | Write Correctly |
|---|---|
| You cannot really see seven million people at one time! | |
| The city has only two two-way streets. | |
| Our research included 7 2-year-olds. | |
| Use 3 7-point scales for reliability. | |
| Check the 1st 4 items on the menu. | |
| The city has a budget of ten million dollars. | |

# Reference Citations Within the Text

### B.4.29a. Cite the Author's Last Name and Year or Years of Publication in the Text

| Incorrect | Correct | Note |
|---|---|---|
| In her study of heavyweight champions, Byson found that . . . | In her study of heavyweight champions, Byson (2009) found that . . . | The author's name is part of the narration. Therefore, only the year is in parentheses. |
| Ticklishson stated that humor is good medicine (2010). | Ticklishson (2010) stated that humor is good medicine. | Type the year immediately after the name. |
| Byson (2015) found that the reaction time of his opponents was sluggish . . . . Byson (2015) also found that . . . | Byson (2015) found that the reaction time of his opponents was sluggish. . . . Byson also found that . . . | Omit the year when the same study is referred to again in the same paragraph if it cannot be confused with another. |
| A study showed that boxing causes brain damage; Hali, 2011 | A study showed that boxing causes brain damage (Hali, 2011). | When the name and the year are not a part of the narrative, enclose both within parentheses. |
| In (2016), MacVinro was the first to show that playing tennis sharpens the tongue. | In 2016, MacVinro was the first to show that playing tennis sharpens the tongue. | If the year also is a part of the narration, do not enclose it in parentheses. |
| Nemson, Jr. (2012) did the study. | Nemson (2012) did the study. | In the text, omit such name-suffixes as *Jr.* or *III*. Add them in the reference list. |
| Patterson's study (2014, October) was not valid. | Patterson's study (2014) was not valid. | In the text, do not cite the month even if it is cited in the reference list. |
| Russell in 1921 and 2005 contended that words do not carry meaning. | Russell (1921/2005) contended that words do not carry meaning. | Russell's book was originally published in 1921, and reprinted in 2005; the publishers of the two editions may be different. See B.4.54 on how to reference such works in the reference list. |

### B.4.30a. Cite Both Names in the Text When a Work Has Two Authors

| Incorrect | Correct IN TEXT | Note |
|---|---|---|
| Tang et al. (2013) found that college courses are incomprehensible. | Tang and Lagassi (2013) found that college courses are incomprehensible. | Cite both the authors in the first and all subsequent citations. |
| Studies have shown that plagiaristic writing is more common than some realize (Brew et al., 2015; True, et al., 2014). | Studies have shown that plagiaristic writing is more common than some realize (Brew & Drew, 2015; True & Crew, 2014). | Cite both the names in the first as well as all subsequent parenthetical constructions. |

B.4  Selected Matters of Scientific Style

# Reference Citations Within the Text

**B.4.29b.**   Cite the Author's Last Name and Year or Years of Publication in the Text

| Incorrect | Write Correctly |
|---|---|
| June John Jinkinson (2007) stated that . . . | |
| In (2008), Torkinson reported that . . . | |
| Jasperson's study has shown that . . . (2011). | |
| Research shows that bilingualism is enriching; Fung, 2016. | |
| Packman III (2012) questioned the validity of such claims. | |
| Nunez completed the study (2014, June). | |
| Skinner in 1975 and 2003 stated that the concept of a free person is a myth. | *Hint:* the same book, reprinted in 2003 |

**B.4.30b.**   Cite Both Names in the Text When a Work Has Two Authors

| Reference Information | Write a Sentence Using the Information |
|---|---|
| 1. Authors: Cheng and Tang<br>Year: 2017<br>Study on: elimination of phonological processes<br>Results: Only some processes were eliminated. | 1. Begin the sentence with the reference. |
| 2. Authors: Haniff and Chwe<br>Year: 2015<br>Study on: incidence of stuttering in general population<br>Result: about 1% | 2. End the sentence with the names in parentheses. |

### B.4.31a. Cite Works With Three to Five Authors Using All the Authors' Names Only the First Time

- Subsequently, cite only the first author's last name and add "et al." to it (without quotation marks).
- Include the year of publication.
- Apply the same rule to parenthetical citations.

| Incorrect | Correct | Parenthetical |
|---|---|---|
| In a study on head injury, Hali et al. (2016) found that . . . (*first citation*) | In a study on head injury, Hali, Byson, and Tedson (2016) found that . . . (*first citation*) The results of the Hali et al. (2016) study were that . . . (*subsequent citation*) | It was reported that . . . (Hali, Byson, & Tedson, 2016). (*first parenthetical citation*) The report confirmed that . . . (Hali et al., 2016). (*subsequent parenthetical citation*) |
| In their study on vocal nodules, Lordon et al., (2015) discovered that . . . (*first citation*) Lordon et al. (2015) showed that . . . (*subsequent citation*) | In their study on vocal nodules, Lordon, Fontana, Tanseko, Pendl, and Tavratino (2015) discovered that . . . (*first citation*) Lordon et al. (2015) showed that . . . (*subsequent citation*) | A study reported that . . . (Lordon, Fontana, Tanseko, Pendl, & Tavratino, 2015). (*first parenthetical citation*) Evidence suggests that . . . (Lordon et al., 2015). (*subsequent parenthetical citation*) |

### B.4.32a. Cite Works of Six or More Authors by Only the First Author

- Follow this rule even for the first citation.
- Type "et al." (without quotation marks) after the first author's last name followed by the year of publication; do not type a comma after the name when only one name is mentioned (e.g., Wang et al.; *not* Wang, et al.).
- Add a comma when more than one name precedes et al. (e.g., Wang, Smith, et al.; *not* Wang, Smith et al.).

| Incorrect | Correct | Note |
|---|---|---|
| Wang, Bhat, Johnson, Hernadez, Allende, and Singh (2009) reported . . . (*six authors, first citation*) | Wang et al. (2009) reported . . . (*first and all subsequent citations*) | Add additional names only when it is necessary to distinguish works of multiple authors. See rule B.4.33a. |
| It was reported that . . . (Wren, Ram, Traveno, Kelly, Trudeau, Svensson, & Boonthenthorpe, 2008) (*seven authors, first parenthetical citation*) | It was reported that . . . (Wren et al., 2008). (*first and all subsequent citations*) | The same rule applies when the author names are in parentheses. |

### B.4.31b. Cite Works With Three to Five Authors Using All the Authors' Names Only the First Time

Show the **first** and one **subsequent** citation.

| Reference Information | Write a Sentence Using the Information |
|---|---|
| 1. Authors: Shanker, Shantler, Samuelson, Whau, and Mistry<br>Year: 2010<br>Study: new surgical methods of closing the complete palatal cleft<br>Results: favorable | 1. Begin the sentence with the names; show first and subsequent citations. |
| 2. Authors: Southerland, Pena, and Pundit<br>Year: 2012<br>Study: new methods of auditory masking<br>Results: no improvement over existing methods | 2. End the sentence showing names within parentheses. |

### B.4.32b. Cite Works of Six or More Authors by Only the First Author

| Reference Information | Write A Sentence Using The Information |
|---|---|
| 1. Authors: Soong, Moong, Moore, Raju, McLaughlin, and Johnson<br>Year: 2001<br>Study on: digital hearing aids<br>Results: very effective | 1.<br><br>*Note:* Name part of the narrative. |
| 2. Authors: Mann, Nath, Fahey, Lahey, Bohey, Johey, and Pinkerton<br>Year: 2000<br>Study on: new speech treatment<br>Results: ineffective | 2.<br><br>*Note:* Name within parentheses. |

## B.4.33a. Distinguish Works of Multiple Authors Published in the Same Year

If two studies published in the same year with a different combination of three or more authors have the same first author, then cite all names if necessary; or cite as many names as needed to distinguish the two studies.

| Incorrect | Correct | Note |
|---|---|---|
| Lordon et al. (2012) have concluded that . . . *(subsequent citation)* *(This study had four authors: Lordon, Fontana, Tanseko, and Pendl)* | Lordon, Fontana, Tanseko, and Pendl (2012) showed that . . . Lordon, Fontana, Tanseko, and Pendl (2012) have concluded that . . . *(All names of this study cited each time)* | Even in subsequent citations, all authors are cited to distinguish the two studies. If not, the two studies would be confused as they both abbreviate to Lordon et al. (2012). |
| Lordon et al. (2010) also have concluded that . . . *(subsequent citation)* *(A different study published in the same year that had a different combination of four authors: Lordon, Fontana, Tanseko, and Jensen)* | Lordon, Fontana, Tanseko, and Jensen (2010) also reported that . . . Lordon, Fontana, Tanseko, and Jensen (2010) also have concluded that . . . *(All names of this other study also cited each time)* | |
| Tinsonn et al. (1998) have found no significant difference. *(This study had seven authors: Tinsonn, Fung, Haniff, Chwe, Boonthenthorpe, Alvarado, and Smith)* | Tinsonn, Fung, et al. (1998) have found no significant difference. | The two studies had six or more authors, published in the same year.<br><br>The addition of a third name distinguishes the two studies. |
| Tinsonn et al. (2005) did not find the method effective. *(This study had six authors: Tinsonn, Fung, Mendoza, Kumar, Azevedo, and Alfonso)* | Tinsonn, Fung, Mendoza, et al. (2005) did not find the method effective. | A comma is added to the last name (before et al.) because of multiple names. |

## B.4.33b. Distinguish Works of Multiple Authors Published in the Same Year

Use the names of as many authors as needed to distinguish the two studies.

| Reference Information | Write A Sentence Using The Information |
|---|---|
| 1. Authors: Rodriguez, Ford, Williams, Johnson, and Benson<br>Year: 2013<br>Study: modeling target responses<br>Result: useful | 1. |
| 2. Authors: Rodriguez, Ford, Williams, Bennet, Bickley, Shekar, and Shinson<br>Year: 2013<br>Study: Incidence of stuttering<br>Results: 1% in the general population | 2. |

### B.4.34a. Join Multiple Author Names With the Conjunction *and* or the Ampersand

- Join the author names with *and* when the citation is part of the narrative.
- Join the author names with *&* (ampersand) when the citation is in parentheses.

| Incorrect | Correct | Note |
|---|---|---|
| A study of Hecker & Donnors (2003) showed that . . . | A survey of Hecker and Donnors (2003) showed that . . . | The names are a part of the narrative. Hence, the conjunction *and* is used. |
| Spitting on the field increases the number of hits (Rosen and Tanseko, 2008). | Spitting on the field increases the number of hits (Rosen & Tanseko, 2008). | The names are in parentheses. Hence, the ampersand is used. |

### B.4.35a. Distinguish the Different First Authors With the Same Surname

- If two or more first authors have the same surname listed in the reference list, add the initials to the first surname even in the text citation.
- Follow this rule even if the years of publication are different.

| Within the Text | In the Reference List | Note |
|---|---|---|
| Studies of those of F. Pomaville (2010) and M. Pomaville and Pomaville (2015) reveal that . . . | Pomaville, F. (2017). *Assessment of communication disorders in children.* San Diego, CA: Plural.<br><br>Pomaville, M., & Pomaville, K. (2015). A review of voice assessment procedures. *Journal of Voice, 28,* 56–69. | Three different authors with the same surname.<br><br>In the case of paired authors, the initials are added only to the first author in the text. |

### B.4.34b. Join Multiple Author Names With the Conjunction *and* or the Ampersand

| Reference Information | Write a Sentence Using the Information |
|---|---|
| 1. Part of narration<br>Authors: Gimmick and Himmick<br>Year: 2000<br>Study: the relation between screaming and vocal nodules<br>Results: positive relation | 1. |
| 2. Citation in parentheses<br>Authors: Byson and Lyson<br>Year: 1992<br>Study: programming maintenance<br>Results: possible to program maintenance | 2. |

### B.4.35b. Distinguish the Different First Authors With the Same Surname

| In the Reference List | Write a Text Sentence |
|---|---|
| Maul, M. (2016). *Assessment of autistic children.* Los Angeles, CA: Mayfair Press.<br><br>Maul, O., & Maul, Q. (2015). Treatment of autistic children. *Journal of Autism, 28,* 56–69. | <br><br><br><br><br>*Note*: Include both the sources in your sentence. |

## B.4.36a. Cite Multiple Works of the Same Author in a Temporally Ascending Order

- **Do not** use the conjunction *and* before the final year (2005, 2007, 2015; but **not**, 2005, 2007, *and* 2015).
- Note that *in press* has no year attached to it.

| Incorrect | Correct | Note |
|---|---|---|
| Studies show that the more exciting the game, the greater the injury to vocal folds (Fontana, 1997, in press, 2001, 1999). | Studies show that the more exciting the game, the greater the injury to vocal folds (Fontana 1997, 1999, 2001, in press). | The earliest publication is cited first; the *in press* citation is always the most recent, hence the last. |
| Studies of Tonsiko and Travlatinova (2001, 1999, 1997, 1996) have shown that verbal abuse is a common locker room strategy. | Studies of Tonsiko and Travlatinova (1996, 1997, 1999, 2001) have shown that verbal abuse is a common locker room strategy. | The incorrect versions are in the descending temporal order of publication. |
| Data suggest that yells that induce vocal nodules excite the players (Rosery & Ruthery, 2001; 1995; 1998). | Data suggest that yells that induce vocal nodules excite the players (Rosery & Ruthery, 1995, 1998, 2001). | The correct versions show references in parentheses in the ascending order. |

## B.4.37a. Attach Alphabetical Suffixes to the Same Author's Multiple Publications in the Same Year

- Repeat the year; do not affix a, b, c, and so forth to year typed only once (1989a, 1989b, 1989c; but **no**t 1989a, b, c).
- In assigning a, b, c, and so forth to studies published in the same year, use the alphabetical order of the first word of titles of articles.

| Incorrect | Correct | Note |
|---|---|---|
| Several studies by Johnson (2000-1, 2000-2, 2000-3, in press-1, in press-2) have shown that . . . | Several studies (Johnson, 2000a, 2000b, 2000c, in press-a, in press-b) have shown that . . . | Multiple *in press* entries also take -a, -b, -c, and so forth. |
| Studies have shown that ball game watching increases brain size (Fontana, 1988-1, 1988-2, 1999-1, 1999-2, in press-1, in press-2; Tanseko, 2001-1, 2001-2, 2001-3, 2002-1, 2002-2). | Studies have shown that ball game watching increases brain size (Fontana, 1988a, 1988b, 1999a, 1999b, in press-a, in press-b; Tanseko, 2001a, 2001b, 2001c, 2002a, 2002b). | Multiple authors, each publishing multiple studies in each of the two years; references in parentheses. |

### B.4.36b. Cite Multiple Works of the Same Author in a Temporally Ascending Order

| Reference Information | Write A Sentence Using The Information |
|---|---|
| Author: McVinro<br>Study: treatment of hoarse voice<br>Studies published in: 2001, 1999, 2000, 1989 | Include the author's name in your narration. |
| Authors: Moncure and Sincure<br>Study: bilingual-bicultural issues<br>Studies published in: 2002, 1996, 1989, 1999 | Enclose the authors' names in parentheses. |
| Author: Foresight<br>Study: future professional issues<br>Studies published in: 2002, 2001, 1999, 1998, 1997 | Enclose the author's name in parentheses. |

### B.4.37b. Attach Alphabetical Suffixes to the Same Author's Multiple Publications in the Same Year

| Reference Information | Write A Sentence Using The Information |
|---|---|
| Author: Sharp<br>Study: advances in cochlear implants<br>Published: four in 2002 | Write the author's name as part of your narration. |
| Author: Bulltit<br>Study: dysphagia assessment techniques<br>Published: three in 1999, two in 2001<br><br>Author: Hiltit<br>Study: dysphagia assessment techniques<br>Published: two in 1989; two in 2001 | Cite the two authors and their publications in parentheses. |

### B.4.38a. Within Parentheses, Arrange the Last Names of Multiple Authors in Alphabetical Order

- Use the last name of the first author to determine the alphabetical order.
- Separate each name with a semicolon.
- Do not type *and* or *&* before the last citation.

| Incorrect | Correct | Note |
|---|---|---|
| (Zoom, 1999; Began, 2000; Push, 1998; Lord, 1997) | (Began, 2000; Lord, 1997; Push, 1998; Zoom, 1999) | Follow the alphabetical, not temporal, order. |
| (Push & Twink, 1999; Began & Quinn, 1990; Lord, Horde, & Board, 1985) | (Began & Quinn, 1990; Lord, Horde, & Board, 1985; Push & Twink, 1999) | The last name of the first author of a study determines the order. The names of multiple authors are joined by an ampersand. |
| (Benson, 1989; Dinson, 1992; Henson, 1990; Nelson, 1986; and, Olsen, 1980) | (Benson, 1989; Dinson, 1992; Henson, 1990; Nelson, 1986; Olsen, 1980) | Omit *and* before the last entry. |
| (Bloodstein, 1987; Epstein, 1995; Fonstein, 1990; & Konstein, 1993) | (Bloodstein, 1987; Epstein, 1995; Fonstein, 1990; Konstein, 1993) | Omit the ampersand before the last entry. |

### B.4.39a. Cite Secondary Sources Sparingly and Correctly

- Secondary sources are books and articles that you found in a source other than the original.
- To maintain scholarly integrity, consult the original sources (books, journal articles).
- Cite no more than just a few unavoidable secondary sources.

| Correct | Note |
|---|---|
| Deepthought's classic study (as cited in Alvarado, 1999) showed that . . . | The date of the original study (*Deepthought's*, in this case) is usually not given. In the reference list, only the secondary source (Alvarado, 1999, in the example) is listed. |

### B.4.38b. Within Parentheses, Arrange the Last Names of Multiple Authors in Alphabetical Order

| Reference Information | Cite The Names Within Parentheses |
|---|---|
| Authors:<br>Thompson, 1999<br>Johnson, 2001<br>Quinn, 2000 | |
| Authors:<br>Zonks and Gonks, 1998<br>Banks and Atkins, 1995<br>Atkins, 1990<br>Kinson, 2001 | |
| Authors:<br>Bayle, 1997<br>Timson, 1996<br>Xenon, 1998<br>Lyson, 2002 | |

### B.4.39b. Cite Secondary Sources Sparingly and Correctly

| Reference Information | Cite Correctly |
|---|---|
| Original study by: Kinkler<br>Found in: Peakson, 2000 | |

### B.4.40a. Cite Correctly the Works With No Author or an Anonymous Author

- In the text, cite the first few words of the title of an article, a book chapter, or a web page within double quotation marks and add the year.
- Italicize the title of a journal, book, or a report.

| In the Text | Note |
|---|---|
| The professional guidelines ("Best Practice," 2016) | This may be from a web page. |
| *Investment for young professionals* (2017) is a useful book. | |
| This is an often stated opinion (Anonymous, 2012). | Anonymous is treated like a name itself. |

## B.4.40b. Cite Correctly the Works With No Author or an Anonymous Author

| Sources | Write Correctly |
|---|---|
| 1. New health care [a web article] | 1. |
| 2. Becoming a Clinician (2017) [a book.] | 2. |
| 3. Many believe in this view [Anonymous source, 2012]. | 3. |

## B.4.41a. Cite Correctly the Classical Works

- Cite the date of publication of translated classic works.
- Add the word trans. as shown.
- APA *Manual* (6th ed.) says that classic Greek and Roman academic works need no reference entries, but many scholars wish to include them (e.g., philosophical texts) as evident in the APA Style Blog (blog.apastyle.org).
- Religious texts such as the Bible and Qur'an may not need entries in the reference list.
- If the reference list includes an entry for it, follow the first example.

| In the Text | In the Reference List |
| --- | --- |
| The Greek philosopher Plato contradicted this view (Plato, 380/1974). | Plato (1974). *The Republic.* ((D. Lee, Trans.). London: Penguin Books. (Original work published ca. 380 B.C.) |
| Aristotle contradicted this view (Aristotle, trans., 1947). | If the text citation is as shown, there is no entry in the reference list. |

## B.4.41b. Cite Correctly the Classical Works

| In the Text | In the Reference List |
|---|---|
| Work: Book by D. Hume<br>Originally Published: 1739<br>Translator: K. Dell<br>Published: 1952<br>Publisher: Academic Press, New York, NY | Show the reference list entry. |
| Work: Socrates<br>Translation Published: 1979 | Show only the text citation with no reference list entry. |

### B.4.42a. Cite Correctly the Year of Publication in Parenthetical Text

| In the Text | Note |
| --- | --- |
| The details may be found elsewhere (e.g., the U.S. Census Report, 2015, Table 5). | The year of publication is preceded and followed by a comma, not brackets. |

### B.4.43a. Cite Correctly the Specific Parts of a Source

- Occasionally, a chapter, a page, a figure, or a table in a source may be cited.
- The source is included in the reference list.

| In the Text | Note |
| --- | --- |
| The latest statics are of clinical concern (Brain Injury Association, 2016, p. 22). | *Page* is abbreviated to small p. |
| The reader is referred to another source (Freed, 2016, Chapter 5). | *Chapter, Table, and Figure* are not abbreviated. |

B.4 Selected Matters of Scientific Style

### B.4.42b. Cite Correctly the Year of Publication in Parenthetical Text

| In the Text | Write Correctly |
|---|---|
| Write a sentence to include the following:<br><br>The American Speech-Language-Hearing Association's Report on Reimbursement<br>Year: 2017<br>Figure: 5 | <br><br><br><br><br>The citation is referenced in the reference list. |

### B.4.43b. Cite Correctly the Specific Parts of a Source

| In the Text | Write Correctly |
|---|---|
| Write a sentence to include the following:<br><br>Health and Human Services<br>Year: 2014<br>Table: 7 | |
| Write a sentence to include the following:<br><br>Author: Skelton<br>Year: 2017<br>Figure: 8-1 | |

# Reference List

## B.4.44. General Guidelines on Using Electronic Sources in Scientific Writing

The Internet, though a convenient and almost an infinite source of information, poses some risks for those who depend on it. Students and even seasoned writers who search for information for their academic and scientific writing should be careful and critical in selecting sources from the Internet. Sources and sites may contain information that is not verified by others or critically reviewed by experts. The careful, scholarly, scientific, and professional writer who evaluates the source to be used in his or her writing would do the following:

- *Ascertain who maintains the website.* Is the web page maintained by a scientific, professional, or governmental agency or organization? Is it owned by an individual? Is it owned by a commercial establishment? Generally speaking, sites owned and managed by scientific, professional, and governmental organizations offer more objective and research-based information than a business that sells products or blogs on which individuals post their opinions. The reader may trust a web page maintained by an organization whose members are specialists in the topic of interest more than sites that are maintained by novice individuals. For instance, on matters of speech, language, and hearing, http://www.asha.org will be a trustworthy site. On general and specific health matters, the various sites of the National Institutes of Health will be trustworthy. Nonetheless, individuals should critically evaluate what they read on any website.

- *Find out if it is an advocacy group's site.* If so, the information offered is evaluated for the viewpoints of the host group.

- *Check whether there are other sources on the Internet or in the print media that will help verify the authenticity and validity of claims made.* The site should refer the reader to other sites or sources that will support the information offered. If not, be skeptical. Typically, good documents on the Internet have references to reputable sources, such as peer-reviewed journal articles.

- *Be critical of any extreme or exaggerated claims or statements.* Such statements may not be based on sound research and may not present information from an objective standpoint.

- *Find out if there are sponsors.* If the information on the web page is filled with advertisers, links, and lures to commercial sites, the information offered should be evaluated in light of such efforts to sell products.

- *Evaluate the information offered on the website for its authorship, reliability, and accuracy.* Who wrote the article on the web page? Is the author an expert? Is the information based on evidence or scientific research? Is the information offered reviewed by experts? Does the site reference articles published in peer-reviewed journals? Is the information cited a valid representation of articles cited in the journals? Answering the last question is critical because a site may cite references from reputable journals, but misrepresent what the articles say.

- *Find out whether readers edit the information offered on the site.* Although this is not bad in itself, a careful writer would be on alert: The information offered on a site that allows anyone to edit, delete, or add information (e.g., *Wiki* sites) may be considered opinions of people, which may or may not be factual.

- *Check the currency of information.* The date of posting or updating is important to ascertain. On some of the web pages, decade-old information may be touted.

## B.4.45. Guidelines on Referencing the Electronic Sources

Addresses of sources of information obtained through the Internet are highly variable. Therefore, any information obtained from the web should be referenced in such a way as to direct the reader to the correct address that helps retrieve the information. In addition to the sixth edition of the APA *Manual* (2010), which gives guidelines for citing information obtained through the Internet, authors should obtain the *APA Style Guide to Electronic References, Sixth Edition.* This guide may be purchased online at http://www.apa.org and downloaded to the user's computer, if preferred.

Scholarly articles and books generally depend on print sources, rather than Internet-only sources with the exception of journals published only online and classic books and materials available online. Most print journals or their articles also have electronic versions.

In citing electronic sources:

- Follow a general rule of citing the print version whenever available, and add electronic retrieval information when that has been supplied as well. Adding DOI and Retrieve from http://www. ending in the exact URL will be sufficient in most cases.

- Follow the reference and citation guidelines that are often found at the right side or at the end of scholarly publications found on materials available online. For example, when you print a document from the website of the American Speech-Language-Hearing Association (ASHA), you can usually find directions on referencing it at the end of the document. For example, at the end of the document, *Code of ethics,* you find:

    **Reference this material as:** American Speech-Language-Hearing Association. (2016). *Code of ethics* [Ethics]. Available from http://www.asha.org/policy/.

- Shift the elements of the article in referencing it to suit the preferred style (e.g., the APA style); not all downloaded articles follow the APA style.

- Generally, include the elements you normally would for a print document; however, it is usually not available, nor is it necessary, to specify the geographic location of the web page publication.

- Specify the document name or title, not just the home page from which the information was drawn.

- Give the date of document publication; if unavailable, give the date of retrieval. The retrieval date is especially important for documents that change over time because of periodic updates. There is no need to specify the retrieval date for books, printed journal articles, and such other materials with a publication date.

- Specify the author's name (if available).

- Give the address, which is the URL; check all the URLs cited in your paper during proofreading (your last chance to make corrections) to make sure that the listed URLs are all active; make necessary corrections.

- Give the home page URL for online dictionaries and encyclopedias.

- Do not add a period, even at the end of a sentence, if there is no period in the address, data path, or directory.

- Use lowercase letters, even for the initial letter of words that start a sentence, if the address, data path, or directory is written that way.

- Do not add typical punctuation marks that are not a part of the address, data path, or directory.

- Note that some sources are available only online, whereas others are available in printed form as well.

- Cite the source you consulted when that source is also available in another form; for instance, if you consulted a printed journal article, cite the printed journal, not its online version, which may also be available.

- Do not include the name of the database in your reference (e.g., it is not necessary to include PubMed or PsycINFO in the reference list).

- Note that *http* stands for *hypertext transfer protocol*, a file transfer mechanism recognized by most Internet browsers (always followed by a colon and two forward slashes: http://).

- Include the Digital Object Identifier (DOI) number if one is shown on the journal article you accessed on a database such as ScienceDirect or PubMed. Because the URLs may be changed, moved, or deleted, readers may be unable to find the original source of the article you cite in your work. However, DOIs are more stable.

- DOI numbers are usually on the abstract page or the first page of the full text, if available. The DOI is usually a long string of numbers, so it is practical to copy it and paste it into your reference of the article.

**Note that a typical URL has the following elements:**

- protocol (standard: http://)

- host name, which is often an organization's home page that is generally but not always preceded by http://www. (e.g., http://www.asha.org/ or http://journals.apa.org)

- path to document (e.g., convention02/registration.html)

- single forward slashes separating certain elements in the URL

Such a URL as specified will be written as follows: http://www.asha.org/convention02/registration.html

(The specified document is about registering online for the national convention of the American Speech-Language-Hearing Association.)

**Note also that the path name**

- is the most case-sensitive of all other elements in the address;
- should be reproduced exactly as it appears (including uppercase and lowercase letters and punctuation, if any); and
- should not be broken with a hyphen; if you need to break a URL in a typed line, do so after a period or a slash.

## B.4.46a. Begin the Reference List on a New Page With a Centered Heading

- A reference list contains all that is cited and only what is cited in the text.
- The list is attached to a paper, a book, or other form of writing.
- Double-space the entire list.
- A bibliography is a comprehensive list of the articles published on a topic and typically stands alone (not attached to any text).

---

Communication Disorders 21

### References

Able, T. K. (2010). *Children with autism: New directions in assessment and treatment* (4th ed.). New York: Sapson Press.

Able, Q. T. (Ed.). (2012). Dream analysis in language therapy with 2-year-old children. *Journal of Language Therapy, 35,* 201–202.

American Speech-Language-Hearing Association. (2001). *Professional practice with multicultural clients.* Washington, DC: Author.

American Speech-Language-Hearing Association. (n.d.). Traumatic brain injury. Retrieved from http://www.asha.org/public/speech/disorders/tbi/

Bhoonthruntup, K. K. (2011a). Outcome of stuttering therapy in 50 adults. *Journal of Fluency Disorders, 35,* 55–98.

Bhoonthruntup, K. K. (2011b). Outcome of stuttering therapy in 50 children. *Journal of Fluency Disorders, 35,* 99–110.

Binger, C., Ragsdale, J., & Bustos, A. (2016). Language sampling for preschoolers with severe speech impairments. *American Journal of Speech-Language Pathology.* Newly Published. doi:10.1044/2016_AJSLP-15-0100

Boyle, M., Coelho, C. A. (1995). Application of semantic feature analysis as a treatment for aphasic dysnomia. *American Journal of Speech-Language Pathology, 4,* 94–98. doi:10.1044/1058-0360.0404.94

Fantastisky, D. Z. (2016). Phonological theories in contemporary linguistics. In D. B. Dream (Ed.), *Current perspectives in theoretical linguistics* (pp. 59–250). Palo Alto, CA: The Obscure Press.

National Institutes of Health. (2014). *Guidelines on laryngeal cancer research.* (DHHS Publication No. BBS-0020). Washington, DC: U.S. Government Printing Office.

Sunson, K. J., Ramson, B. B., Thomson, A. D., Nelson, S. J., Boreson, T. D., Geekson, F. L., & Zinson, G. G. (2015). Seven authors is the maximum you can list in a reference list. *Journal of Complicated References, 269,* 18–30.

Torin, J. G., Vokin, S., Lenin, L. B., Benin, O., Menin, P., Renin, R. S., . . . Norin, A. S., (2016). In referencing a work with 8 or more authors, cite the first six names, type three ellipsis points, and then add the last author name. *Journal of Complicated References, 270,* 15–25.

Vomen, M. [Michelle]. (2014). Add the first name to the reference when two last names and their first name initials are the same. *Journal of Complicated References, 268,* 10–12.

Vomen, M. [Monika]. (2013). I am now differentiated from my academic arch enemy Michelle Vomen. *Journal of Complicated References, 267,* 19–21.

Williamson, T. T., IV. (2010, March 15). America's successful schools. *Newsweek, 225,* 50–58.

Zero, A. L. (2017). Restrict the use of et al. to appropriate text citations because it is now banished from the reference list. *Journal of Complicated References, 274,* 7–12.

---

*Note:* The boxed display does not show double spacing or one-inch margins, both required in a manuscript. The references shown are attached to a paper called "Communication Disorders."

# B.4 Selected Matters of Scientific Style

## B.4.46b. Begin the Reference List on a New Page With a Centered Heading

Write a page header, an arbitrarily selected page number, and the word *references* with the right characters and in the correct position. Then, inventing the necessary information, write correctly reference entries for

- a book with two authors;
- a chapter written by one author published in a book edited by two editors;
- a journal article published by two authors, print version with DOI (see B.66 General Guidelines on Referencing the Electronic Sources);
- a journal article published by two authors;
- a book written and published by an organization (e.g., ASHA);
- a piece of information retrieved from an online source;
- a journal article with seven authors; and
- a journal article with nine authors.

## B.4.47a. In the Reference List, Arrange References in Alphabetical Order

- Use the last name to determine the alphabetical order.
- Alphabetize the names of multiple authors by the surname of the first author.
- Alphabetize names letter by letter, but exclude the initials.
- Arrange prefixes in their strict alphabetical order. Ignore an apostrophe attached to a prefix (M').
- Consult the biographical section of *Merriam-Webster's Collegiate Dictionary* to find the order in which surnames with articles and prepositions are arranged (names with *de, la, du, von*, etc.).
- When listing several works by the same author, but some with and some without coauthors, start with those works that do not have coauthors.

| Incorrect | Correct | Note |
| --- | --- | --- |
| McNeil, A. S. (2010)<br>Macmillan, J. J. (2008) | Macmillan, J. J. (2008)<br>McNeil, A. S. (2010) | *Mac* precedes *Mc* |
| Thomson, A. B. (2016)<br>Thomas, Z. X. (20015) | Thomas, Z. X. (2015)<br>Thomson, A. B. (2016) | Alphabetized letter by letter. Ignore the initials. |
| Tonseko, K. J., & Fontana, P. J. (2001)<br>Tonseko, K. J., & Lordon, T. P. (2017)<br>Tonseko, K. J. (2013) | Tonseko, K. J. (2013) Tonseko, K. J., & Fontana, P. J. (2001)<br>Tonseko, K. J., & Lordon, T. P. (2017) | Enter the single author first. Alphabetize the second authors, too: *Tonseko & Fontana* before *Tonseko & Lordon*. |

## B.4.48a. Arrange Multiple Works of the Same Single Author From the Earliest to the Latest Year

| Incorrect | Correct | Note |
| --- | --- | --- |
| Able, P. J. (2017)<br>Able, P. J. (1992)<br>Able, P. J. (1989) | Able, P. J. (1989)<br>Able, P. J. (1992)<br>Able, P. J. (2017) | For each single author, arrange the works from the earliest to the latest year. |
| Benson, L. S. (2016) Benson, L. S. (2008) Benson, L. S. (2002) | Benson, L. S. (2002) Benson, L. S. (2008) Benson, L. S. (2016) | |

### B.4.47b. In the Reference List, Arrange References in Alphabetical Order

| Reference Information | Arrange the Names Alphabetically |
|---|---|
| McMinnan, L. D., 2010<br>McDonald, U. G., 2015<br>McFarrin, M. P., 2012<br>Van Riper, C., 1975<br>Axelrod, A. K., 2016<br>Herbert, B. H., 2009<br>Hernadez, N. K., 2013<br>Alvarado, B. C., 2014<br>von Kirk, D., 2011<br>de Klerk, Q. Q., 2017 |  |

### B.4.48b. Arrange Multiple Works of the Same Single Author From the Earliest to the Latest Year

| Reference Information | Arrange the Names in the Correct Order |
|---|---|
| Larson, K. (2016)<br>Larson, K. (2007)<br>Larson, K. (2002) |  |
| McDonald, P. (2014)<br>McDonald, P. (2001)<br>McDonald, P. (2007) |  |

### B.4.49a. Alphabetize the Titles of Several Works of the Same Author Published in the Same Year

In alphabetizing the titles, ignore the articles *A* and *The* at the beginning of the title. Attach the lowercase letters a, b, c, and so forth to the year of publication.

| Incorrect | Correct | Note |
| --- | --- | --- |
| Lagassi, A. R. (2015a). Problems of clay courts.<br>Lagassi, A. R. (2015b). Advantages of short-handled rackets. | Lagassi, A. R. (2015a). Advantages of short-handled rackets.<br>Lagassi, A. R. (2015b). Problems of clay courts. | The first word of the title is used to alphabetize: *Advantages* precedes *Problems*. |
| Massood, P. T. (2010a). Some advantages of the circular paper clip.<br>Massood, P. T. (2010b). The case of the missing paper clip. | Massood, P. T. (2010a). The case of the missing paper clip.<br>Massood, P. T. (2010b). Some advantages of the circular paper clip. | The article *The* is ignored in arranging these two entries. |

### B.4.50a. Arrange the Multiple Works of the Same Author Published in a Different Year, in a Temporally Ascending Order

| Incorrect | Correct | Note |
| --- | --- | --- |
| Nelson, B. D. (2001). AIDS in the modern world.<br>Nelson, B. D. (1998). Beads around the neck.<br>Nelson, B. D. (2002). Lost in theories. | Nelson, B. D. (1998). Beads around the neck.<br>Nelson, B. D. (2001). AIDS in the modern world.<br>Nelson, B. D. (2002). Lost in theories. | The titles are not alphabetized. |

### B.4.51a. Alphabetize the Different Authors With the Same Last Name According to Their Initials

| Incorrect | Correct | Note |
| --- | --- | --- |
| Able, Q. T. (1993)<br>Able, A. A. (1982) | Able, A. A. (1982)<br>Able, Q. T. (1993) | The year of publication does not matter. |
| Tavratinova, S. N. (1987)<br>Tavratinova, B. D. (1993) | Tavratinova, B. D. (1993)<br>Tavratinova, S. N. (1987) | |

### B.4.49b. Alphabetize the Titles of Several Works of the Same Author Published in the Same Year

| Reference Information | Alphabetize According to the Titles |
|---|---|
| Belwae, T. P. (1989a). A potential explanation of muddy football fields.<br><br>Belwae, T. P. (1989b). Crashing and winning: The cultural underpinnings of football. | |
| Cisnero, S. M. (1990a). Cities in decay: An agenda for rebuilding American cities.<br><br>Cisnero, S. M. (1990b). Banking on the neighborhood. | |

### B.4.50b. Arrange the Multiple Works of the Same Author Published in a Different Year, in a Temporally Ascending Order

| Incorrect | Arrange Correctly |
|---|---|
| Nayyar, C. D. (2001). All can learn.<br>Nayyar, C. D. (1998). Help for the homeless.<br>Nayyar, C. D. (2002). Polish the self-image. | |

### B.4.51b. Alphabetize the Different Authors With the Same Last Name According to Their Initials

| Reference Information | Alphabetize According to the Initials |
|---|---|
| Nelson, Z. T. (2016)<br>Nelson, B. S. (2013)<br>Nelson, A. P. (2015) | |
| Ramig, L. T. (2017)<br>Ramig, C. C. (2011)<br>Ramig, B. D. (2015) | |

## B.4.52a. Format Each Entry in the Reference List With a Hanging Indent of 5 Spaces

- Use the word processor's default setting for hanging indents.
- Note that each entry is treated as a separate paragraph with its hanging indent.

| Incorrect | Correct | Note |
|---|---|---|
| Lagassi, A. R. (1991a). Advantages of short-handled rackets. *Journal of Rackets, 4,* 55–90.      Lagassi, A. R. (1991b). *Problems of clay courts.* New York: The Racket Press. | Lagassi, A. R. (1991a). Advantages of short-handled rackets. *Journal of Rackets, 4,* 55–90. Lagassi, A. R. (1991b). *Problems of clay courts.* New York: The Racket Press. | Type flush left the first line of each entry. Indent the second and the subsequent lines of each entry by five spaces, by using the word processor's *hanging indent* feature. |

## B.4.53a. Use the Specified Abbreviations in Reference Lists

Note that in reference lists, most of the abbreviations are placed within parentheses, and may include other elements (e.g., number of pages, report, edition, etc.).

| Abbreviation | For | Note |
|---|---|---|
| (2nd ed.) | second edition | Lowercase abbreviations. |
| (p.) or (pp.) | page (pages) | |
| (n.d.) | no date | |
| (Vol.) or (Vols.) | Volume or Volumes | Uppercase abbreviations. |
| (Ed.) or (Eds.) | Editor or Editors | |
| (Trans.) | same for Translator or Translators | |
| (Rev. ed.) | Revised edition | |
| (No.) | Number | |
| (Pt.) | Part | |
| (Rep.) | Report | |
| (Tech.) | (Technical) | |
| (Suppl.) | Supplement | |

### B.4.52b. Format Each Entry in the Reference List With a Hanging Indent of 5 Spaces

Invent a journal name, volume number, and page numbers for both the references.

| Incorrect | Rewrite Correctly |
|---|---|
| Sharma, P. K. (1989). Mothers teach language to their children.<br>    Tackle, K. K. (1990). Tackle football and the moral fiber. | |

### B.4.53b. Use the Specified Abbreviations in Reference Lists

| Unabbreviated | Write the Correct Abbreviation |
|---|---|
| edition | |
| Revised edition | |
| second edition | |
| Editor (Editors) | |
| Translator(s) | |
| page (pages) | |
| Volume | |
| Number | |
| Part | |
| Report | |
| Technical | |
| Supplement | |
| No date | |

# Selected Examples of References

## Printed Journal Articles

### B.4.54a. Printed Journal Articles in Reference Lists

- Format each entry with a hanging indent, using the word processor's default setting; each entry is set as a separate paragraph.
- Enter one space between author initials, after the last initial, before starting the article title, and before the journal name.
- Type a comma after the last initial of the first author, and join the names of two authors with an ampersand (&); type a period after the year in parentheses.
- Capitalize all important words of the journal name; do not abbreviate it; italicize the journal name and the volume number, (but no *volume* or its abbreviation).
- Enter the page number or numbers as the last entry without *p.* or *pp.*; end the entry with a period; do not italicize the page numbers.
- Write "in press" without the quotation marks for articles in press.
- If a publication has no date, type n.d. in parentheses instead of the year of publication.
- Give the month (for monthlies) or month and date (for dailies) after the year in parentheses.
- Type the journal issue number following the volume number only if the journal is paginated by issue (not continuously numbered within a volume).
- Include the Digital Object Identifier (DOI) number if available even for printed sources; copy them exactly, with no period at the end; no additional retrieval information is needed.

| Correct | Note |
| --- | --- |
| Hadley, P., Rispoll, M., & Hsu, N. (2016). Toddlers' verbal lexicon diversity and grammatical outcome. *Language, Speech, and Hearing Services in Schools, 47,* 44–58. doi:xx.xxxxx | Even though all DOIs start with the numeral 10, they are unique to each article and its publisher; copy it exactly. Read more about the doi system at http://www.doi.org/. |
| Crapp, T. C., & Crass, C. T. (2017). Dead people violate the laws of physics. *Journal of Metaphysics, 55*(7), 20–70. doi:xx.xxxxx | Issue number added, but with no italics and no space after the italicized volume number. |
| Hazelnut, L. M., & Beachnut, P. M. (in press). Nutty theories in naughty disciplines. *Journal of Speculative Psychology*. | A comma precedes an ampersand. The journal title is italicized. |
| McVenro, D. (2015, December). The relation between umpire judgments and player verbal outbursts. *American Sportsman, 520,* 1230–1240. | Example of an article published in a monthly magazine. |
| United States Diversity Commission. (n.d.). The diverse America. Retrieved from http:/www.usdc.gov/qtrrpt/2001/sbtoc97.htm. | (n.d.) replaces the year when a publication date is unknown. Do not include the retrieval date unless the content itself is likely to change over time (e.g., *Wiki* documents). |

*Note:* These printed exemplars are not double-spaced; but your typed references should be.

# Printed Journal Articles

### B.4.54b. Printed Journal Articles in Reference Lists

| Reference Information | Correctly Write the References |
|---|---|
| Author: P. E. Turkeltaub<br>Year: 2015<br>Article Title: Brain stimulation and the role of the right hemisphere in aphasia recovery<br>Journal: *Current Neurology and Neuroscience Reports*<br>Volume: 15<br>Pages: 72–79<br>DOI:10.1007/s11910-015-0593-6 | |
| Author: S. L. Nunez<br>Year: in press<br>Article Title: Models of counseling in speech and hearing<br>Journal: *American Journal of Speech-Language Pathology* | |
| Authors: C. C. Woo, and M. Leon<br>Year: 2013<br>Article Title: Environmental enrichment as treatment for autism.<br>Journal: *Behavioral Neuroscience*<br>Volume: 127<br>Issue number: 4<br>Pages: 487–497<br>(Pages in each issue are numbered separately.)<br>DOI: 10.1037/a0033010 | *Note:* Both DOI and doi are used by different sources. |

### B.4.55a. Arrange Correctly the Articles With Multiple Authors

- Enter one space between the initials.
- Insert a comma before an ampersand.
- Include all two, three, four, five, six, and seven author names of a work.

| Correct | Note |
| --- | --- |
| Hellbent, H. B., & Heavenbound, L. T. (2017). | Include both the names of a work, and up to **seven** names. |
| James, B., Conns, L., Beams, B., Krapp, T. T., Lapp, L. Deems, D., & Leans, J. (2016). | A work with **seven** names.<br><br>The reference list will never contain more than seven names (see the next exemplar). |
| Moll, D., Kole, K., Ball, A., Dole, B., Teal, T., Seal, Z., . . . Neal, P. (2015). | In the case of **eight** or more authors, reference the first **six** authors, and then insert three ellipsis points, and add the **very last** author's name of the work.<br><br>There is no *et al.* in the Reference List. |

### B.4.56a. Reference Correctly the Different Forms of Journal Publications

| Correct | Note |
| --- | --- |
| Broadhead, K. D. (Ed.). (2001). Ineffective but popular stuttering therapies [Special issue]. *Journal of Stuttering Therapy, 55*. doi:xx.xxxxx | Referencing an entire [Special issue] of a journal. Note the absence of page numbers. Note the brackets, not parentheses. |
| Joke, B. D. (2001). Psychology of self-image. *Journal of Pop Psychology Monographs, 20*. doi:xx.xxxxx | A monograph, published as a supplement to a journal, but bound separately. |
| Guzman, L., & Bizzman, B. (2002). Campus drinking [Monograph]. *Journal of Educational Sociology, 66*, 120–190. doi:xx.xxxxx | A [Monograph] bound into a journal. Note the brackets, not parentheses. |
| Wide, J. D., Narrow, B. K., & Long, L. (2002). A new normative study on phonological acquisition. *Journal of Phonology, 10*(Suppl.5), 2–45. doi:xx.xxxxx | A (Supplement) to a journal. Note the parentheses, not brackets. |

### B.4.55b. Arrange Correctly the Articles With Multiple Authors

| Reference Information | Correctly Write the References |
|---|---|
| Authors: B. D. Jasper and K. D. Master<br>Year: 2001<br>Article: Communicative intents<br>Journal: *Intuitive Language Pathology, 190,* 15–35. |  |
| Authors: T. T. Ladd, C. Badd, S. Lode, L. Jode, K.. Node, and Z. Goad<br>Year: 2002<br>Article: Do not believe in it.<br>*Journal of Metaphysics, 50,* 30–40. |  |
| Authors: D. Monsen, D. Benson, K. Johnson, A. Nonsense, G. Dollard, B. Miller, S. Terror, and T. Caam<br>Year: 2000<br>Article: Yawning as treatment for voice disorders<br>Journal: *Journal of Communication Disorders, 52,* 30–60. |  |

### B.4.56b. Reference Correctly the Different Forms of Journal Publications

| Reference Information | Correctly Write the References |
|---|---|
| Editor: M. K. Kim<br>Year: 2015<br>Special issue: Therapies that work *Journal of Stuttering Therapy, 75.* |  |
| Author: S. S. Grim<br>Year: 2013<br>Monograph number 15, published as a supplement to a journal, but bound separately: Psychology of peace. *Journal of Peace Psychology* |  |
| Authors: O. Lukes<br>Year: 2016.<br>A monograph bound into a journal: Eating in town. *Journal of Romantic Dining,* vol. 66, pp. 120–190. |  |
| Author: J. D. Jogg<br>Year: 2017<br>A supplement to a journal: A study on morphologic learning.<br>*Journal of Language* vol. 10, Supplement 5, pp. 2–45. |  |

## Magazines and Newspaper Articles

### B.4.57a. Reference Correctly the Publications From Magazines and Newspapers

| Correct | Note |
|---|---|
| Kraft, J. P. (2001, September 10). America's drug war. *Newsweek*, 35–45. | A weekly magazine with no volume number. |
| Local therapist offers new treatment for autism. (2016, September 9). *Los Angeles Times*, p. B10. Retrieved from http://www.xxxxxx | Newspaper articles with no author. In the reference list, alphabetize according to the first significant word. |
| New ways of treating heart disease (2014, December 15). The Fresno Bee, pp. C5, C7, C9–11. | Add the retrieval information if read online. In the text, cite a short title with the year (e.g., "Local therapist, 2001"); use double quotation marks. |
| Thomson, B. L. (2002, Fall). State legislature renews the licensure law. *CSHA*, 5–6. | Article in a newsletter with an author. If no author, alphabetize the title. |

## Abstracts

### B.4.58a. Reference Correctly the Article Abstracts Used as the Primary Source

- The writer may have read only an abstract, which needs to be referenced (as in a database that contains only abstracts or periodically printed abstracts of journal articles).
- The printed source may publish only an abstract of articles (as ASHA does of its annual convention presentations).

| Correct | Note |
|---|---|
| Kemer, J. J. (2001, August 29). Preventing aspiration [Abstract]. *ASHA Leader, 6*(15), 59. | The word *Abstract* in brackets (not italicized). The year is followed by the month and date. |
| Kimm, T. T., & Limm, P. P. (2002). Treatment of aphasia: A review [Abstract]. *Society for Aphasia Abstracts, 10*, 59. | Example of a printed abstract source that the writer consulted. |
| Knudsen, O. O. (2001). Cognitive processes as ghosts of neuroscience. *Mexican Journal of Behavior Science, 5*, 55. Abstract retrieved from http://www.xxxxxx | Example of an abstract obtained from an electronic database. Copy the exact URL. |

## Magazines and Newspaper Articles

### B.4.57b. Reference Correctly the Publications From Magazines and Newspapers

| Reference Information | Correctly Write the References |
|---|---|
| Author: Biff, L. P.<br>Date: 2011, November 15<br>Article: School violence is declining<br>Published in: *Time* (weekly)<br>Pages: 10–15 | |
| Article: The clinic in town saves life<br>Date: 2014, July 10<br>Published in: *New York Times*<br>Page: B20 | |
| Article: Failed treatment for autism disappoints parents<br>Date: 2016, October 10.<br>Published in: *Buffalo Times*<br>Pages: D4, D7, D10–12 | |
| Zinson, L. L. (2001). Licensure laws are about to sunset in several states.<br>Date: 2016, Winter<br>Published in: *Speech and Hearing* (newsletter)<br>Page: 20 | |

## Abstracts

### B.4.58b. Reference Correctly the Article Abstracts Used as the Primary Source

| Incorrect | Correctly Write the References |
|---|---|
| Author: Zen, B. B.; Date: 2001, August 29 Article presented: Preventing stuttering Form: Abstract; Published in: *ASHA Leader;* Volume 8, issue 15, page 20 | |
| Johns, T. T., & Hams, P. P.; Year: 2002 Article: Treatment of autism; Abstract Published in: *Association for Autism Abstracts; volume 12,* page 90 | |
| Author: Kompleks, B. O.; year 2001 Article: Stuttering is awfully complex. Journal: *British Journal of Communication; volume 75,* pages 45–55. Abstract Retrieved from http://www.xxxxxx | |

## Books and Book Chapters

### B.4.59a. Books in Reference Lists

- Use the word processor's *hanging indent* format of paragraphs.
- Italicize the title of the book. Capitalize only the first letter of the title and subtitle.
- Enter one space between the year and the title, and between the title and the place of publication.
- Type the abbreviated word *Jr.* after the last initial, if applicable.
- Type the abbreviated edition number (e.g., 2nd ed.) or the words "Rev. ed." (for *revised edition*; without quotation marks) after the title and place within parentheses.
- Type the name of the city of the publisher.
- If the city is not well known or could be confused with another location, type the abbreviated name of the state. Use the U.S. Postal Service abbreviations for the states.
- Type the publishing company's name exactly as it appears in the book being referenced.
- For books written and published by corporations, agencies, or associations, type the word "Author" (without the quotation marks) for the publisher.
- For books originally published in one year and reprinted or reissued later by another publisher, give both of the years and specify both of the publishers.

| Correct | Note |
|---|---|
| American Psychological Association. (2010). *Publication manual of the American Psychological Association* (6th ed.). Washington, DC: Author. | The publisher and the author are the same (a corporate author). *DC* is added to Washington because it could be confused with the state of Washington. |
| Boczquats, N. S. (2015). *Oceanography and communication: A new frontier.* Chicago: Blue Heaven Press. | One space separates the year and the title and the title and the place of publication. |
| Histrionik, K. L., Jr., & Stoic, P. L. (2017). *Neurotic behavior* (2nd ed.). Los Angeles: Angeles Publishing Company. | *Jr.* after the initials. The book edition in parentheses, not italicized. A comma precedes the ampersand even though only two names are referenced. |
| Null, B. D. (2002). *Numbers in civilization* (Rev. ed.). New York: Sappleton. | (Rev. ed.) for revised edition. |
| Blinton, W., & Blinton, H. (1999). *Hope for America.* Hope, AR: Optimist Press. | The state abbreviation is added because the city is not well known. A colon—not a period—follows the state abbreviation. |
| Katz, A., Bats, B., Hats, S., Mats, I., Bits, B., Notes, L., . . . Chats, K. (2001). *Problems of writing with multiple authors.* New York: Cooperative Press. | If a book has more than eight authors, type only the first six names, add three elliptical points, and the last name as shown. No *ampersand* or *et al.* |
| Russell, B. (1921/2005). *The analysis of mind.* Mineola, NY: Dover Publications, Inc. [Originally published in 1921 by Allen & Unwin, London, England.] | The 2005 publication is not a revision or a new edition; it is a re-issue of the same 1921 publication; the author who cited the book may not have read it in its original print. |
| *The American heritage dictionary of the English language* (5th ed.). (2011). New York: Houghton Mifflin Company. | A book with no author or editor; alphabetize the book by the first significant word in the title, in this case: American. |

*Note:* The examples are independent of each other and are not to be confused with an alphabetized reference list.

## Books and Book Chapters

### B.4.59b. Books in Reference Lists

Write the state abbreviation, not the full name.

| Reference Information | Correctly Write the References |
|---|---|
| Author: K. D. Wong<br>Title: *Bilingual speech-language pathology*<br>Year: 2013<br>Edition: Second<br>Publisher: Word Publishing Company<br>City: Ames, Iowa | |
| Authors: S. S. Simms, T. T. Tinns, and K. K. Kimms<br>Title: *Central auditory problems*<br>Year: 2015<br>Edition: Revised<br>Publisher: Nelson Publishers<br>City: New York, New York | |
| Author: N. C. Gordimeir<br>Title: *Hearing aids of the future*<br>Year: 2017<br>Publisher: The Future Press<br>City: Hazleton, Tennessee | |
| Author: American Speech-Language-Hearing Association<br>Title: *Your professional organization*<br>Year: 2015<br>City: Rockville Pike, Maryland<br>Publisher: American Speech-Language-Hearing Association | |
| Authors: A. Saks, B. Lots, C. Jolts, D. Dykes, E. Estes, F. Fin, G. Gats, H. Hykes, and I. Ikes<br>Title: *It can be done*<br>Year: 2002<br>Publisher: Nightmare Press<br>City: Clovis, California | |
| Author: J. B. Singleton<br>Title: *Fulfilled single life*<br>Years: 1850, original publication by Companion Press, New York, New York; reissued in 2009 by Content Press, Monterey, California | |
| Book: *Merriam-Webster's collegiate dictionary*, 11th edition<br>Year: 2005<br>Publisher: Merriam-Webster<br>City: Springfield, Massachusetts | *Hint:* Write the name of the publisher, not the author. |

## B.4.60a. Edited Books and Chapters in Edited Books

- Note that you can either reference a chapter in an edited book or the entire edited book, depending on what is cited in the text.
- Inn referencing a chapter, use the name of the chapter author (not the editor) in alphabetizing the list.
- After the editor's last name, type in parentheses the abbreviated word (Ed.) for one editor or (Eds.) for multiple editors; type (ed.) for an edition of a book.
- Italicize the book title, not the chapter title.
- Place the author's initials at the end of the surname (*as usual*).
- Place the editor's initials at the beginning, not the end of the surname (*not as usual*).
- Type the pages of the chapter after the title and within parentheses.

| Correct | Note |
|---|---|
| Baker, K. V. (2015). The unconscious. In C. Hart (Ed.), *Unknown states of consciousness* (pp. 305–395). New York, NY: Mystery Publishing House. | In the text, the author of the chapter, not the editor of the book, is cited (Baker, 2015, not Hart, 2015). The page numbers are for the cited author's chapter only. |
| Cantun, U. O. (2001). The invisible and the unmeasurable. In K. Panth & C. Hanth (Eds.), *Ghosts within skulls* (2nd ed.) (pp. 35–95). Fresno, CA: Ghostly Press. | Chapter cited from the second edition of an edited book. There is no comma after the first editor's name and before the ampersand. |
| Hunt, C. P., & Holms, G. S. (Eds.). (2001). *Mysteries of mental events*. Clovis, CA: Invisible Publishers. | This reference is for an entire edited book, not a chapter in it. (Eds.) for Editors. |
| Xong, K. C. (Ed.). (2002). *Split brain is just as good* (2nd ed.). Los Angeles: NeuroPress. | Entire edited book is cited in the text. (Ed.) for Editor, (ed.) for edition. |
| Kent, B. (Ed.). (1990–2001). *Speech-language pathology* (Vols. 1–5). New York: Hudson Press. | Reference to a multi-volume edited book published over several years. Citation in the text: (Kent, 1990–2001). |
| James, J. (Ed.) (2017). *Language disorders*. Retrieved from http://www.xxxxxx | An edited book published only online. |
| Adams, A. (Ed.) (2015). *Sociology of morality*. doi:xxxxx | An online edited publication with only a DOI. |

## B.4.60b. Edited Books and Chapters in Edited Books

| Reference Information | Correctly Write the References |
|---|---|
| Editors: Johns, L. B., and Bangs, R. K. Book title: *Clinical ethics*.<br>Year: 2017<br>Publisher: College Press<br>City: Los Angeles, CA | |
| Editor: Montu, M. L.<br>Year: 2011<br>Book: Language therapy in the mind<br>[An online publication] | |
| Author: Jackson, N. O.<br>Chapter title: Speech-language pathologist and the bilingual child<br>Year: 2005<br>Pages: 135–175<br>Book title: *Education in the Next Century* Editors: Cantor, A. K., and Bantor, B. L. Publisher: Century Press<br>City: Portland, OR | |
| Editor: Lent, B.<br>Years: 2010–2017<br>Book title: *Speech and Hearing Science*<br>Volumes 1–7<br>Publisher: Mechanical Press.<br>City: San Francisco, CA | |

## Proceedings, Presentations, and Reports

### B.4.61a. Proceedings of Conferences and Symposia

| Correct | Note |
|---|---|
| Peacock, P. L., & Lyon, A. D. (2002). Cooperation in the animal kingdom. In E. L. Phant & H. I. Pottoms (Eds.). *Proceedings of the Tenth Conference on the Animal Kingdom* (pp. 23–57). Boston, MA: Cobra Press. | The title of proceedings published as a book is italicized and capitalized as shown (because it is a proper noun). If this is an online publication as well, give the DOI. |
| Ram, B. (2017, June). *Case load of school clinicians.* D. Davis (Chair). Symposium conducted at the meeting of the Fresno County Office of Education, Fresno, CA. | Presentation at a symposium, not published. If available online, give the DOI. |

### B.4.62a. Unpublished Convention Paper or Poster Presentations

See B.4.56a for referencing published abstracts of convention presentations.

| Correct | Note |
|---|---|
| Idlemann, P. S. (2015, November). *Variables related to doing nothing.* Paper presented at the Annual Meeting of the American Anti-Workaholic Association, Bullhead City, AZ. | "Meeting," "convention," and so forth should be accurate. Give the year and the month in parentheses. Italicize the title of the presentation. |
| Hernandez, K. S. (2017, November). *Clinician's ethical dilemmas.* Poster presented at the Annual Convention of the American Speech-Language-Hearing Association, San Antonio, TX. | A poster presentation. |

### B.4 Selected Matters of Scientific Style

## Proceedings, Presentations, and Reports

### B.4.61b. Proceedings of Conferences and Symposia

| Reference Information | Correctly Write the References |
|---|---|
| Author: D. V. Quietson<br>Paper: Hearing impairment in rock musicians<br>Pages: 87–97<br>Title of the book: *Proceedings of the 10th national conference on noise and hearing loss*<br>Editors of the book: C. D. Noysman and F. S. Loudman<br>Year: 2014<br>City: Centralia, IL<br>Publisher: Peace Press | |
| Author: Ahlander, E. (2016, September). *Early treatment for stuttering.*<br>Chair: L. Johns.<br>Symposium conducted at the meeting of the Clovis Unified School District, Clovis, CA. | |

### B.4.62b. Unpublished Convention Paper or Poster Presentations

| Reference Information | Correctly Write the References |
|---|---|
| Author: B. J. Beans<br>Paper: A new method of scoring language samples<br>Presented at: National Convention of the American Speech-Language-Hearing Association<br>Date: November, 2012<br>City: Atlanta, GA | |
| Author: S. Hilton<br>Year: April 2015<br>Poster title: Toddlers are scholars<br>Presented at: Annual Conference of Child Language Society<br>Place: Los Angeles, CA | |

### B.4.63a. Reports From Organizations and Government Agencies

| Correct | Note |
|---|---|
| National Child Health and Human Development. (2001). *How not to write research proposals* (DHHS Publication No. QRS-00910). Washington, DC: U.S. Government Printing Office. Retrieved from http://www.xxxxxxxxx | "Publication No.," "Report No.," and so forth are in parentheses (without the quotation marks). Copy the URL to avoid errors. |
| Alcocer, B. J. (2002). Eating habits and heart diseases. In J. D. Kang & L. D. Lang (Eds.), *The healthy heart* (NIH Publication No. 02230, pp. 200–250). Washington, DC: U.S. Department of Health and Human Services. Retrieved from http://www.xxxxxxxxx | An article or a chapter in a report published by a department of the U.S. government. |
| Norm, J. J. (2000). *Invariably fixed stages of cognitive development* (Report No. 15). Washington, DC: National Cognition Association. | The period is typed after the closing parenthesis; no period is typed at the end of the actual title of the report. |
| Osgood, O. (2001). *Teacher training in the U.S.* (Report No. NCRTL-RR-90-3). East Lansing, MI: National Center for Research on Teacher Learning. (ERIC Document Reproduction Service No. ED203050) | A report obtained from the Educational Resources Information Center (ERIC). No period at the end of the entry. |

### B.4.64a. Printed and Online Reference Works

| Correct | Note |
|---|---|
| *Merriam-Webster's collegiate dictionary* (11th ed.). (2005). Springfield, MA: Merriam-Webster. | |
| Kriegel, U. (n.d.). Self consciousness. *The internet encyclopedia of philosophy*. Retrieved from http://www.xxxxxxxx | Copy the exact URL. |

### B.4.63b. Reports From Organizations and Government Agencies

| Reference Information | Correctly Write the References |
|---|---|
| Organization: National Institute of Public Health (NIPH); year: 2015; title of publication: *Threats to Public Health*; publication #PQ-01-S25; city: Washington, DC; from: U.S. Government Printing Office. | |
| Author: Azvedo, L. J. (2014); title: Autism and language disorders; in P. J. Chew & J. K. Kew (Eds.), *New directions in autism* (NIH Publication No. 02-240, pp. 210–270); Washington, DC: U.S. Department of Health and Human Services. | |
| Authors: Hogg, G. H., & Bogg, B. D.; year: 2011; title: *Ironing habits and academic achievement* (Tech Rep. No. 200); place: Vancouver, British Columbia, Canada: University of Western Canada, Psychosocial Research Institute. | |

### B.4.64b. Printed and Online Reference Works

| Reference Information | Correctly Write the References |
|---|---|
| Author: B. James, article: Aristotle, year: 2015, published in: Stanford Encyclopedia Retrieved from http://plato.stanford.edu/entries/Aristotle/ | |
| Editor: Butterfield, J. Printed book: Fowler's dictionary of modern English usage.; 4th edition; year: 2015; Publisher, Oxford University Press; place: Oxford, UK | |

## Unpublished Articles, Dissertations, and Theses

### B.4.65a. Unpublished Articles, Theses, or Dissertations

| Correct | Note |
|---|---|
| Dimm, B. J. (2010). *Why some articles do not get published.* Unpublished manuscript. | Titles of unpublished works are italicized while those of published ones are not. If available online, give the URL. |
| Godson, J. K. (2011). *Levels of aspiration and academic performance.* Unpublished manuscript, Department of Psychology, University of California, Los Angeles. | An unpublished manuscript obtained from a university department. |
| Badson, H. P. (2015). *Cognitivists confuse the brain for the mind.* Manuscript submitted for publication. | A manuscript in the process of being published. |
| Smiley, S. S. (2017). *Relationship between toilet training and frequency of smiling in high school classrooms.* Unpublished master's thesis, Sharp College of Education, Needles, CA. | A master's thesis not abstracted in *Masters Abstracts International (MAI)*. Use the same format for unpublished doctoral dissertation. |
| Brightly, B. B. (2014). *Relation between hair color and academic learning.* Retrieved from http://www.xxxxxxx | If retrieved from an institutional database (such as a university), copy the full URL. |
| Zinson, D. C. (2002). *Fathers' role in children's language learning.* Unpublished master's thesis, University of Toronto, Toronto, Canada. | The name of the city, state, and the country are specified when a thesis or dissertation is from a university outside the United States. |

### B.4.66a. Theses and Dissertations in *Abstracts International*

Note that abstracts of most theses and dissertations are published in their respective *Abstracts International*. If only the abstract is read, reference the name of the abstract, volume number, and page number.

| Correct | Note |
|---|---|
| Allen, T. H. (2013). The role of the unconscious in language treatment. (Doctoral dissertation, Unaware University, 2001). *Master's Abstracts International, 92,* 540. | Abstracted in MAI, but the reader got a copy from the university. Both are cited; the dissertation title is not italicized. |
| Gardner, G. N. (2010). Horticultural concepts in explaining human behavior. *Dissertation Abstracts International, 89,* (05), 435B. (UMI N0. 989876) | Abstracted in DAI, but obtained from University Microfilms International (UMI), which offers this service; both are cited. |

# Unpublished Articles, Dissertations, and Theses

### B.4.65b. Unpublished Articles, Theses, or Dissertations

| Reference Information | Correctly Write the References |
|---|---|
| Author: Henkly, T. K.; year, 2015 Unpublished article: How to get published in speech and hearing. | |
| Author: Carter, J. J., year, 2012 Unpublished article: Peace on earth. Obtained from: Emory University City: Atlanta, GA | |
| Author: Gyon, G. V.; year, 2010 M.A. thesis, not in MAI: Evaluation of an early language intervention package University: Downstate University City: Rocks, NJ | |
| Author: Meyersson, M.; year, 2002 Unpublished doctoral dissertation: *Mothers' role in her child's cognitive development.* University: University of London; City: London: Country: UK | |

### B.4.66b. Theses and Dissertations in *Abstracts International*

| Reference Information | Correctly Write the References |
|---|---|
| Author: Borgen, T. H.; year 2016<br>Title of doctoral dissertation found in DAI, but obtained from the university: What is in the mind?<br>University: Mental University<br>Dissertation Abstracts International, volume 92, page 300 | |
| Author: Branch, L. L.; year, 2013<br>Title of doctoral dissertation, abstracted in DAI, but obtained from UMI: A plant grows into a tree.<br>Dissertation Abstracts International, volume 55, page 40, UMI N0. 967345 | |

## Note to Students Working on Theses or Dissertations

The graduate schools of most universities and the specific department have a set of guidelines on the preparation of theses and dissertations. The university and departmental guidelines that generally accept the APA style may have special guidelines that deviate in certain respects from the APA style. Therefore, students should consult both the APA style and the guidelines of their department and the graduate school.

# B.5. Writing Sections of Research Papers and Proposals

## B.5.1. General Guidelines on Completed and Proposed Empirical Studies

Completed research and a research proposal are different in their content. Generally, the two types of writing follow the same format, including such major headings as Abstract, Method, Results, Discussion, and References. Various subheadings also may be similar if not the same.

Students initially write a thesis or dissertation proposal and submit it to a university committee for approval. Once the research is completed, a thesis or a dissertation is written as an empirical report submitted for publication.

Generally, sections of a completed study are written in the past tense, whereas a proposal is written in the future tense. There are some variations in specific journal styles on these matters. Therefore, the author should read a few sample articles from the journal to which he or she plans to submit the paper for possible publication.

## B.5.2. Sections of a Research Paper

| Printed Notes | Class Notes |
|---|---|
| **Abstract**<br><br>An abstract is a brief description of the problems, the methods, the procedures, and the results of a scientific study in direct and nonevaluative language. It is written not only to give a summary of the article, but also to attract the reader to the whole article. In manuscripts, abstracts are printed on a separate page. In printed articles, they are placed just before the introductory section begins.<br><br>According to the APA *Manual* (2010), a good abstract is accurate, self-contained, concise, specific, nonevaluative, coherent, and readable. The *Manual* suggests a range of 150 to 250 words for abstracts. For the actual number of words, the author should consult the guidelines of the specific journal to which the article will be submitted. Most computer word processors give an automatic count of the total number of words, characters, and spaces in a document or its selected section.<br><br>To conserve space, authors can write abstracts in active voice. All numbers may be written in numerals instead of words. By recasting a sentence, authors can avoid use of a number at its beginning is avoided. | |

Students often find it difficult to write an abstract of a paper. Writing an attractive and comprehensive abstract requires skills in precision writing. Exercises in abstracting a few papers are necessary to learn this skill.

An abstract, though brief, may have to be revised several times, especially if the first draft is too long or vague. With a keen eye on wordiness, students can trim their abstracts to size.

## Introduction

The text of the paper starts with an introductory section without a heading. This section introduces: (1) the general area of investigation; (2) the general findings of past investigations; (3) the specific topic of the current investigation; (4) a review of selected studies that have dealt with the topic in the past; (5) the methods, results, conclusions, methodological problems, and limitations of the past studies; (6) the questions that remain to be answered; (7) the significance of the current investigation; and (8) the specific problem or research questions investigated in the present study.

The introduction should move from the general topic of investigation to the particular, specific research question investigated in the study. A critical review of previous studies sets the stage for the current investigation by pointing out gaps in our knowledge. This review should be fair, objective, and direct. The review should make it clear to the reader the need for the study and the reasoning behind it. The review should show how the present study is related to past research while also pointing out its innovative aspects.

Toward the end of the introduction, the research question should be formally stated. Hypotheses, if proposed, may be stated at this point. The research questions and hypotheses must be written in direct, clear, and terse language. A good introduction gives sufficient background to the study and justifies its execution. By the end of this section, the reader should gain a clear understanding of the context of the study and why it was done.

| Printed Notes | Class Notes |

## Method

The second section describes the method in detail for two reasons: (1) to give sufficient information so the reader can understand the methods and procedures of the study and judge their appropriateness to investigate the research questions asked and (2) to permit direct and systematic replications of the study.

The method section consists of at least three subsections: (1) the participants, (2) the apparatus or materials, and (3) the procedure. Additional subsections (and subheadings), such as *Baselines* or *Experiment 1*, *Experiment 2*, may be necessary.

Do not confuse the *Method* with *Procedures*. A broader term than *procedures*, *Method* is a level 1 heading and *Procedures* a level 2 heading.

## Participants

The relevant characteristics of the participants (gender, age, education, cultural background, occupation, family background, health, geographical location, and communicative behaviors) are described. The number of participants and how they were selected also are specified in this subsection.
In clinical studies, the participants' diseases and disorders should be described in both qualitative and quantitative terms. Generally, any subject characteristic thought to influence the results should be described.

It is helpful to describe, when appropriate, the ethnocultural background of participants in a study. It is preferable to identify an ethnocultural group in the most precise terms possible. For example, instead of simply describing participants as *Asian Americans*, it may be helpful to specify, for example, that *20 Vietnamese and 20 Japanese American women* participated in the study. Such specificity helps determine the generality of reported findings.

## Materials

This subsection describes the physical setting of the study and the names and model numbers of equipment used. Routine equipment such as furniture may simply be mentioned, but description of any scientific or electronic instrument used should contain the name of the manufacturer and the model number. Instruments the investigator fabricates should be described in greater detail.

Standardized or nonstandardized tests and other assessment or rating procedures should be summarized. Photographs, diagrams, or additional descriptions may be included in an appendix if the apparatus is unusual or rarely used.

## Procedures

This subsection describes in detail how the study was implemented. The experimental design should be specified and described or justified in detail if uncommon. The author should describe all stimuli presented to the subjects (including instructions given), how variables were measured and manipulated, and the temporal sequence of various conditions arranged in the study.

Differences in the treatment of groups of participants should be described, as well as the procedures for establishing reliability of the data. In reporting clinical treatment studies, the author should describe in detail the treatment procedures and how they were implemented. The methods by which the treatment effects were measured and evaluated also should be described.

Other procedural information may be included in this section. In making this section complete, the author should follow the rule of providing all information necessary to replicate the study.

## Results

The results section opens with a brief statement of the problem investigated and the general findings of the study. An overview of the results is followed by detailed quantitative, qualitative, graphic, and tabular presentations of the findings. These findings are reported without evaluations and interpretations.

Tables and graphs may be used to display data and to supplement, not duplicate, the text. Statistical or other procedures of data analysis should be specified and, when necessary, justified.

In organizing the results of a study, the student must consult the APA *Manual* and several exemplary articles published in the professional journal to which the author plans to submit the paper for publication.

## Discussion

In the discussion section, the author points out the meaning and significance of the results. This section is typically opened with a brief statement of the problem and the major findings. Discussion includes primarily the theoretical and applied implications of the findings. The current findings are related to those of previous investigations.

Limitations of the study also are pointed out, along with suggestions for further research. Ideally, a discussion is an integrative essay on the topic investigated, but it is written in light of the study's data. It should answer the research questions posed in the introduction, as well as support or refute any hypotheses presented. Clarity and directness are important here. Excessive speculation on the causes of unexpected data should be avoided.

## References

The references section lists publications and other sources of information cited in the paper. The reference list should be accurate. It should be prepared according to an accepted format, such as that of the APA *Manual*. A reference list should list all, and only, the sources cited in the paper.

## Note to Students on Different Formats of Journal Articles

Besides research papers (empirical reports), scientific and professional journals publish review papers, theoretical papers, tutorials, commentaries, and other kinds of papers. Each type of paper has a prescribed format. Students should consult journals in their discipline and understand types of papers and their formats.

# B.6. Electronic Manuscript Preparation, Editing, and Proofreading

## B.6.1. Electronic Manuscript Preparation

**Printed Notes** | **Class Notes**

### Changed Times

Now, almost all scientific journals and book publishers require electronic files of articles and book chapters, unlike the printed copies of the past. It is no longer necessary to send a hard copy containing a manuscript of any size. This has reduced the cost of mailing and the time needed to process the manuscript through the editorial and production process.

Authors may send papers and chapters as e-mail attachments or use a site where files are shared. For example, Dropbox is a site where one can upload a manuscript that may be retrieved by all those who are authorized to see it. Authors receive reviews of their manuscripts, the copyedited versions, and the page proofs electronically. Consequently, transactions between the authors, editors, and production departments can be instantaneous.

### Evolving Practices

Electronic manuscript preparation guidelines, though becoming more standardized and uniform, are still evolving. Different publishers of journals and books have different guidelines. A few publishers may still require an initial submission on hard copy, but may attach copyedited manuscripts in Microsoft Word or other word-processor formats to e-mails sent to the authors. A few publishers may send printed page proofs by mail, although this practice is disappearing fast. Authors now receive electronic page proofs in PDF files.

### Print and Online Journals

Print journals were the standard in the past. But journals never printed on paper and published only in their electronic form online are gaining popularity, acceptability, and respectability. Articles published in many online journals are now peer reviewed just like those in print journals.

| Printed Notes | Class Notes |
|---|---|

During the past few years, there has been a steady increase in the number of online scientific journals offered free of cost to anyone interested in reading them. These *open-access* journals also are based on the philosophy that scientific articles should be available to the public free of charge, because most scientific research is supported by public or private charities.

Online journals may be produced more efficiently than print versions. Obviously, authors submit articles online, but the same is true for print journals. Also, the two kinds of journals have the same editorial process: no paper is exchanged between the authors, editors, and peer reviewers. But once the articles are accepted for a particular issue of a journal, the online journal editors can quickly convert the papers into PDF files, have them reviewed by the authors, and publish them immediately. Although there is cost associated with running and maintaining an online journal website, no time is spent nor cost borne to produce the issue in the print form and mail it to subscribers. When a particular issue is published online, those who have registered their names with the site get an e-mail, alerting them about the publication. Many online journals can be freely accessed; few or no print journals are free.

## Print Journals of the American Speech-Language-Hearing Association

Members of the American Speech-Language-Hearing Association (ASHA) are allowed full and free electronic access to its contents. Each journal has a subscription fee for receipt of a printed copy.

All ASHA journals use the APA style and accept papers only electronically. To submit a paper to one of the ASHA journals, authors should log on to the ASHA website: http://www.asha.org, click on "Publications" for general information, and then select guidelines specific to the journal being considered for submission. Authors also can log on to http://mc.manuscriptcentral.com/asha, a central point for submitting papers, and follow the instructions. Questions relative to a specific journal may be sent to its e-mail address (e.g., ajslp@asha.org, for the *American Journal of Speech-Language-Pathology*). Acceptable file formats include plain text, Microsoft Word, PowerPoint, Excel, and PDF.

| Printed Notes | Class Notes |
|---|---|

It is important to remember that ASHA guidelines may change periodically and that before submitting an article online to one of its journals, authors should prepare the article according to the current APA *Manual* (6th edition, as of this writing). Guidelines change because there are constant technological improvements that make it easier for authors to submit articles and revise them. Therefore, it is not practical to summarize ASHA's manuscript preparation guidelines or those of any other print or electronic journal; any such summary might soon be dated. Authors should follow the latest guidelines of the journal to which an article is being submitted.

## Submission for Convention or Conference Presentations

Most professional organizations, including ASHA and state associations, invite papers to be submitted online for presentations at their annual conventions or other kinds of conferences. Formats for convention and conference presentations vary, depending on the type of presentation (e.g., oral presentations, posters, symposia, workshops, etc.). The format for specific kinds of presentations also varies across organizations.

Online submission guidelines for convention and conference presentations are periodically updated with newer and more user-friendly features. Therefore, presenters should consult the latest guidelines in preparing their oral or poster presentation proposals. E-mail invitations that organizations send to their members to submit proposals contain links to the site on which the authors may prepare their proposals.

## Book and Book Chapter Publications

Writing a book or a book chapter requires the author to follow the style manual of the publishing house to which the manuscript is expected to be submitted. Most publishers expect the manuscript to be prepared in Microsoft Word or Mac Word formats. An in-house copy editor will edit the manuscript in the Word format.

After the author reviews the copyedited manuscript and makes changes, the publishing house will convert the file into a PDF document to create page proofs. The author then reviews the page proofs and sends them back to the publisher. This section highlights electronic manuscript preparation; the next two sections offer information on electronic copyediting and proofreading.

It should be noted that book manuscripts do not strictly conform to the APA style or any other standard style (e.g., the Modern Language Association, American Medical Association, or Chicago styles). Each book publishing company has its own style manual, although many in behavioral sciences (including speech-language pathology) do follow the general guidelines of APA or another standard style. Medically oriented book publishers may follow elements of the American Medical Association's style manual.

Unlike journal articles, books are designed with a concern for readability, aesthetic appeal, and pedagogical devices that help readers learn the information the books offer. Journal articles are faithful to the selected style. Books, however, may differ in their style. For example, heading styles may be distinctly different in a book that otherwise generally follows the APA style.

## Electronic Manuscript Preparation

At the college level, students begin to prepare academic and term papers according to an accepted style; in the case of speech-language pathology and audiology, the students learn to write in the APA style. Graduate or doctoral students who write research articles for publication prepare their manuscripts according to the publisher's guidelines.

In essence, electronic manuscript preparation requires advanced word-processing skills and a thorough knowledge of an accepted style manual (e.g., the APA style or the style manual of a book publishing house or journal publisher).

### B.6 Electronic Manuscript Preparation, Editing, and Proofreading

**Printed Notes**

## General Guidelines on Electronic Manuscript Preparation

- Find out the file format the journal or the book publisher requires you to use.
- Understand the basic as well as the advanced features of the word processor that you use.
  - Most advanced features that are useful in preparing electronic manuscripts relate to the *format* of the file that you create.
  - Various options for formatting the manuscript are available under FORMAT shown on the toolbar menu.
  - Prepare a skeleton of the article or the book chapter by creating the different levels of headings and subheadings; use the STYLES and FORMATTING feature under FORMAT on the main toolbar; a heading created as a style under formatting will help create consistent heading levels and any level may be changed to a higher- or lower-level heading by a click of the mouse.
  - Format the paragraphs to automatically set each with a 5-space indent and set the margin on all sides at 1 inch.
  - Create a header that automatically repeats on each page; find the HEADER and FOOTER feature under HOME view on the main toolbar and follow the directions. Follow the APA format to create headers.
  - Format the reference list with a hanging indent feature, so that each entry is treated as a separate paragraph with the first line typed flush left and the subsequent lines indented up to five spaces.
  - To see the menu related to reviewing and tracking changes in the file, click on REVIEW on the main toolbar.
  - Familiarize yourself with the TRACK CHANGES feature, found under the *review* toolbar menu; tracking changes will be more useful in editing and revising the manuscript rather than in initial preparation, but the sooner you master the features of tracking changes in the document, the better it will be. See the next section on tracking changes and electronic editing of manuscripts.

**Class Notes**

**Printed Notes**

- Find out the style the publisher wants you to use; we are mostly concerned with the APA style in this book, because it is the adopted style of the American Speech-Language-Hearing Association. Note that the APA style applies mostly to academic writing and journal articles.
  - Note the differences between the APA style that you may have mastered and the publishing house's required style.
  - Many elements of the APA style are simply matters of acceptable writing and, therefore, are appropriate to adopt.
- Understand the basic as well as the advanced features of the APA style or the book publisher's style manual.
  - Even if the publisher will change the style while designing the article or book (e.g., heading styles), follow the recommended style and leave the design aspects to the publisher's typesetter.
  - Find out how the publishing house or journal publisher will handle copyediting and proofreading. Because it is likely that both will be handled electronically, get a head start on learning how to use the REVIEW option on your word processor. That way, you will be ready to check the copyedited manuscript. Also, learn how to use the Adobe Acrobat Pro (professional) program so that you will be ready to proofread the PDF file that you receive later.
- Send the completed manuscript as an e-mail attachment to the journal editor or book publisher; if the book chapters are long, consider attaching only a few chapters at a time to an e-mail.
- For conference and convention presentations, you will most likely prepare the proposal online, on the website of the inviting organization, and submit the completed proposal electronically.
- See the next section for additional information on **electronic manuscript editing** and the subsequent section on **electronic proofreading.**

**Class Notes**

## B.6.2. Electronic Manuscript Editing and Revising

**Printed Notes** | **Class Notes**

### The Editorial Process

An author's submission of a completed manuscript is the beginning of the editorial process. Some book publishers may want the author to submit a completed sample chapter to begin planning the book's design.

The editorial process is designed to make necessary revisions in the manuscript by having it reviewed by experts who may offer suggestions on improving the manuscript. Reviewers will evaluate the reliability and validity of the information, the research procedures used, and the importance of the data offered in a research paper. They may have comments to improve the clarity of expression and to eliminate errors of omission or commission.

The editorial process of journal articles and books may differ to some extent. The purpose of these two kinds of writing is different, and the editorial process is suited to the specific purpose.

### Editorial Process of Journal Articles

The editor or the associate editor of journals will send all articles submitted for possible publication to editorial consultants or reviewers. The publication of the article is contingent on the reviewers and consultants' recommendations. If the article is otherwise acceptable, but needs a revision, the author is asked to make the recommended changes. If the article is not acceptable because of faulty procedures or insignificant research questions investigated, the author may receive a rejection letter.

If the article has a potential for publication, the editor will ask the author to carefully read the reviewers' comments and make the recommended changes. It will be up to the author to accept or reject the suggestions. Although there is no guarantee of final acceptance of the paper, the author who makes the recommended changes and resubmits the paper may improve his or her chances of getting it published in the journal.

The author may receive the reviewers' and the editor's comments via e-mail attachments, or they may be posted on the journal's secured website. Each author will have a specific password that allows him or her to access the reviews of the submitted article.

## Editorial Process of Book Manuscripts

Some book authors may submit a completed but unsolicited manuscript to a publisher who has not offered a prior publishing contract. This is similar to submitting a paper to a journal for possible publication. In many cases, however, the author may submit to a publisher only a book proposal, a tentative table of contents, and perhaps a sample chapter or two. Authors with a good track record, on the other hand, may be invited by a publisher to write a specific book and may be offered a publishing contract.

As noted in the previous section, books and book chapters are prepared electronically, following the style guide of the publisher. Most elements of the APA style can be used in preparing the manuscript, as those elements apply to all kinds of writing. Once the manuscript is completed, the author sends it to the in-house editor of the publishing firm as an e-mail attachment. When the editor receives the completed manuscript, the editing process begins.

The in-house editor of the publishing company is likely to send the manuscript to selected expert reviewers, similar to those who review journal articles. These reviewers will critically examine the book for its coverage, content, writing style, currency in the discipline, clarity of expression, accuracy of information presented, research base of the claims made, and usefulness to the intended audience. They may have general comments about the writing style and adherence to the selected style (e.g., the APA style). For the most part, expert reviewers do not closely edit the manuscript for writing problems, but make only general comments. Their main concern is the content of the book.

Reviews are written as a separate document and sent to the editor. Many reviewers also make comments on the electronic manuscript to help the author revise it. Some reviewers may make comments on the printed copy.

### Printed Notes

The editor receives the reviews and the manuscript (electronic or printed) with comments on it. The editor then makes a summary of the reviewers' comments, adds his or her own recommendations, and sends the manuscript to the author, usually as an e-mail attachment. The electronic file or the printed copy, if it contains the reviewers' comments, is sent to the author as well.

## Electronic Revision of Manuscripts

Editors and reviewers offer comments for improving the manuscript, but it is always the author who revises the writing. Considering all the recommendations of the editor and the reviewers, the author makes changes in the manuscript's electronic file and sends it back to the editor as an e-mail attachment. Manuscript revision at this stage is no different from the author's own revisions of the writing on the computer screen. Unless the editor requests that the revisions are visible in the manuscript, there usually is no need to show them.

When the editor accepts the final revision the author submits, the journal or book production process begins. The first step in this process is copyediting the manuscript. Before an accepted journal article, a complete book, or a book chapter is typeset, the copy editor processes it.

## Copyediting

Although not necessarily an expert in the subject matter, a copy editor plays a critical role in refining and polishing the manuscript. The editor ensures that the text is concise, consistent, logically and sequentially expressed, grammatically correct, and easy to read. The editor checks to be sure the text is factually correct—for example, spelling of names of organizations, accuracy of important dates, and so on. The copy editor compares the citations in the text to the entries in the reference list to ensure that what is cited is in the references section and that what is in the references section is indeed cited in the text. The copy editor checks the tables and figures and other illustrations to be sure they are placed and referenced correctly.

### Class Notes

**Printed Notes**

The copy editor ensures strict adherence to the selected style guide and edits the manuscript for stylistic uniformity. The copy editor queries the author about errors, oversights, omissions, ambiguities, confusing sentences, and so forth, and when appropriate, may offer suggestions for changes.

The copy editor will also double-check the manuscript's heading styles and the general layout, based on those that the typesetter will use. In some cases, the editor will make notations on the manuscript that suggest various design elements of the manuscript.

Finally, the copy editor will meet deadlines in order to help maintain set production schedules and, therefore, must be able to work well under pressure.

The author does not have to accept all the changes the editor suggests, but they are worthy of serious consideration. If the editor has a problem understanding some parts of the writing, the target audience may have an even greater problem understanding it.

## Review and Revision of Copyedited Manuscripts

Electronic revision of all kinds of manuscripts requires the same skill and approach. In revising an electronic manuscript, the author should use certain editing features built into word processors such as Microsoft Word.

To **turn on the editing features** of Microsoft Word, first click on *Review* on the top taskbar. Several reviewing and editing options will appear.

At this point, click on the Track Changes tab so that the author and editor can see the changes made in the manuscript. Each person's entry will be identified by the person's name so that all readers of the manuscript can see who suggested what changes, who inserted new material, and who deleted old material. Note that deleted elements do not disappear, but are shown on the screen. Each author's changes, entries, comments, and so forth will appear in a different font color; the name of the person who made the changes also may be shown.

**Class Notes**

## B.6 Electronic Manuscript Preparation, Editing, and Proofreading

### Printed Notes

Both the editor and the author can insert comments to each other. A click on *Insert* on the top taskbar will drop down a few menu items; then clicking on *Comment* will allow any comments to be inserted into the document. Comments appear typically on the right or the left margin, as set by the user. An editor who does not understand a sentence may insert a comment, and the author may then insert comments to answer the copy editor's queries.

It is important to answer all the queries the editor enters in the manuscript. These queries may point out inconsistencies, missing citations or references, or other kinds of errors. The author may make corrections or enter comments; if no corrections are needed, in some cases, the author may want to justify keeping the original text.

Documents that different people edit can be viewed several ways. Under the *Review* taskbar options, the following views of the document are available:

- *Original:* In this view, no changes or revisions are shown
- *Original showing markups:* In this view, the original draft and all the subsequent changes are seen
- *Final showing markups:* In this view, changes, edits, and comments are all seen; the first draft may not be shown
- *Final:* In this view, no changes and edits are shown

The View of a document, of course, can be switched back and forth. Once the *Track* option is turned on and the document is prepared or edited, all changes are stored; one may choose to see them or not see them by switching the view option.

The *review* pane on the taskbar also allows one to accept or reject a change suggested by an editor or reviewer. Two options allow the author to "Accept all changes" or "Reject all changes." For the final version of the manuscript, the author can delete all comments made in the document. When changes are accepted, the final version will have incorporated the changes; when they are rejected, the final version will not have the unacceptable comments or edits.

### Class Notes

## Printed Notes

Authors send the copyedited files, with suitable changes made to them, back to the publisher as e-mail attachments or upload them to a central service (e.g., Dropbox). The authors may not accept or reject all changes before saving the documents; instead, they may insert comments to accept or reject a particular change and make only those changes that are acceptable. The copy editor may save the final version as accepted before sending it to the typesetter.

After the manuscript is typeset, the author proofreads the manuscript, as discussed in the next section.

## Class Notes

_____

_____

_____

_____

_____

_____

_____

_____

### B.6.3. Electronic Proofreading

| Printed Notes | Class Notes |
|---|---|

#### What Is a Page Proof?

A *page proof* is a verified and finally checked piece of typeset and printed material. A proofed document is supposedly free of errors, inconsistencies, grammatical problems, and so forth. Although one can proof a handwritten or typewritten piece of writing, a *proof* in the publishing world is printed material that looks like the final published material. It is meant to be finally checked by the author. A proof, though printed, is only a trial print. Limited changes can still be made, and format adjustments are possible.

A proof is the last chance the author gets to work with the manuscript; when sent back to the publisher, the proofed material is printed and bound as soon as possible. This last chance to check the accuracy of the material is limited, however. Authors cannot rewrite sections of the paper or the book at this stage because any change will be expensive, and the authors will bear the cost of typesetting the material again and of repaginating it. Publishers allow corrections only for typographic (spelling) errors, changes in the publication year of cited (and referenced) sources, or gross mistakes, for which the authors will pay nonetheless. Corrections of the typesetter's errors are not charged to the author.

#### PDF Documents

Most authors receive the page proofs as PDF (Portable Document Format) documents. This format has solved one of the nagging problems in electronic manuscript preparation and information exchange: incompatibility of different word processors and computer operating systems. Files exchanged in such varied platforms lost many of their formatting features. When text prepared on any platform and in any word processor is converted into a PDF file, the document has a professionally typeset look. It looks like printed material, and when the document is electronically transmitted to other individuals, the format is maintained.

| Printed Notes | Class Notes |
|---|---|

PDF documents can be prepared on any computer, with any software application (e.g., any word processor), or on any operating system. Adobe (Adobe Systems Incorporated) developed this file exchange system and offers two versions: The *Acrobat Reader*, which is free, and the *Acrobat Professional*, which must be purchased. Most computers come loaded with the free Acrobat Reader.

Compared to Microsoft Word documents, PDF documents are more secure; others reading the document cannot make changes unless the originator of the document enables them to edit it. The professional version of Adobe Acrobat allows the originator of a document to "Enable Usage Rights in Adobe Reader" by clicking that option under "Advanced" on the toolbar. Most publishing houses send page proofs to the authors with security rights enabled so that the authors can edit the proofs. Authors who have Adobe Acrobat Pro installed on their computers can open the page proofs with that program and make their corrections even if the security rights are not enabled.

Once the usage (security) rights are enabled, authors can make corrections in the Adobe Acrobat Reader program. However, the changes the authors make within the program will be incorporated into the final version of the document only by the compositor (typesetter). On the other hand, if the authors have their own professional version, they have the option of incorporating and finalizing the document, although the publisher may request that the authors do not finalize the proofs because the editor and the compositor will finalize them after reviewing all changes the authors make.

Learning to use the editing features of documents in either the enabled Adobe Acrobat Reader or the Adobe Acrobat Pro version takes time and patience, but most people can learn to use the essential features of the program in a relatively short time. Authors have no choice but to learn how to use the program because they must proofread their manuscripts in PDF files.

| Printed Notes | Class Notes |
|---|---|

## Proofreading PDF Versions of Manuscripts

The authors receive their PDF page proofs as e-mail attachments. As in the Microsoft Word program, authors or editors can insert comments, text, figures, and other materials into a PDF document. Advanced editing options may be used to include sound, animation, and other features in the document. Existing text may be deleted or otherwise modified. Inserted and deleted text will be marked until the document is finally accepted and signed off. When multiple people comment on the documents, the original author will know who made what comment.

To begin proofreading and making corrections, the author should launch Acrobat Pro and then open the file to be proofed. The top taskbar on the Acrobat is similar to that of Microsoft Word and includes buttons such as FILE, VIEW, EDIT, COMMENTS, TOOLS, and so on. Clicking on them accesses several drop-down menus with options that the author can select.

The single most useful option for proofreading is TOOLS, which shares certain common menu items with COMMENTS. When clicking on TOOLS, the author sees several branching or layered options necessary to proof the document, including:

- **Comments and markup:** This is a useful collection of tools. Clicking on this option opens many essential features for proofreading:
  - **Sticky note:** The author can add a sticky note for the editor and place it in the margins and move it around. This is helpful in answering any final queries the copy editor may have for the author, or to alert the typesetter about any formatting problems the author sees.
  - **Text edits:** Probably the most essential of all, the *Text edit* tool gives the author a chance to correct the proofs with several specific branching functions:
    - Highlight selected text
    - Underline selected text
    - Cross out selected text to be deleted
    - Replace selected text by typing new words
    - Add note to the selected text
    - Insert new text at cursor

- **Forms:** This tool allows the author to insert forms or modify them, although at the stage of proofreading, such actions are discouraged.
- **Edit:** Under this tool, the author has options such as Copy, Paste, Spell-Check, and Find.
- **Document:** Under this tool, the available options include Insert Page, Delete Page, Replace Page, Rotate Page, Header Footer, and so forth.

It is essential for authors to work with a few PDF files to become comfortable with using them and the features needed in proofing the typeset article or book. The program comes with an online user's manual.

PDFs are secure documents; they show all changes and comments until the changes are finally accepted and signed off. It usually is not recommended at this stage that the author click on Accept all Changes, because the editor and the typesetter need to see the comments, changes, and corrections.

Authors will send the proofed pages back to the editor or typesetter electronically. The authors' responsibilities for the publications are usually over when the proofed papers or books are sent back to the publisher. The authors will next enjoy the fruits of their labor in the form of an article printed in a journal or of a printed and bound book.

# PART C

# Professional Writing

# C.1. Introduction to Professional Writing

Professional writing includes writing diagnostic or assessment reports, treatment plans, progress reports, and professional correspondence. As there is no standard accepted by all clinics, the headings and the formats of these reports vary. Furthermore, *clinical reports need not follow all aspects of the APA style*, which is most relevant to scientific writing. Clinical reports may use different margins, paragraph styles, indentations, phrases (incomplete sentences), and one-sentence paragraphs. Clinical reports may contain lists. Most of these may contradict the APA style requirement. However, most other principles of good writing and those of scientific writing, including clarity, brevity, and an objective tone apply to professional writing as well.

On the following pages, you will find examples of various clinical reports. I expect that the student clinicians and supervisors or instructors will use these as examples only; they are not meant to be prescriptive. Nonetheless, it is better for the beginning student to master a format than to enter the initial clinical practicum with no such format. Experienced clinicians will have learned to vary the style to suit their employment setting and audience.

Clinicians in public schools, medical settings, and university clinics write vastly different kinds of reports. Reports vary not only in their formats, but also in the amount of details given. Although some assessment reports are long enough to fill several pages, others are short enough to fill only a single page. Some contain connected prose; others contain only symbols, abbreviations, phrases, and brief observations. Generally, reports written in medical settings are briefer than those written in university speech and hearing clinics. Therefore, some student clinicians in university clinics ask why they are expected to write detailed reports that are uncommon in the "real world."

There are at least two good reasons for teaching student clinicians how to write reports with complete sentences and connected prose. First, even in settings that routinely require brief reports written without complete sentences, there may be occasions when detailed, formal reports with extensive supportive evidence are required. When treatment has to be justified to a third party who pays for services or when a report comprehensible to other professionals has to be written, the clinician has to use a more narrative, cogent, and well-organized style. Second, the one who knows how to write a detailed report should have very little trouble writing brief reports. But the clinician who has learned only a brief and disconnected style will have great difficulty in writing elaborate, well-reasoned, well-organized narrative reports when needed.

The student clinicians should study the examples carefully and compare them with those written in their clinic. A simple rule of clinical practicum is to follow the guidelines of the setting in which that experience is offered. Therefore, it is the student clinicians' responsibility to find out what is acceptable in their setting.

## C.2. Formats of Diagnostic Reports

*Diagnostic reports* are also known as *assessment reports* and *evaluation reports*. Those three terms may be used interchangeably. Choose the term that is used in your setting.

### Elements of a Diagnostic Report

Although the formats vary, all diagnostic reports contain the following kinds of information:

- History of the client, the family, and the disorder
- Interview of the family, the client, or both
- Orofacial examination
- Hearing screening
- Speech and language samples
- Disorder-specific assessment, including standardized and client-specific assessment procedures
- Diagnostic summary
- Recommendations

On the following pages, you will see outlines of typical diagnostic reports. Note the following:

- The various headings and subheadings may vary across clinics and clinicians.
- Most clinicians include information of the kind the headings suggest.
- All headings and subheadings are not needed for all clients.

## C.2.1. Outline of a Typical Diagnostic Report on a *Child Client*

**University Speech and Hearing Clinic**
**Victorville, California**
**Diagnostic Report**

| | |
|---|---|
| Client: | Date of Birth: |
| Address: | Clinic File Number: |
| City: | Date of Report: |
| Telephone Number: | Diagnosis: |
| Referred By: | Clinician: |

**Background and Reasons for Referral**

**History**

*Birth and Development*

*Medical History*

*Family, Social, and Educational History*

## Assessment Information

*Orofacial Examination*

*Hearing Screening*

*Speech Sound Production and Speech Intelligibility*

*Language Production and Comprehension*

*Fluency*

*Voice*

## Diagnostic Summary

## Recommendations

Submitted By _____
        Thomas Jefferson, B.A.
        Student Clinician

Client's or Parents' Signature _____

Approved By _____
        Mary Lincoln, M.A., CCC-SLP
        Speech-Language Pathologist and Clinical Supervisor

## C.2.2. Outline of a Typical Diagnostic Report on an *Adult Client*

**University Speech and Hearing Clinic**
**Jefferson City, North Carolina**
**Diagnostic Report**

Client:                                    Date of Birth:

Address:                                   Clinic File Number:

City:                                      Date of Report:

Telephone Number:                          Diagnosis:

Referred By:                               Clinician:

**Background and Reasons for Referral**

**History**

*Medical History*

*Family and Social History*

*Educational and Occupational History*

## Assessment Information

*Orofacial Examination*

*Hearing Screening*

*Speech Sound Production and Speech Intelligibility*

*Language Production and Comprehension*

*Fluency*

*Voice*

## Diagnostic Summary

## Recommendations

Submitted By _____
        June Ahmed, B.A.
        Student Clinician

Client's Signature _____

Approved By _____
        April Summers, M.A., CCC-SLP
        Speech-Language Pathologist
        Clinical Supervisor

## C.2.3. Anatomy of a Diagnostic Report

**University Speech and Hearing Clinic**
**1479 Wide Avenue**
**Boomtown, CA 90909**

> The name of the clinic. Typically centered; may be all caps or in uppercase and lowercase; bold.
>
> The type of report

**Diagnostic Report**

**Client:** Lynda Pen                  **Date of Birth:** xx-xx-xx

**Address:** 555 N. Cedar #000         **Clinic File Number:** 87003

**City:** Fresno, CA 93726             **Diagnosis:** Language and Articulation Disorders

**Telephone Number:** 555-0634         **Date of Report:** xx-xx-xx

**Referred By:**                       **Clinician:**

> Identifying information.

### Background and Reasons for Referral

On September 15, 1997, Lynda Pen, a 7-year, 1-month-old female, was evaluated at the University Speech and Hearing Clinic. She was referred by Dr. James Osborne, a pediatrician. Lynda's delayed expressive speech was the reason for referral. Mrs. Susan Penn brought her daughter to the clinic and provided the case history information.

> **Level 1 Heading (L1H)**
>
> Indented (5 spaces) paragraphs.
>
> Describe when, who, and how old the referred person was and to which clinic the person was referred and why.

### History

*Prenatal and Birth History*

Mrs. Pen reported that she experienced preeclampsia 5 months into her pregnancy. At 30 weeks of gestation, Lynda was delivered by a cesarean section. Birth weight was 5 pounds and 8 ounces. Because of cardiac murmurs and a premature birth, Lynda did not thrive during her first 6 months of development.

> (L1H)
>
> **Level 2 Heading (L2H)**
>
> Start with prenatal and birth history. Mother's health during pregnancy. Birth: normal or otherwise. Early development. Health during infancy and early childhood.

## Developmental History

Lynda's developmental milestones were reported to be delayed for both physical and communicative behaviors. Mrs. Pen reported that Lynda walked at 26 months and "used a few single words" at 24 months. Mrs. Pen stated that currently Lynda's speech consists of 10–15 word approximations.

> **(L2H)**
> Describe later development and physical growth. Communicative behaviors. Current status.

## Medical History

Mrs. Pen reported that Lynda had a single instance of otitis media at 9 months of age. At 10 months of age, Lynda underwent a specialized heart surgery called pulmonary banding to prevent further damage to her lungs. At 2 years of age, Lynda was operated on at the University of California Hospital in San Francisco by Drs. T. S. Mouster and O. S. Houster for anterior skull reconstruction. At the age of 2 years and 2 months, Lynda underwent open-heart surgery to repair cardiac murmurs. The Medical Genetics Team at Valley Children's Hospital has reported that Lynda has a probable chromosome abnormality with extra material on chromosome 14q.

> **(L2H)**
> Summarize significant medical history, including sensory problems, medical and surgical treatment, and any previously made diagnostic statements.

## Family, Social, and Educational History

Mrs. Pen did not recall any members of her family or those of her husband's as having speech or language problems. Lynda is the only child of Mr. and Mrs. Pen. Mr. Pen is a high school teacher, and Mrs. Pen is an insurance underwriter. Lynda's grandmother, who lives with Mr. and Mrs. Pen, usually watches her when the parents are at work.

Lynda sometimes plays with a younger child in the neighborhood. According to Mrs. Pen, Lynda generally plays cooperatively with children who are younger than she is.

> **(L2H)**
> Describe the family history of communicative problems.
>
> Describe the family.
>
> How many children?
>
> Client's education and occupation.
>
> Who takes care of the child?
>
> Child's companions and play activities.

Lynda attended the clinic of Exceptional Parents Unlimited from May 1987 to April 1988. Mrs. Pen reported that Lynda interacted well with her peers, although the frequency of her social interactions was limited. Lynda is not currently attending school.

> Describe the previous clinical and education programs of relevance and the current educational level.

## Assessment Information

(L1H)

### Orofacial Examination

(L2H)

An orofacial examination was conducted to evaluate the structural and functional integrity of the orofacial mechanism. The examination revealed a broad nasal bridge and prominent epicanthal folds. The teeth were marked by a Class III malocclusion. During smiling, there was bilateral retraction at the angle of the mouth. A narrow, inverted v-shaped palate also was noted. Because of Lynda's lack of cooperation, movements of the velum and the lateral pharyngeal walls were not observed. Labial and lingual mobility was deemed adequate for normal speech production.

> Describe the orofacial examination:
>
> Integrity of oral and facial structures.
>
> Give a general description of the face, mouth, tongue, teeth, hard and soft palate, and movement of the soft palate and the tongue.

### Hearing Screening

A hearing screening conducted at 25 dB for 500, 1000, 2000, and 4000 Hz revealed essentially normal hearing.

### Speech Sound Production and Speech Intelligibility

Lynda's speech was assessed through a standardized test and a recorded conversational speech sample. To assess Lynda's speech sound production in fixed word positions, the Goldman-Fristoe Test of Articulation was administered. Her performance on this test revealed numerous speech sound errors, as summarized in the following table.

> (L2H)
>
> First, say how speech production was assessed.
>
> Give the full name of tests administered.
>
> A reference to a test may not be necessary in clinical reports.
>
> Do not ignore speech samples.

|  | Initial | Medial | Final |
|---|---|---|---|
| Substitutions | t/s; d/p<br>d/dr; k/kr;<br>p/pl; s/sl;<br>t/tr | s/z | |
| Omissions | /f, v, t, n,<br>s, z, l, r, w,<br>h, fl, st/ | /b, m, f,<br>d, n, s,<br>l, r/ | /p, b,<br>m, f, v,<br>t, n, s,<br>r, k/ |
| Distortions | /s/ | | |

*List errors of articulation noted on the test or tests administered.*

*Arrange the errors of articulation in a table as shown.*

A 90-utterance speech sample was audio-recorded. An analysis of this sample revealed the following additional errors:

|  | Initial | Medial | Final |
|---|---|---|---|
| Substitutions | p/b; b/m; t/s; y/l | | |
| Omissions | /m, k/<br>/st, fl/ | /g/ | /d, l, k/<br>/ts/ |
| Distortions | /z, s/ | | |

*Describe the speech sample.*

*List the errors of articulation noted in the speech sample.*

*Arrange the errors of articulation in a table like this.*

Because of her numerous speech sound errors, Lynda's speech was generally unintelligible. With contextual cues present, her speech intelligibility was only 11.9% on a word-by-word basis and 15% on an utterance-by-utterance basis.

*Describe the effects of articulation errors on intelligibility.*

### *Language Production and Comprehension*

Lynda's language production was assessed mainly through a language sample. She responded to questions and was asked to describe pictures in storybooks. Through this method, a 90-utterance language sample was obtained. An analysis of this sample showed a mean length of utterance (MLU) of 1.13 for words. She did not produce any syntactically complete sentences as she said mostly one-word phrases. Because of reduced speech intelligibility marked by sound substitutions and omissions, Lynda's use of morphologic features could not be assessed.

*(L2H)*

*Describe how you assessed language production.*

*Give names of tests you administered.*

*Describe the method of analysis.*

*Describe the results of analysis.*

Lynda's comprehension of words was assessed by administering the Receptive One Word Picture Vocabulary Test (ROWPVT). The results were as follows: Raw score, 52; standard score, 77; percentile rank, 6; age equivalency, 4 years, 6 months.

### Voice and Fluency

Based on clinical observations, Lynda's vocal pitch and intensity were judged appropriate for her age. Because of her limited speech and language production, Lynda's fluency also was limited. However, clinically significant amounts or durations of dysfluencies were not observed.

## Diagnostic Summary

The overall results of the assessment of Lynda Pen's speech and language production show a severe speech sound disorder combined with expressive language difficulties. Many omitted and substituted phonemes and inconsistent production of others have reduced Lydia's speech intelligibility. Expressive language was limited mostly to one-word utterances. This resulted in limited fluency although her vocal characteristics were within the limits of normal variations. The assessment results also suggest that Lynda's comprehension of language was limited.

## Recommendations

It is recommended that Lynda Pen receive treatment for her speech and language problems. Although her problems are severe, Lynda was attentive and cooperative throughout the assessment process, and parental support was evident. Therefore, with consistent treatment, prognosis for improvement in

## C.2 Formats of Diagnostic Reports

speech intelligibility and language skills is judged to be good. Among others to be determined later, the treatment targets may include the following:

1. Spontaneous naming of pictures of her family members with 90% accuracy.

2. Spontaneous production of selected functional words with 90% accuracy.

3. Production of phrases and sentences in a carefully graded sequence.

4. Correct production of selected phonemes.

> List the potential targets as shown.
>
> List as many targets as seem appropriate.

Submitted By _____
        LaTeena LeBueque,
        B.A. Student Clinician

Parent's Signature _____
        Susan Pen, Mother

Approved By _____
        Benton Q. Bentley, M.A., CCC-SLP
        Speech-Language Pathologist
        Clinical Supervisor

> Name and signature of the student clinician
>
> Parents' signature
>
> Signature and name, degree, ASHA certificate, and title of the supervisor

## C.3. Sample Diagnostic Reports

**Note to Student Clinicians**

On the following pages, you will see samples of diagnostic (assessment) reports. Study them for the general content and format of diagnostic reports. Compare the samples with the format used in your clinic. Take note of variations in headings and their styles used in your clinic. Consult with your clinic director or clinical supervisor to select an approved format and acceptable variations, if any.

## C.3.1. Sample Diagnostic Report: *Speech Sound Disorder*

**University Speech and Hearing Clinic**
**Midstate University**
**Middletown, Montana**

**Diagnostic Report**

Client: Pennifer Forbes                     Date of Birth: xx-xx-xx

Address: 1326 E. Harvard                    Clinic File Number: 9-Qr101

City: Middletown, Montana                   Date of Report: xx-xx-xx

Telephone Number: 555-0719                  Diagnosis: Speech Sound Disorder

Referred By: Jane Pendelton, M.D.           Clinician: Missouline Montoya

### Background and Reasons for Referral

Pennifer Forbes, a 5-year, 4-month-old female, was seen on February x, xxxx, for an evaluation at the Speech and Hearing Clinic at the Midstate University, Middletown, Montana. Dr. Pendelton, a pediatrician, referred her to the clinic because of her articulation problems. Pennifer was accompanied to the clinic by her mother, Mrs. Jane Forbes, who served as the informant.

### History

Mrs. Forbes reported that Pennifer's speech is difficult to understand. She said that her daughter leaves out sounds in her speech resulting in such words as "nake" for "snake." Pennifer also substitutes one sound for another. According to the mother, Pennifer says, "tat" for "cat." Pennifer has previously received speech therapy at Big Sky Speech and Hearing Center for remediation of her articulation disorder. The 3-month treatment she received resulted in some improvement, but Pennifer's speech problems are still significant.

Pennifer's birth and developmental history is not remarkable. Her motor and speech development was typical, as judged by Mrs. Forbes. Pennifer has enjoyed good health with no diseases of significance.

*Family, Social, and Educational History*

Pennifer is the second of three children. Mrs. Forbes did not report a family history of communicative disorders. Mrs. Forbes, a high school graduate, manages a restaurant. Mr. Forbes, who has a 10th-grade education, is a maintenance man with the local school district.

Pennifer attends a kindergarten school and is reportedly doing well. However, other students and the teacher have complained about her unintelligible speech.

## Assessment Information

*Orofacial Examination*

An orofacial examination was performed to assess the function and integrity of the oral and facial structures. Pennifer's lips and hard palate appeared symmetrical at rest. She was able to perform a variety of labial and lingual tasks. The anterior and posterior faucial pillars were within normal limits. Vertical movement of the pharyngeal wall was observed upon the phonation of /a/.

*Hearing Screening*

Using a Maico portable screening audiometer (model MA-20A), the clinician screened Pennifer's hearing at 25 dB HL for 500, 1000, 2000, and 4000 Hz. At all frequencies, Pennifer passed the screening bilaterally.

*Speech Sound Production and Speech Intelligibility*

To assess Pennifer's speech sound production, a conversational speech sample was recorded. In addition, the Goldman-Fristoe Test of Articulation (GFTA) was administered to assess speech sounds in fixed positions. An analysis of the speech sample and Pennifer's performance on the GFTA revealed the following errors:

|  | Initial | Medial | Final |
|---|---|---|---|
| Substitutions | /s/ for /k/; /d/ for /g/; /t/ for /s/; /w/ for /r/; /b/ for /f/; /t/ for /tʃ/; /t/ for /ʃ/; /j/ for /z/; /b/ for /bl/; /b/ for /br/; /d/ for /dr/; /bl/ for /fl/; /t/ for /kl/; /l/ for /sl/; /d/ for /st/ | /l/ for /t/; /t/ for /ʃ/; /b/ for /v/; /d/ for /g/; /b/ for /f/; /t/ for /tʃ/ | /k/ for /t/; /p/ for /b/ |
| Omissions |  | /k/ and /θ/ | /g/, /k/, /d/, /f/, /s/, /t/, /ʃ/, /tʃ/, /θ/, /l/, /d/, /z/, /p/ |
| Distortions |  | /z/ |  |

The Khan-Lewis Phonological Analysis was administered to assess Pennifer's phonological error patterns. Pennifer's overall score of 32 on the test was calculated into an age equivalency of 2 years, 9 months. The analysis revealed the following phonological processes:

Deletion of final consonants

Palatal fronting

Velar fronting

Stridency deletion

Stopping of affricates and fricatives

Cluster simplification

Final devoicing

Liquid simplification

Because of numerous speech sound errors, only 23% of Pennifer's utterances were intelligible. In addition, most of her misarticulations were not stimulable. Pennifer correctly imitated only /k/, /g/, /s/, and /f/. However, a diadochokinetic test showed essentially normal rates.

### *Language Production and Comprehension*

Pennifer's conversational speech during the interview and assessment showed essentially normal language structure and use except for several missing grammatical morphemes. It is possible that missing grammatical morphemes are caused by missing speech sounds. The mean length of utterance (MLU) of her speech sample was 5.4 morphemes, which is within normal limits for her age.

### *Voice and Fluency*

Though difficult to understand, Pennifer's speech had normal rhythm. The rate of dysfluencies was within the normal range. Therefore, no further analysis of the dysfluency rate was made. In addition, Pennifer's voice was judged to be within normal limits.

## Diagnostic Summary

Pennifer Forbes exhibited a severe speech sound disorder characterized by multiple errors and limited speech intelligibility. Unless treated, her speech sound disorder is likely to have negative social and educational consequences. Because Pennifer was stimulable for some of the consonants, the prognosis with treatment for improved speech intelligibility is good.

## Recommendations

It is recommended that Pennifer receive treatment for her speech sound disorder. As her articulation of speech sounds and intelligibility improve, Pennifer's language may be further evaluated to see if morphological features emerge. If they do not, language treatment may be offered.

Submitted By _____
        Missouline Montoya, B.A.
        Student Clinician

Parent's Signature _____
        Jane Forbes, Mother

Approved By _____
        Akbar Jamal, M.A., CCC-SLP
        Speech-Language Pathologist
        Clinical Supervisor

## C.3.2. Sample Diagnostic Report: *Voice Disorder*

**Balmtown University Speech and Hearing Clinic**
**Balmtown, New York**

**Diagnostic Report**

Name: Valine Wrenn

Date of Birth: xx-xx-xx

Age: 25

Address: 1919 S. Dakota #Q108-R

City: Fresno, CA 98705

Telephone: 555-0608

Date of Examination: xx-xx-xx

Clinical Classification: Voice Disorder

Clinic File No: 08a-7314

Referred By: Dr. Hanna Eismer

Examiner: Janina Presham

Informant: Self

### Background and Presenting Complaints

Valine Wrenn, a 25-year-old female, was seen for a speech and language evaluation at the Balmtown University Speech and Hearing Clinic on April xx, xxxx. She was referred to the clinic by her otolaryngologist, Dr. Eismer. Her presenting complaints were difficulty speaking loudly and difficulty speaking for long periods. She also noted a "lack of excitement" in her voice and difficulty producing sounds at the ends of sentences caused by a low pitch. Valine came to the clinic by herself and provided all the information.

### History

*Early History*

Valine reported that her voice always sounded "funny" since early childhood. During her high school years, she became aware of a low pitch and monotone quality after listening to herself on audiotape. Valine did not recall previous consultations or treatment for her voice problem. She thought that her developmental history was unremarkable.

*Medical History*

On March xx, xxxx, Valine received a medical evaluation by Dr. Hanna Eismer, an otolaryngologist. Dr. Eismer reported Valine as having normal external auditory canals and tympanic membranes. The nose and oral cavities were also clear. A fiberoptic endoscope was used to examine Valine's larynx. Vocal fold structure and motion were reported to be normal. There was no evidence of vocal nodules or lesions. The vocal folds were described as being minimally erythematous (redness of tissue) and slightly swollen on the free edge.

Valine is allergic to such substances as molds, trees, and grasses. When she is close to one of them, phlegm in the throat and postnasal drip tend to increase. Valine recently began using Beconase (an inhalant) to relieve the allergies. Valine typically experiences excessive colds resulting in phlegm and postnasal drip approximately once a month beginning in October or November, and lasting about a week. Valine thought that her colds were caused by stress and emotional problems. She temporarily discontinued the use of the Beconase while using Afrin and Neo-Synephrine for the colds. Excessive phlegm resulted in frequent coughing and throat clearing.

### *Family, Social, and Educational History*

Valine is a student at Balmtown University, Balmtown, New York, majoring in speech communication. She is divorced and lives with her 3-year-old daughter, Haline. Either the television or the radio is on in Valine's apartment for the majority of the time she is at home. While speaking to her daughter, Valine rarely shouts or yells through the apartment. Instead, she makes an effort to go into the room where her daughter is. Valine noted that she frequently sings for personal pleasure. She sings in numerous and varied settings, including at home, in the car, and on campus. She has between two to five telephone conversations per day, ranging from 2 to 30 minutes in length. Valine does not habitually drink coffee, tea, soft drinks, or alcoholic beverages. She does drink at least two glasses of low-fat milk every day. Valine mentioned that friends easily identify her voice and describe it as being "low and sexy." Valine typically experiences a feeling of tightness in the throat when nervous, as well as a higher pitch, lower intensity, and difficulty projecting her voice.

## Assessment Information

### *Orofacial Examination*

An orofacial examination was conducted to assess the integrity of oral and facial structures. Valine's facial features appeared symmetrical, with lingual and labial mobility adequate for speech. However, restricted oral mobility was noted during speech. Velopharyngeal closure was acoustically deemed adequate during repeated productions of /a/. Diadochokinetic rates were within normal limits.

### *Hearing Screening*

Using a Maico portable screening audiometer (model MA-20A), the clinician screened Valine's hearing at 25 dB HL for 500, 1000, 2000, and 4000 Hz. At all frequencies, Valine passed the screening bilaterally.

### *Speech Sound Production and Comprehension*

Valine's speech production and comprehension were informally assessed. Her conversational speech and her interaction during the interview did not reveal speech sound errors or comprehension problems. Therefore, these aspects of her communicative behaviors were judged to be within normal variations.

### *Language and Fluency*

Valine's language and fluency were assessed informally. Her conversational speech during the assessment period did not suggest problems of language structure or use. Her fluency and rates of dysfluencies also were judged to be within normal variations.

### *Voice*

Valine's fundamental frequency ranged between 150 Hz and 200 Hz on the fundamental frequency indicator. This pitch was determined to be low for Valine's gender and stature. During the interview, frequent glottal fry and hoarseness of voice were observed. A later analysis of the audiotaped speech sample revealed that glottal fry and hoarseness were more likely to occur on downward inflections of most utterances. On approximately 60% of her utterances, either glottal fry, hoarseness, or both were observed. However, Valine's breath support appeared adequate for speech.

## Diagnostic Summary

Valine Wrenn's history suggests vocally abusive behaviors. She uses a habitual pitch that is too low for her. This may have resulted in excessive glottal fry. Her low vocal focus may have adversely affected the extent to which she could project her voice.

## Recommendations

It was recommended that Valine Wrenn receive voice therapy. Valine was found to be stimulable for higher pitch levels. Therefore, prognosis for improved pitch level under treatment was judged to be good. Specific recommendations for treatment include the following:

1. Eliminating glottal fry by raising Valine's habitual pitch to a more optimal level during spontaneous conversational speech produced in nonclinical settings.
2. Decreasing such abusive vocal behaviors as ineffective management of colds and allergies, improper fluid intake, and singing and speaking in noisy situations.

Submitted By _____
        Janina Presham, B.A.
        Student Clinician

Client's Signature _____
        Valine Wrenn

Approved By _____
        Dambly Doumbleson, M.A., CCC-SLP
        Clinical Supervisor
        Speech-Language Pathologist

## C.3.3. Sample Diagnostic Report: *Aphasia and Apraxia*

**University Speech and Hearing Clinic**
**Tinkyville, Tennessee**

**Diagnostic Report**

Name: Lynn M. Zoolanfoos

Address: 111 E. Cornell

City: Tinkyville, TN 43704

Telephone Number: 677-229-9850

Clinician: Maxine Traoumer

Referred By: Dr. Mendelsohn

Date of Birth: xx-xx-xx

Clinic File Number: 910019

Diagnosis: Aphasia and Apraxia

Date of Report: xx-xx-xx

Supervisor: Galaxy Galvestrouton, M.A., CCC-SLP

Assessment Date: xx-xx-xx

### Background and Reasons for Referral

Lynn Zoolanfoos, a 44-year-old female, was referred to the Speech and Hearing Clinic at the Tinkyville State University in Tinkyville, Tennessee. Her physician, Dr. Muskwhiter Mendelsohn, referred her for a speech-language evaluation following a stroke.

Lynn's speech and language were evaluated in two sessions. She was seen on September xx, xxxx, and October xx, xxxx. Lynn was unaccompanied to the diagnostic sessions. She suffered an initial stroke in July xxxx. On September xx, xxxx, she experienced a second stroke that resulted in right hemiplegia, expressive and receptive aphasia, and verbal apraxia.

### History

*Medical History*

Lynn has a history of heart problems. She resides with her mother, Gladys Miller, who experiences severe emphysema and is on continuous oxygen. Lynn and her mother have a home care aide who comes into the home six hours a day.

Lynn reported she wears braces on her right leg and right hand and uses a cane to assist with walking. Lynn enjoys activities such as bowling and watching television. She now wants to improve her writing skills.

*Previous Speech and Language Services*

For the past six months, Lynn has received speech and language services at the Community Hospital Speech and Hearing Department. Previous treatment targets include the production of two- to four-word phrases, correct production of initial and final consonants in single words, auditory comprehension of two- and three-step directions and two- and three-element questions, and reading comprehension of three- to six-word sentences.

## Assessment Information

Lynn cooperated during the evaluation and showed excellent motivation for continuing therapy. She was keenly interested in the assessment tasks. She said that she wanted to improve her speech and language skills.

### *Orofacial Examination*

An orofacial examination was performed to evaluate the functional and structural integrity of the oral and facial complex. Facial features including lips at rest were judged symmetrical and normal in appearance and function. The tongue was normal in appearance, but its lateral movements were sluggish. There were groping behaviors while attempting to draw the tip of the tongue along the hard palate. A slight neutroclusion was noted. The hard palate was narrow, with a high arch and a small bony outgrowth along the midline. Pronounced rugae were evident in the premaxillary region. The soft palate was of adequate length and elevated vertically and posteriorly to achieve closure. Velopharyngeal functioning was acoustically judged to be adequate during production of /a/. An assessment of diadochokinetic rates revealed slowness suggesting weakness in circumoral and lingual musculature. The productions also were characterized by substitutions suggesting verbal apraxia.

### *Voice*

Lynn's voice characteristics were subjectively judged based on her conversational speech. Except for a hyponasal resonance, her voice was judged appropriate for her age and gender.

### *Hearing Screening*

A hearing screening was performed bilaterally at 25 dB HL for 500, 1000, 2000, and 4000 Hz. Lynn passed at all frequencies bilaterally.

### *Speech Production*

The Apraxia Battery for Adults was administered to verify the presence of apraxia and provide a rough estimate of the severity of the disorder. The summary of scores included the following:

| *Subtest I* | Diadochokinetic Rate |
|---|---|
| Pt | 13 |
| Tk | 10 |
| Ptk | 6 |
| *Subtest II* | Increasing Word Length |
| 1-syllable average | 1.8 |
| 2-syllable average | 1.7 |
| 3-syllable average | 1.9 |
| Deterioration in performance score | 0 |
| *Subtest III* | Limb Apraxia and Oral Apraxia |
| Limb Apraxia | 34 |
| Oral Apraxia | 39 |

| | |
|---|---|
| *Subtest IV* | Latency and Utterance Time for Polysyllabic Words |
| Latency Time | 93 seconds |
| Utterance Time | 2 seconds |
| *Subtest V* | Repeated Trials Test |
| Total Amount of Change | +1 |
| *Subtest VI* | Inventory of Articulation Characteristics of Apraxia |
| Total YES Items | 2 |

Lynn's performance on the subtests reveals searching behaviors for making gestures and a low score on articulation characteristics of apraxia.

### Language Production and Comprehension

A 76-utterance, 157-word language sample was obtained. The mean length for these utterances was 2.19 for words and 2.42 for morphemes. Word finding difficulties were noted. Automatic speech was evident in some of her replies.

To make an initial assessment of Lynn's aphasia, the first three items of each subtest of the Western Aphasia Battery were administered as a screening test. In the following table, Lynn's scores are listed in the left-hand column. Several subtests were scored beyond the first three items. These scores are listed in the right-hand column. The scores were as follows:

| | Client's subscores on first three items/Maximum | Client's subscores beyond the first three items/Maximum |
|---|---|---|
| Spontaneous Speech | | |
| Information Content | 6/10 | |
| Fluency | 5/10 | |
| Yes/No Questions | 9/9 | 36/42 |
| Auditory Word Recognition | 9/27 | |
| Sequential Commands | 6/6 | 8/22 |
| Repetition | 6/6 | 60/70 |
| Word Fluency | 2/20 | |
| Sentence Completion | 4/6 | 6/10 |
| Responsive Speech | 0/6 | |
| Reading | 20.5/32 | 30.5/52 |
| Writing | 31.5/100 | |
| Praxis | 6/6 | 27/30 |
| Drawing | 3/9 | |
| Calculation | 0/4 | |

Lynn performed well on tasks involving auditory comprehension for yes/no questions, auditory comprehension of one-part sequential commands, verbal repetition of single words and two- to five-word phrases, sentence completion, and reading single words. Errors were noted during tasks involving oral reading of phrases and sentences, spelling, writing (except for writing numbers and her own name and copying printed words), calculation, drawing, responsive speech, word fluency, auditory word recognition, spontaneous speech, and two-part sequential commands. Lynn's performance on the Praxis subtest did not suggest oral or verbal apraxia. An Aphasia Quotient and a Cortical Quotient were unobtainable because of partial presentation of the test.

## Diagnostic Summary

Lynn's performance on various assessment tasks suggested a moderate to severe expressive and receptive aphasia with anomia. A mild verbal apraxia was also suggested.

## Recommendations

Speech and language treatment is recommended for Lynn. With treatment, prognosis for improved communication skills is judged to be good because of the high levels of motivation and cooperation Lynn showed during assessment. Immediate treatment goals recommended for her include the following:

1. Improve expressive language.
2. Teach consistent productions of selected functional words and phrases. These productions may include a variety of communication modes (gesturing, drawing, speaking, writing) to improve communicative effectiveness.
3. Teach four- to six-word sentence completion performance with 90% accuracy.
4. Improve receptive language in reading.
5. Teach correct responses to questions about silently read material with 90% accuracy.

Submitted By _____
        Maxine Traoumer, B.A.
        Student Clinician

Client's Signature _____
        Lynn Zoolanfoos

Approved By _____
        Galaxy Galvestrouton, M.A., CCC-SLP
        Speech-Language Pathologist
        Clinical Supervisor

## C.3.4. Sample Diagnostic Report: *Stuttering*

**University Speech and Hearing Clinic**
**Freemont University**
**Valleyville, California**

### Diagnostic Report

Name: James Foxx

Date of Birth: xx-xx-xx

Address: Graves 312 B

City: Valleyville, CA 90710-3342

Telephone Number: 555-3235

Referred By: Self

Assessment Date: xx-xx-xx

File Number: Rs92019

Diagnosis: Stuttering

Date of Report: xx-xx-xx

Informant: Self

Clinician: Meena Wong

### Background and Presenting Complaint

James Foxx, a 21-year-old male, was seen for a speech and language evaluation at the Freemont University Speech and Hearing Clinic on February x, xxxx. He had applied for services for his stuttering after he read an article in the campus newspaper about the speech and hearing services on campus. James is a student at the university, majoring in computer science.

### History

James reported that, according to what his parents have told him, his stuttering began when he was about 3 years of age. From the age of 4 through 9 years, James received treatment for his stuttering at J. R. Cronin Elementary School in Dublin, California. At age 7, he also received approximately a year of treatment at Motherlode University, Red Wing. He has not received treatment since that time. James reported that the severity of his stuttering fluctuates depending on his mood, and it is more pronounced in stressful situations.

He reported increased frequency of stuttering when he speaks to strangers, his instructors, and his father. He thought he was less dysfluent when he speaks to his mother, brother, sister, and close friends. He said that he would rather not order at restaurants, buy tickets at counters, introduce himself, or answer telephone calls. He did not think that he has difficulty with specific words or sounds.

*Family and Social History*

James lives on campus. His parents live in Merced, California. He is the oldest of three children. His younger brother and younger sister do not have communication problems. He believes that his maternal uncle and his son both stutter. James is not aware of any person on his father's side who stutters.

James lives with a roommate in a dorm on the campus. He says that his verbal interactions with his roommate are limited. He has other friends with whom he spends more time. Reportedly, he has difficulty asking for dates because he is worried that he might stutter badly.

### Educational and Occupational History

James has had part-time jobs in various businesses. He said that his stuttering was always a frustrating problem in the workplace. He usually avoided speaking to his supervisors. He tended to seek work that did not involve much oral communication.

James is studying for a degree in computer science. He is doing well in his courses. He does not think that his stuttering has negatively affected his coursework or relationship with his instructors. He plans to work for a private company when he finishes his degree. He is concerned about being able to communicate under job pressure. James appeared to be highly motivated for treatment, as he wants to be able to speak fluently.

## Assessment Information

### Orofacial Examination

An orofacial examination was performed to assess the structural and functional integrity of the oral mechanism. The examination did not reveal anything of clinical significance.

### Types and Frequency of Dysfluencies

To analyze the types and the frequency of dysfluencies, a conversational speech sample was recorded. James was also asked to bring an audiotaped conversational speech sample within the next three days. An analysis of the two samples revealed the following types and frequency of dysfluencies.

| Dysfluency Types | Clinic Sample<br>Total Words: 1231<br>Frequency of Dysfluency | Home Sample<br>Total Words: 1071<br>Frequency of Dysfluency |
|---|---|---|
| Interjections | 86 | 26 |
| Pauses | 29 | 9 |
| Part-word reps | 68 | 60 |
| Whole-word reps | 9 | 57 |
| Audible prolongations | 52 | 4 |
| Silent prolongations | 7 | 4 |
| Revisions | 8 | 6 |
| Incomplete phrases | 2 | 1 |
| **Total** | **261** | **167** |
| **Percent Dysfluency Rate** | **21** | **15.6** |

Both of the speech samples contained pauses from 5 to 25 sec in duration. His sound and silent prolongations typically exceeded 1 sec. James's rate of speech was calculated between 110 and 150 words per minute depending on the amount and duration of pauses and prolongations. He intermittently rushed groups of words. Overall rate of speech was variable depending on amount of dysfluencies.

An occasional eye blink and hand movements associated with dysfluencies were observed during the interview. These motor behaviors were most often associated with part-word repetitions and silent and sound prolongations.

### *Speech and Language Production and Language Comprehension*

An informal assessment of a 100-utterance, 1,231-word, conversational speech and language sample did not reveal any speech sound production errors or expressive language problems. Therefore, these skills were judged appropriate for his level of education. No language comprehension problems were noted during the interview.

### *Voice*

James spoke with laryngeal tension and hard glottal attack approximately 50% of the time. Tension and abrupt initiation of voice were often associated with dysfluencies. Nonetheless, he exhibited appropriate vocal intensity, intonation, and inflectional patterns.

### *Hearing Screening*

A bilateral hearing screening was administered at 25 dB HL for 500, 1000, 2000, and 4000 Hz. James responded to all frequencies.

## Diagnostic Summary

Analysis of the conversational speech samples revealed that James Foxx exhibited a severe fluency disorder with 18% to 21% dysfluency rates. His dominant dysfluencies were repetitions, prolongations, interjections, and pauses.

## Recommendations

It is recommended that James Foxx receive treatment for his stuttering. With treatment, prognosis for fluent speech is judged to be good as a brief duration of trial therapy suggested that stuttering may be eliminated with recommended fluency skills. The following fluency skills may be taught within a fluency-shaping program:

1. Teaching appropriate airflow, rate reduction, and gentle phonatory onset.
2. Production of 98% fluent speech within the clinic.
3. Maintenance of at least 95% fluency in extraclinical situations.

Submitted By _____
        Meena Wong, B.A.
        Student Clinician

Client's Signature _____
        James Foxx

Approved By _____
        Nancy Lopez, M.A., CCC-SLP
        Speech-Language Pathologist
        Clinical Supervisor

# C.4. Practice in Diagnostic Report Writing

In practicing diagnostic report writing in the next section, use the information given on the left-hand pages and write your report on the right-hand pages. Give appropriate headings and subheadings. Invent missing information.

Take note that the information on the left-hand pages is often written in an abbreviated style. You should not simply copy these truncated constructions. You should use the information to write formal, well-connected, sentences.

## C.4.1. Diagnostic Report: *Speech Sound Disorder*

> Data Sheet. Use these data to write your report on the opposite page. Use the correct headings.

Name of the clinic, city, and state: (invent)

*Write the name and address of the clinic.*

*What kind of report?*

### Diagnostic Report

Mathew Moon, client; age, 8; address: (invent); telephone: (invent); clinician: yourself; date of assessment: (invent); diagnosis: articulation disorder; referred by: Dr. Lydia Bong, a counselor.

**(L1H)**

*Identifying information*

*Arrange appropriately*

### Background and Reasons for Referral

Use the information above

No prior assessment at this facility

Informant: Mr. Sonny Moon, father

Date seen and evaluated (invent)

**(L1H)**

*Who, how old a person, referred when, to which clinic, and why?*

> Write your report. Use the information on the data sheet. Invent information as needed.

> Data Sheet. Use these data to write your report on the opposite page. Use the correct headings.

## History

*Birth and Development*

Normal pregnancy, cesarean delivery

No other prenatal or natal complications

Normal infancy

Delayed motor development, but no specific information

First words at 18 months

Soon language development somewhat accelerated to approximate the normal.

*Medical History*

Frequent middle ear infections; frequent medical treatment

Mild conductive hearing loss according to previous clinical reports

Frequent attacks of cold and allergies

Chicken pox at age 4

---

(L1H)

(L2H)

Prenatal, birth

Mother's health

Early development

Early language development

---

(L2H)

Diseases of significance

> Write your report. Use the information on the data sheet. Invent information as needed.

> Data Sheet. Use these data to write your report on the opposite page. Use the correct headings.

*Family, Social, and Educational History*

An older brother (10 years), a younger sister (2 years)

None with a communicative disorder

Mother: college graduate; a real estate broker

Father: high school graduate; car repairman

Mathew, in 2nd grade, doing below-average school work, was held back the first year in school

He plays well with other children.

Parents say he is cooperative, affectionate, and well behaved;

Gets group speech treatment at his school once a week for 20 minutes.

---

**(L2H)**

Family
How many children?

Any family history of communicative problems?

Parents' education and occupation

Educational information

Child's companions and social behavior

Any other information about the family

> Write your report. Use the information on the data sheet. Invent information as needed.

> Data Sheet. Use these data to write your report on the opposite page. Use the correct headings.

## Assessment Information

*Orofacial Examination*

Class II malocclusion

Sluggish lingual movements

No other findings of significance

**(L1H)**

**(L2H)** Describe the orofacial examination: integrity of oral and facial structures.

Give a general description of the face, mouth, teeth, tongue, hard and soft palate, and movement of the soft palate and the tongue.

*Hearing Screening*

Screened: 500, 1000, 2000, and 4000 Hz at 25 dB HL

Failed at all tested frequencies.

Needs a complete audiological examination; will be referred to an audiologist

**(L2H)** What frequencies were screened and at what level?

What were the results?

### C.4 Practice in Diagnostic Report Writing

> Write your report. Use the information on the data sheet. Invent information as needed.

Data Sheet. Use these data to write your report on the opposite page. Use the correct headings.

*Speech Sound Production and Intelligibility*

Conversational speech sample

Goldman-Fristoe Test of Articulation

Numerous errors in both

In the initial position of words, omitted: /b, d, p, f, v, r, k/; substituted: t/k; distorted: /z, s/

In the medial position of words, omitted: /b, m, f, z, s, l, g, r/

In the final position of words, omitted: /b, d, p, f, v, r, k, t, l, m, n, s/

The same errors in conversational speech

Intelligibility with contextual cues: 60% for utterances

---

**(L2H)**

How was speech sound production assessed?

Give the full name of tests administered. Do not ignore speech samples.

Summarize the errors in a table.

What was the speech intelligibility?

> Write your report. Use the information on the data sheet. Invent information as needed.

Data Sheet. Use these data to write your report on the opposite page. Use the correct headings.

*Language Production and Comprehension*

Speech-language sample: 120 utterances

MLU: 3.0 words

Analysis of conversational speech for missing grammatical features

Many morphologic features missing, but consider the errors of articulation

(invent missing morphologic features, including the regular plural, possessive, prepositions)

Limited sentence structures

Tests administered:

Peabody Picture Vocabulary Test, 3rd ed. (PPVT III), Form A

    Results: Raw score, 108; standard score, 100; percentile, 50; age equivalency, 8–0.

Expressive Vocabulary Test (EVT)

    Results: Raw score, 80; standard score, 101; percentile, 53; age equivalency, 8–2.

> (L2H)
>
> How did you assess language production?
>
> How did you analyze the results?
>
> What were the results of the analysis?
>
> How did you assess comprehension?
>
> What were the results?

*Voice and Fluency*

Informally assessed through conversational speech samples

Judged to be within normal limits

> (L2H)
>
> How did you assess voice and fluency?
>
> What is your evaluation?

> Write your report. Use the information on the data sheet. Invent information as needed.

> Data Sheet. Use these data to write your report on the opposite page. Use the correct headings.

### Diagnostic Summary

Multiple misarticulations

Speech intelligibility: 60%

Normal voice and fluency

Limited language structures; many missing morphologic features

### Recommendations

Treatment recommended

With treatment, good prognosis

Goal is to teach the misarticulated phonemes

A later, more detailed language assessment

A program to train parents in maintenance techniques

An audiological assessment

Submitted By _____

Parent's Signature _____

Approved By _____

---

**(L1H)**
Summarize the communicative problems.

**(L1H)**
Do you recommend treatment?

What are the priority treatment targets?

Who submitted the report?
Write the name, degree, and title.

Parent's name and signature.

Who approved the report?
Write the name, degree, certification, and title of a clinical supervisor.

> Write your report. Use the information on the data sheet. Invent information as needed.

## C.4.2. Diagnostic Report: *Child Language Disorder*

> Data Sheet. Use these data to write your report on the opposite page. Use the correct headings.

Name of the clinic, city, and state: (invent)

*[Write the name and address of the clinic.]*

### Diagnostic Report

Sylvia Sun, client; age, 5 years, 2 months; address: (invent); telephone: (invent); clinician: yourself; date of assessment: (invent); diagnosis: Language Disorder; referred by: Dr. Chang Loongson, a physician.

*(L1H) What kind of report? Identifying information. Arrange appropriately*

### Background and Reasons for Referral

Date seen at the clinic (invent)

Use the information above

No prior assessment at this facility

Informant: Mrs. Katie Sun, mother

*(L1H) Who, how old a person, referred when, to which clinic, and why?*

C.4 Practice in Diagnostic Report Writing

Write your report. Use the information on the data sheet. Invent information as needed.

Data Sheet. Use these data to write your report on the opposite page. Use the correct headings.

## History

**Birth and Development**

Normal pregnancy, delivery

No significant prenatal or natal complications

Normal infancy

Delayed language and motor development

First words at 22 months

Two-word phrases not until 28 months

Errors of articulation

"Does not speak in complete sentences" (mother)

"Does not know many words" (mother)

**Medical History**

One episode of high fever and convulsions at age 16 months

Prone to frequent episodes of coughs, colds, and allergic reactions

Chicken pox at age 4

Slow physical growth

---

(L1H)

(L2H)

Prenatal, birth

Mother's health

Early development

Early language development

---

(L2H)

Diseases of significance

> Write your report. Use the information on the data sheet. Invent information as needed.

> Data Sheet. Use these data to write your report on the opposite page. Use the correct headings.

*Family, Social, and Educational History*

An older sister (8 years), a younger brother (3 years)

Sister diagnosed as developmentally delayed, enrolled in special education

No parental concern about the younger brother's speech and language

Older sister: language delayed, getting treated in school

Mother: a high school graduate; a receptionist in an auto body repair shop

Father: high school graduate; plumber

Enrolled in a kindergarten program

Needs special attention

Does not play cooperatively

Has a few companions who are much younger

---

(L2H)

Family

How many children?

Any family history of communicative problems?

Parent's education and occupation

Educational information

Child's companions and social behavior

Any other information about the family

### C.4 Practice in Diagnostic Report Writing

> Write your report. Use the information on the data sheet. Invent information as needed.

Data Sheet. Use these data to write your report on the opposite page. Use the correct headings.

**Assessment Information**

*Orofacial Examination*

No malocclusion

Sluggish lingual movements

Slow diadochokinetic rate

No other findings of significance

(L1H)

(L2H)

Describe the orofacial examination: integrity of oral and facial structures.

Give a general description of the face, mouth, teeth, tongue, hard and soft palate, and movement of the soft palate and the tongue.

*Hearing Screening*

Screened: 500, 1000, 2000, and 4000 Hz at 25 dB HL

Passed at all tested frequencies

(L2H)

What frequencies were screened and at what level?

What were the results?

### C.4 Practice in Diagnostic Report Writing

> Write your report. Use the information on the data sheet. Invent information as needed.

> Data Sheet. Use these data to write your report on the opposite page. Use the correct headings.

### Speech Sound Production and Speech Intelligibility

Conversational speech sample

Goldman-Fristoe Test of Articulation: Second Edition

Numerous errors in both

In the initial position of words, omitted: /b, d, t, l, g, m, n, k/; distorted: /z, s/

In the medial position of words, omitted: /b, m, f, z, s, l, g, r/

In the final position of words, omitted: /b, d, p, r, k, t, m, n, s/

The same errors in conversational speech

Intelligibility with contextual cues: 80% for utterances

---

**(L2H)**

How was speech production assessed?

Give the full name of tests administered. Do not ignore speech samples.

Summarize the errors in a table.

What was the speech intelligibility?

### C.4 Practice in Diagnostic Report Writing

Write your report. Use the information on the data sheet. Invent information as needed.

> Data Sheet. Use these data to write your report on the opposite page. Use the correct headings.

*Language Production and Comprehension*

Language sample: 60 utterances

Shown pictures, objects, and toys to evoke language

MLU: 4.0 words

Analysis of conversational speech for missing grammatical features and pragmatic functions

Limited vocabulary

Many morphologic features missing (invent missing morphologic features, e.g., the plural *s*, present progressive *ing*, past tense *ed*)

Typically, three- to four-word utterances

Few grammatically complete sentences

Limited sentence structures and few sentence varieties

Difficulty in maintaining topic and in conversational turn taking

Tests administered:

Receptive One-Word Picture Vocabulary Test (ROWPVT)

    Results: Raw score, 46; standard score, 85; percentile, 16; age equivalency, 4–0

Expressive One-Word Picture Vocabulary Test (EOWPVT)

    Results: Raw score, 40; standard score, 82; percentile, 11; age equivalency, 3–10

Clinical judgment during interview and language sampling

Comprehension of conversational speech: Approximately that of a 3-year-old

*Voice and Fluency*

Informally assessed through conversational speech samples

Limited fluency because of limited language

Voice judged to be within normal limits

---

**(L2H)**

How did you assess language production?

What tests?

How did you analyze the results?

What were the results of the analysis?

How did you assess language comprehension?

What were the results?

---

**(L2H)**

How did you assess voice and fluency?

What is your evaluation?

### C.4 Practice in Diagnostic Report Writing

Write your report. Use the information on the data sheet. Invent information as needed.

> Data Sheet. Use these data to write your report on the opposite page. Use the correct headings.

### Diagnostic Summary

Multiple sound errors

Speech intelligibility: 80%

Normal voice but limited fluency

Limited vocabulary and language structures; many missing morphologic features pragmatic problems; deficiency in language comprehension

**(L1H)** Summarize the communicative problems.

### Recommendations

Treatment recommended

With treatment, good prognosis

Initial goal is to expand vocabulary, teach early morphemes, and basic sentence structures.

Later goal is to teach correct articulation of phonemes, pragmatic features.

A more detailed language assessment before initiating treatment

Parent training in a home treatment and maintenance program

**(L1H)**
Do you recommend treatment?

What are the priority treatment targets?

Submitted By _____

Parent's Signature _____
               Mrs. Katie Sun

Approved By _____

Who submitted the report?
Write the name, degree, and title.

Parent's name and signature

Who approved the report?
Write the name, degree, certification, and titles of a clinical supervisor.

## C.4 Practice in Diagnostic Report Writing

Write your report. Use the information on the data sheet. Invent information as needed.

## C.4.3. Diagnostic Report: *Stuttering*

> Data Sheet. Use these data to write your report on the opposite page. Use the correct headings.

Name of the clinic, city, and state: (invent)

*Write the name and address of the clinic.*

### Diagnostic Report

Marvin Lenson, client; age, 32; address: (invent); telephone: (invent); clinician: yourself; date of assessment: (invent); diagnosis: stuttering; referral: self.

*(L1H)*
*What kind of report?*
*Identifying information*
*Arrange appropriately*

### Background and Reasons for Referral

Use the information above

Date evaluated (invent)

Several prior assessments and treatments at various clinics with no lasting effects

Informant: Self

Client reported that: stuttering started when he was about 5 (according to his mother)

Has had prior treatment throughout the school years

Does not recall treatment techniques except that he was encouraged to think before talking

Stuttering varies across situations; but more stuttering when talking to strangers; his boss; more fluent talking to wife; avoids telephones, ordering in restaurants, and talking to groups

*(L1H)*
*Who, how old a person, referred when, to which clinic, and why?*
*Summarize the history of stuttering.*

### C.4 Practice in Diagnostic Report Writing

> Write your report. Use the information on the data sheet. Invent information as needed.

> Data Sheet. Use these data to write your report on the opposite page. Use the correct headings.

## History  (L1H)

### Birth and Development  (L2H)

Mother had told the client that everything was normal. — Prenatal, birth

Mother's health during pregnancy reportedly normal — Mother's health

Normal infancy — Early development

Normal motor development

Advanced early language development, as told by parents — Early language development

Considers himself verbally competent; likes to read and write; has good vocabulary and command of the language.

### Medical History  (L2H)

Nothing of clinical significance — Diseases of significance

*Note:* In the case of most adult clients, *Birth and Development* may not be a necessary heading. However, when information that is relevant for a given disorder is available, it should be included.

C.4 Practice in Diagnostic Report Writing 323

> Write your report. Use the information on the data sheet. Invent information as needed.

> Data Sheet. Use these data to write your report on the opposite page. Use the correct headings.

*Family, Social, and Educational History*

An older brother (37 years), a younger sister (27 years), a younger brother (24 years)

Older brother used to stutter but has been mostly fluent for the past 10 years; has had unspecified treatment.

A maternal uncle (65) still stutters.

A paternal aunt (62) used to stutter but has been fluent for many years.

Has no family history of other communicative disorders.

Both hold doctoral degrees

Mother: a pediatrician

Father: a clinical psychologist

Client holds a master's degree in structural engineering

Works for a construction company

Married; wife owns a clothing store

One daughter (3); speaks normally

---

(L2H)

Family

How many children?

Any family history of communicative problems?

Parents' education and occupation

Educational and occupational information

Personal information

> Write your report. Use the information on the data sheet. Invent information as needed.

> Data Sheet. Use these data to write your report on the opposite page. Use the correct headings.

## Assessment Information

*Orofacial Examination*

Nothing of clinical significance

**(L1H)**

**(L2H)**

Describe the orofacial examination: integrity of oral and facial structures.

*Hearing Screening*

Screened: 500, 1000, 2000, and 4000 Hz at 25 dB HL

Passed the screening

**(L2H)**

What frequencies were screened and at what level?

What were the results?

### C.4 Practice in Diagnostic Report Writing

> Write your report. Use the information on the data sheet. Invent information as needed.

> Data Sheet. Use these data to write your report on the opposite page. Use the correct headings.

*Speech and Language Production*

Informally assessed as the client was interviewed

Judged to have normal articulation and superior language skills

Speech intelligibility was 100% for utterances with or without knowledge of contexts.

**(L2H)**

How were speech and language production assessed?

What was the speech intelligibility?

Summarize the observations.

*Voice*

Informally assessed as the client was interviewed

Vocal qualities judged to be normal

**(L2H)**

How assessed?

Summarize the observations.

### C.4 Practice in Diagnostic Report Writing

> Write your report. Use the information on the data sheet. Invent information as needed.

> Data Sheet. Use these data to write your report on the opposite page. Use the correct headings.

*Assessment of Fluency*

Conversational speech sample: 2,000 words

Oral reading sample: 500 words

Two home samples of at least 1,000 words each requested for later analysis

Analysis of types and frequency of dysfluencies (all types)

Calculation of percent dysfluency rate

Results:

In conversational speech:

Part-word reps, 57; sound prolongations, 48; syllable interjections, 28; whole-word reps, 39; pauses (1 sec or more), 45; broken words, 21

Total number of dysfluencies: 238

Percent dysfluency rate: 11.9

Oral reading:

Part-word reps: 42; sound prolongations: 39; syllable interjections: 34; whole-word reps: 53; pauses (1 sec or more): 54; broken words: 21

Total number of dysfluencies: 243

Percent dysfluency rate: 48.6

Eye blinks, knitting of the eyebrows associated with sound prolongations and word repetitions

---

**(L2H)**

How did you assess fluency and stuttering?

How did you analyze the results?

What were the results of the analysis?

Describe the frequency and types of dysfluencies in oral reading

Describe the associated motor behaviors

> Write your report. Use the information on the data sheet. Invent information as needed.

> Data Sheet. Use these data to write your report on the opposite page. Use the correct headings.

### Diagnostic Summary

Clinically significant dysfluency rate: 11.9%

Part-word reps, sound prolongations, syllable interjections, whole-word reps, pauses, and broken words

Higher dysfluency rate in oral reading: 48.6

Few associated motor behaviors

**(L1H)**
Summarize the dysfluency rates.

Specify the types.

### Recommendations

Treatment recommended

With treatment, good prognosis

Goal is to teach the skills of fluency (gentle phonatory onset, rate reduction through syllable prolongation, and appropriate airflow management).

Self-monitoring skills for maintenance

**(L1H)**
Do you recommend treatment?

What are the priority treatment targets?

Submitted By _____

Client's Signature _____
            Marvin Lenson

Approved By _____

Who submitted the report?

Write the name, degree, and title.

Client's name and signature

Who approved the report?

Write the name, degree, certification, and titles of a clinical supervisor.

> Write your report. Use the information on the data sheet. Invent information as needed.

## C.4.4. Diagnostic Report: *Voice Disorder*

> Data Sheet. Use these data to write your report on the opposite page. Use the correct headings.

Name of the clinic, city, and state: (invent)

| Write the name and address of the clinic.

### Diagnostic Report

Raj Mohan, 35 years; address: (invent); telephone: (invent); clinician: yourself; date of assessment: (invent); diagnosis: Voice Disorder (Inadequate Loudness); referred by: Dr. Melanie Mallard, an otolaryngologist.

| (L1H)
| What kind of report?
| Identifying information
| Arrange appropriately

### Background and Reasons for Referral

Use the information above

No prior assessment; date assessed (invent)

Informant: Self

Client reports that: his voice is too soft for his occupation (high school teacher); voice gets tired too soon during the working days; students complain because of too soft voice; has had the problem for the past two years; not much variation

| (L1H)
| Who, how old a person, referred when, to which clinic, and why?
| Summarize the history of the voice disorder.

> Write your report. Use the information on the data sheet. Invent information as needed.

> Data Sheet. Use these data to write your report on the opposite page. Use the correct headings.

## History

*Birth and Development*

No relevant information; eliminate this heading in the report

*Medical History*

Ear, Nose, and Throat (ENT) specialist's report negative; normal laryngeal structures

No medical basis for the symptoms

ENT recommends voice treatment.

(L1H)
___

(L2H)
___

(L2H)
___
Diseases of significance

> Write your report. Use the information on the data sheet. Invent information as needed.

> Data Sheet. Use these data to write your report on the opposite page. Use the correct headings.

*Family, Social, and Educational History*

The only child in the family

No history of voice disorder or other communicative disorders

Mother: college graduate; a college counselor

Father: college graduate; a college admissions officer

**(L2H)**

Family
How many children?

Any family history of communicative problems?

Parents' education and occupation

C.4 Practice in Diagnostic Report Writing

> Write your report. Use the information on the data sheet. Invent information as needed.

> Data Sheet. Use these data to write your report on the opposite page. Use the correct headings.

### Assessment Information

*Orofacial Examination*

Negative (means nothing of clinical significance)

*Hearing Screening*

Screened: 500, 1000, 2000, and 4000 Hz at 25 dB HL

Passed at all frequencies

---

(L1H)

(L2H)

Describe the orofacial examination: integrity of oral and facial structures.

(L2H)

What frequencies were screened and at what level?

What were the results?

### C.4 Practice in Diagnostic Report Writing

> Write your report. Use the information on the data sheet. Invent information as needed.

> Data Sheet. Use these data to write your report on the opposite page. Use the correct headings.

### *Speech, Language, and Fluency*

Based on the observation of conversational speech during interview, judged to be within normal limits

Speech 100% intelligible with or without contextual knowledge

**(L2H)**

How were they assessed?

What was the speech intelligibility?

## C.4 Practice in Diagnostic Report Writing

> Write your report. Use the information on the data sheet. Invent information as needed.

> Data Sheet. Use these data to write your report on the opposite page. Use the correct headings.

### Voice

Subjectively rated on a 5-point scale from very soft to very loud (1 = very soft; 5 = very loud)

Received a rating of 2, soft voice

Also measured with a sound level meter with the microphone placed at 8 in. from the client's face

Measurement showed 45 dB, judged too soft

Additional data: in each class period, the client's students request some five to six times to speak louder

Was asked to baserate the frequency with which the students request him to speak louder over five consecutive days

---

**(L2H)**

How was voice assessed?

What were the results?

### C.4 Practice in Diagnostic Report Writing

> Write your report. Use the information on the data sheet. Invent information as needed.

> Data Sheet. Use these data to write your report on the opposite page. Use the correct headings.

### Diagnostic Summary

Self-report, clinical judgment, and instrumental measurement suggest a voice that is too soft to meet the demands of the client's social and occupational life.

**(L1H)** Summarize the voice disorder.

### Recommendations

Treatment recommended

With treatment, good prognosis

Shape a louder voice considered appropriate for classroom teaching

Reduce or eliminate the number of student requests to speak louder by shaping appropriately louder voice

**(L1H)** Do you recommend treatment?

What are the priority treatment targets?

Submitted By _____

Who submitted the report?

Write the name, degree, and title.

Client's Signature _____
             Raj Mohan

Client's name and signature

Approved By _____

Who approved the report?

Write the name, degree, certification, and titles of a clinical supervisor.

> Write your report. Use the information on the data sheet. Invent information as needed.

## Note to Student Clinicians

Contact your clinic secretary for additional examples of assessment reports. Take note of variations in formats. Practice writing reports according to your clinic format. Use the practice formats presented in this section.

# C.5. Comprehensive Treatment Plans

Treatment plans written for clients vary across professional settings. The plans written in university clinics are perhaps more detailed than those that are written in other settings. A student who learns to write detailed and comprehensive treatment plans can easily write less extensive and briefer reports. Examples of more and less detailed treatment plans follow.

Treatment plans, like assessment reports, need not follow the APA format in every respect. Heading styles will vary; the examples that follow use different styles to illustrate this variety. One-sentence paragraphs, lists (incomplete sentences), and other deviations from the APA style may be acceptable in treatment plans, especially in those that are brief.

Student clinicians are encouraged to see these varied forms and styles as intended reflections of practice across clinics. The variations should not be thought of as inconsistencies. Student clinicians need to find out the accepted format in their clinic by talking to their clinic director and clinical supervisor.

On the following page, we begin with an exemplar of a comprehensive treatment plan which is more detailed than brief treatment plans and may include the following:

1. A brief summary of previous assessment data
2. Treatment targets
3. Treatment and probe procedures
4. Maintenance program
5. Follow-up and booster treatment procedures

A student who writes a comprehensive treatment plan understands the total management program for a client. The student may or may not complete the program in a semester or quarter. Nonetheless, writing a comprehensive treatment program is a good exercise in visualizing the entire treatment sequence from the beginning to the end, which goes beyond a clinical practicum to what clinicians do in professional settings. After assessing their clients, clinicians develop comprehensive treatment plans for them. Therefore, although the student clinicians complete only a portion of a treatment plan, it is desirable to think of the total treatment program for a client.

## C.5.1. Comprehensive Treatment Plan: *Speech Sound Disorder*

### University Speech and Hearing Clinic

### Treatment Plan

Name: Oliver Driver

Date of Birth: xx-xx-xxxx

Address: 312 N. South #111

City: Martinsville, CA 94812

School: University Preschool

Diagnosis: Articulation Disorder

File No.: 900111-3

Semesters in Therapy: 1

Date of Report: xx-xx-xxxx

Telephone: 782-9832

### Background Information

Oliver Driver, a 4-year-old-male child, began his first semester of speech treatment at the University Speech and Hearing Clinic in February, xxxx. Oliver's speech and language were evaluated January 15, xxxx. The evaluation revealed a speech sound disorder characterized by substitutions, omissions, and reduced intelligibility. See his folder for a diagnostic report. Treatment was recommended to train correct production of misarticulated phonemes to increase speech intelligibility. Based on Oliver's cooperative behavior during assessment, prognosis for improved articulation was judged as good.

### Target Behaviors

The **final target** for Oliver is to produce all phonemes correctly in conversational speech with at least 90% accuracy.

The **initial target** is to produce selected phonemes correctly. Based on their inconsistent production during assessment, the following phonemes were selected for the initial treatment: /p/, /m/, /s/, /k/, and /g/. Production of each phoneme was baserated with 20 stimulus words administered on modeled and evoked discrete trials with the following correct baseline response rates:

| Phonemes | Evoked | Modeled |
| --- | --- | --- |
| /p/ | 15% | 17% |
| /m/ | 10% | 24% |
| /s/ | 12% | 22% |
| /k/ | 18% | 20% |
| /g/ | 14% | 17% |

Treatment began after the baserates were obtained. The following general treatment procedures will be used during the semester. The procedures will be modified as suggested by Oliver's performance data. These changes will be described in the final progress report.

## Treatment and Probe Procedures

Each target phoneme will initially be trained at the word level. When Oliver's probe response rate at the word level meets a 90% correct criterion, training will be initiated on two-word phrases. A similar probe criterion will be used to shift training to sentences and then to conversational speech.

Intermixed probes in which trained and untrained words, phrases, or sentences are alternated will be administered every time Oliver meets a tentative training criterion of 90% correct response rate on a block of 20 evoked training trials. Oliver will be trained to meet this criterion at each level of response topography (words, phrases, and sentences).

Initially, the clinician will provide stimulus pictures. Subsequently, Oliver will be required to find at least five pictures in magazines that represent the target sound and bring them to the clinic sessions. After he correctly produces a target sound on five consecutive trials, he will paste a picture that represents the just-trained sound in a book. This book will be used for both clinic and home practice.

Training will begin at each level with discrete trials and modeling. The clinician will show Oliver a picture, ask a question ("What is this?"), and model the response (word or phrase). Oliver will then be required to imitate the clinician's production. When Oliver correctly imitates the target sound on five consecutive trials, modeling will be discontinued. The clinician will show Oliver a picture and ask, "What is this?" to evoke a response.

At the modeled and evoked word levels, verbal reinforcement will be administered on an $FR_1$ schedule for correct productions. At the phrase and sentence levels, an $FR_4$ schedule will be used. At the conversational level, verbal reinforcement will be delivered on an approximate $VR_5$ schedule. All incorrect productions at each level will immediately be interrupted by saying, "stop."

Modeling will be reintroduced if Oliver gives two to four incorrect responses on the evoked trials. Shaping with manual guidance will be used as necessary.

The clinician will chart all productions in all treatment sessions. Oliver also will chart productions with an X under the *happy face* (correct responses) or X under the *sad face* (incorrect responses). At the end of each session, Oliver will assist the clinician in recording his progress on a graph.

It is expected that different target sounds will reach the training criterion at different times. Therefore, the clinician expects to train several sounds at different response topographies in each session. Some sounds may be trained at the word level, whereas others may be trained at the phrase or even sentence level. When the initially selected target sounds meet the criterion of a 90% correct probe rate in conversational speech in the clinic, new target sounds will be baserated and trained.

## Maintenance Program

After Oliver produces the target sound with 90% accuracy at the evoked word level, his mother, Mrs. Janice Driver, will be asked to participate in treatment. Initially, she will observe the treatment procedure. Soon, Mrs. Driver will be taught to present stimulus items and chart correct and incorrect productions. She will be taught to immediately reinforce the correct productions and stop Oliver at the earliest sign of an inaccurate production.

After Oliver's mother identifies correct and incorrect responses with at least 80% accuracy in the clinic session, she will be taught to work with him at home. Mrs. Driver will begin with such structured activities as reciting from a list or reading from the book that Oliver will be developing in treatment. Assignments will progress to monitoring and recording speech during dinner and phone conversations with Oliver's grandmother, who will be encouraged to prompt and then praise the correct productions. The clinician, Oliver, and his mother will review tape-recorded home assignments. The mother will be given feedback on the procedures implemented at home.

When Oliver produces the target sound with 90% accuracy in conversation in the sessions, he will be taken out of the clinic to practice correct productions in nonclinical situations. The clinician will take Oliver for a walk on campus and talk with him. Subsequently, he may be taken to the campus bookstore, library, cafeteria, and other places. Eventually, his speech may be monitored informally in shopping centers and restaurants.

When Oliver's speech is 98% intelligible and his sound productions are 90% correct, he may be dismissed from treatment. A follow-up visit will be scheduled for six months after dismissal. Based on the initial follow-up results, booster treatment, treatment for persistent errors, or additional follow-up assessments will be planned.


Submitted By _____
        Marla Model, B.A.
        Student Clinician


Client's Signature _____
        Mrs. Janice Driver


Approved By _____
        Barbara Sierra, M.S., CCC/SLP
        Speech-Language Pathologist
        Clinical Supervisor

# C.6. Brief Treatment Plans

Brief or short-term treatment plans, also known as lesson plans, are probably used more frequently than longer ones. The scope of these plans varies across clinics and supervisors. Some plans describe what will be done in only a session or two. Others might describe treatment objectives and procedures planned for a week, a quarter, or a semester. Even those that describe the plan for a semester may not be as comprehensive as a complete treatment plan. In some plans, only the treatment objectives may be listed. However, all treatment plans—long or short—should contain a statement of prognosis and a description of target behaviors, treatment procedures, and performance criteria.

The examples of brief treatment plans given on the following pages show slightly different formats in which they can be written. The sampling of formats is not comprehensive; the examples suggest a few basic variations. Heading styles and paragraph formats are varied purposefully.

## C.6.1. Brief Treatment Plan: *Fluency Disorder*

**Speech and Hearing Clinic**
**Eastern State University**
**Bedford, California**

James Foxx, a 23-year-old male, was seen on February x, xxxx, for a speech evaluation at the Speech and Hearing Clinic of Eastern State University, Bedford, California. The results of the evaluation indicated a severe fluency disorder with a 21% dysfluency rate in conversational speech. His dysfluencies were characterized by repetitions, prolongations, pauses, interjections, and revisions. A fluency treatment program was recommended. With consistent treatment, prognosis for improved fluency was judged to be good.

A fluency-shaping program was selected for James. The program consists of the following final treatment objective and specific target fluency skills:

**Final Treatment Objective:** A dysfluency rate that does not exceed 5% in James's home and other nonclinical settings.

### Target Behaviors

1. **Appropriate management of airflow.** To produce and sustain fluency in conversational speech, the clinician will teach James to inhale and then immediately exhale a slight amount of air before phonation. He also will be taught to sustain a smooth flow of air throughout his utterances.
2. **Gentle onset of phonation.** James will be taught to initiate phonation in a soft and easy manner.
3. **Reduced speech rate through syllable prolongation.** James will be taught to prolong vowels to reduce his speech rate and to achieve continuous phonation.
4. **Continuous phonation.** Throughout an utterance, James will be taught to maintain continuous phonation by not pausing between words.
5. **Normal prosody.** Maintenance of normal prosodic features with a dysfluency rate that does not exceed 5%.

### Treatment Procedures

1. A baseline of dysfluency and speech rates in conversational speech will be established before starting treatment.
2. Treatment will begin at the phrase or short sentence level.
3. The target fluency skills will be taught one at a time, beginning with inhalation and slight exhalation. Gentle onset will then be added, followed by syllable prolongation and other target skills.
4. As James sustains 98% stutter-free speech at each level of response complexity, utterance length will be increased.
5. The clinician will give instructions and model target responses consistently in the beginning stages and as often as necessary in subsequent stages of treatment.
6. The clinician will verbally reinforce the production of all target behaviors, including the resulting fluency.

7. The clinician will give corrective feedback for incorrect responses, including dysfluencies; this feedback will be given at the earliest sign of a dysfluency or mismanagement of a target fluency skill.
8. When James sustains speech with 2% or less dysfluency, normal prosodic features will be trained by having him increase his speech rate and by using normal intonational patterns.
9. As James sustains 98% fluency in conversational speech, maintenance procedures will be implemented. James's wife and a colleague of his will be trained in evoking and reinforcing skills of fluency. James will be taught to self-monitor his fluency skills. The clinician will take James to extraclinical situations to evoke and reinforce his fluency skills. Home speech samples will be used to judge maintenance of fluency.
10. Follow-up will be scheduled for 3, 6, and 12 months postdismissal. Booster treatment will be arranged as needed.

Signed _____
      Gloria Marquez, B.A.
      Student Clinician

I understand the results of the evaluation and agree to the recommended treatment plan.

Signed _____ Date _____
      James Foxx

_____
Henriette Borden, Ph.D., CCC-SLP
Speech-Language Pathologist
Clinical Supervisor

## C.6.2. Brief Treatment Plan: *Speech Sound Disorder*

**Valley Speech and Hearing Center**
**Nordstrom, Maine**

Rudy Amos, a 7-year and 3-month-old boy, was referred to the Valley Speech and Hearing Center for assessment and treatment of a speech sound disorder. According to an assessment made on February xx, xxxx, Rudy's speech sound disorder is limited to omissions of the following phonemes in both the word initial and final positions: /k, l, s, t, r/, and /z/. Treatment was recommended. Prognosis for improvement was judged excellent because Rudy was readily stimulable and highly cooperative during a brief period of trial therapy.

The treatment began on February xx, xxxx. A baserate showed 0% to 10% accuracy on the target phonemes. The baserates on modeled and evoked trials were similar.

The treatment will have the following final goal, specific objectives, and procedures.

**Final treatment goal:** Correct production of target phonemes maintained in conversational speech produced in the natural environment with at least 90% accuracy.

**Objective 1.** Correct production of misarticulated phonemes in the initial, medial, and final word positions with a minimum of 90% accuracy.

**Procedures:** Pictures that help evoke words with the target sounds in all word positions will be used. Instructions, demonstrations, and visual feedback will be used, as found necessary. Modeling will be provided, and, if necessary, various sound-shaping techniques will be used to refine the imitated responses. Rudy will be verbally reinforced for progressively better imitations of modeled responses. Corrective feedback will be given for incorrect responses.

When Rudy meets the training criterion of 90% correct production of words for a block of 20 treatment trials, an intermixed probe will be conducted. Training and probe trials will be alternated until this criterion is met.

**Objective 2.** Correct production of misarticulated phonemes in phrases and sentences.

**Procedures:** Training will be shifted to phrase level when Rudy meets the probe criterion for words and to sentence level when his responses at the phrase level meet the probe criterion. Picture description and controlled conversation will be used to evoke target phrases and sentences. Modeling will be provided as needed. Correct responses will be reinforced on a variable schedule designed to progressively reduce the amount of feedback. Corrective feedback will be given for all incorrect responses.

**Objective 3.** Correct production of misarticulated phonemes in conversational speech with varied audiences.

**Procedures:** Initially, the clinician will evoke conversational speech and model and reinforce correct productions. When Rudy's accuracy of production in conversational speech reaches at least 80%, other persons will serve as the audience.

**Objective 4.** Correct production of target phonemes in extraclinical situations.

**Procedures:** Rudy will be taken out of the treatment room to various settings on the campus to strengthen the correct production of the target phonemes. Correct productions will be prompted and reinforced in a subtle manner in such places as the campus bookstore and restaurants.

**Objective 5.** Teaching Rudy's mother to evoke and reinforce correct productions in conversational speech at home.

**Procedures:** The mother will be asked to initially observe the sessions and later participate in the treatment sessions. Mrs. Amos will be taught to recognize the correct productions and to immediately praise Rudy. Mrs. Amos will be asked to hold brief and informal treatment sessions at home. Recorded home speech samples will be used to assess the correct production of phonemes at home.

**The dismissal criterion:** A 90% or better correct production of the target phonemes in conversational speech produced in extraclinical situations. Periodic home speech samples, recorded by the mother, will be used to assess this criterion.

The procedure will be modified as found necessary during the treatment sessions.

Follow-up evaluations will be conducted 3, 6, and 12 months after the dismissal. Booster treatment will be scheduled as needed.


Signed _____
     Mohamed Ali, M.A., CCC-SLP
     Speech-Language Pathologist


I understand the treatment program, and I agree to it.


Signed _____
     Ms. Lydia Amos
     Mother

## C.6.3. Brief Treatment Plan: *Child Language Disorder*

**Speech and Hearing Clinic**
**Southern State University**
**Johnstonville, Louisiana**

Timothy Krebs, a 4-year, 2-month-old boy, was evaluated at the Speech and Hearing Clinic at the Southern State University on February x, xxxx. The evaluation revealed a severe language disorder. Case history and assessment data showed that his language performance is limited to a few words and phrases. A detailed assessment report can be found in Timothy's file. A language treatment program was recommended.

Timothy will be seen two times weekly in sessions lasting 45 min. His father, Mr. John Krebs, will accompany him to the clinic and will participate in treatment sessions. It is judged that prognosis for improved language performance is good if treatment is consistent and a home treatment and maintenance program is sustained. The following treatment objectives were selected for this semester (fall, xxxx).

### Initial Treatment Objective

Correct production of selected functional words at 90% accuracy.

With the help of Timothy's father, the following 20 targets consisting of single words or two-word phrases of high functional value were selected for initial treatment:

| cup | sock | milk | shoe | Jenny (sister) |
| --- | --- | --- | --- | --- |
| juice | more | eat | give me | walking |
| no more | I want | cookie | candy | bath |
| shirt | look! | Hi | Binny (dog) | John (friend) |

Timothy did not produce any of these words on evoked or modeled baseline trials.

### Subsequent Treatment Objectives

1. Correct production of additional words
2. Expansion of single words into phrases and sentences
3. Production of early morphological features (present progressive, regular plural, possessive, prepositions, pronouns, etc.)

### Initial Treatment Procedures

1. Pictures, objects, toys, acted-out situations, and role-playing will be used as stimuli to evoke the target words or phrases.
2. The clinician and the father will take turns in evoking the target words or phrases.
3. Initially, gross approximations will be reinforced by verbal praise and such natural reinforcers as handing an object, complying with a request, and so forth. Subsequently, only better approximations will be reinforced.

C.6 Brief Treatment Plans

4. All correct and incorrect productions will be measured in each treatment session.
5. When single words meet the training criterion of 90% accuracy across two sessions, intermixed probes will be conducted to assess generalized production.
6. Words that meet the 90% accurate probe criterion will be expanded into phrases and phrases that meet the same probe criterion will be expanded into simple sentences.
7. The father will be asked to conduct similar treatment sessions at home and bring recorded samples of sessions for evaluation and feedback.

## Subsequent Treatment Procedures

1. Additional words, selected in consultation with the father, will be trained using the same procedure described under initial treatment procedures.
2. Additional words will be expanded into phrases and sentences.
3. Selected morphologic features will be initially trained in words and later expanded into phrases and sentences.

It is expected that Timothy will need extended treatment and that both the treatment objectives and procedures will be modified in light of his performance data. The father's participation in training from the beginning will help maintenance. A more complete maintenance program will be developed later.

Signed _____
    Trisha Muniz, B.A.
    Student Clinician

I understand the results of the evaluation and agree to the recommended treatment plan.

Signed _____
    Mr. John Krebs

Signed _____  Date _____
    Maya Real, M.A., CCC-SLP
    Speech-Language Pathologist
    Clinical Supervisor

## C.6.4. Brief Treatment Plan: *Voice Disorder*

### The Sunshine Speech and Hearing Center
### Zingsville, Vermont

Roshana Hersh, a 21-year-old female college student, was seen at the Sunshine Speech and Hearing Center on March xx, xxxx, for a voice evaluation. The evaluation suggested a pattern of vocal abuse associated with a persistent hoarseness of voice, low pitch, and socially inappropriate intensity. Her vocal abuse consists mainly of excessive talking over the telephone and shouting at children she supervises as a teacher's aid in a kindergarten school. The detailed case history and assessment data can be found in her file. A treatment program to improve her voice quality was recommended. Considering her high degree of motivation for improvement that she expressed during the interview, prognosis with treatment for improved vocal quality was judged to be good.

### *Treatment Targets*

**Goal 1:** Production of clear voice at least 90% of the time Roshana speaks by reducing the hoarseness of voice

    **Objective 1a.** Reduced amount of talking over the phone

    **Objective 1b.** Reduced amount of shouting at the school

**Goal 2.** Increased vocal pitch

    **Objective 2a.** Higher pitch at the level of words and phrases

    **Objective 2b.** Higher pitch at the level of conversational speech

**Goal 3.** Decreased vocal intensity

    **Objective 3a.** Softer voice at the level of words and phrases

    **Objective 3b.** Softer voice at the level of conversational speech

### *Treatment Procedures*

**Objectives 1a and 1b.** During the first week, the frequency and durations of Roshana's telephone conversations will be baserated. She will be asked to keep a diary to record the number of daily telephone conversations and their durations. During the second week, Roshana will be asked to reduce by 10% the amount of telephone conversation time. She may achieve this by either reducing the frequency of telephone conversations or only their durations. She will continue to record the frequency and duration of telephone conversations. In subsequent weeks, she will be asked to progressively decrease the amount of time spent on the telephone until the duration is reduced by about 50%.

The frequency of shouting also will be similarly baserated. Roshana will then be asked to reduce the frequency of shouting behavior in 10% decrements until the frequency approaches zero.

**Objectives 2a and 2b.** The Visi-Pitch will be used to shape a higher pitch consistent with Roshana's gender and age. The treatment will start at the word and phrase level and move on to the conversational speech level.

**Objectives 3a and 3b.** The Visi-Pitch will be used to progressively decrease the vocal intensity until it is clinically judged to be appropriate for Roshana. The treatment will start at the word and phrase level and move to the conversational speech level.

A maintenance program that includes an analysis of speech samples from home and periodic follow-up and booster treatment will be implemented.


Signed _____
       Pero Boss, B.A.
       Student Clinician


I understand the results of the evaluation and agree to the recommended treatment plan.


Signed _____
       Roshana Hersh


Signed _____    Date _____
       Moss Nero, M.A., CCC-SLP
       Speech-Language Pathologist
       Clinical Supervisor

# C.7. Individualized Educational Programs

In public schools, clinicians are required by law to develop individualized educational programs or family service plans. Clinicians in a typical university or hospital speech and hearing clinic essentially do the same. Individual treatment plans described so far are comparable to individualized educational programs.

Clinicians often do not have time to write lengthy or narrative treatment plans for the children they serve. Therefore, most public school clinicians use printed forms to select treatment targets for the children they treat. Formats vary across school districts, some being more detailed than others. In this section, a few examples of printed individualized education plans for speech-language services are provided.

## C.7.1. IEP: Treatment of Child Language Disorder

**Central Coast Unified School District**
**Individualized Educational Plan for Speech and Language Services**
**Oral Language and Verbal Expression**

Student's Name _____ Date of Birth _____

School _____ Grade _____ Date _____

Speech-Language Pathologist _____

Criteria for Placement _____

**Goal:** To improve oral language and verbal expression

| Present Level of Performance: *See assessment report* | Target Date | Met On (Date) | Not Met |
|---|---|---|---|
| Objectives:<br>By x/xx [specify the date] the student will complete the following objectives with 90% accuracy as measured by pre- and posttests, specialist's observations, client-specific procedures, or other procedures (specify):<br><br>_____<br>_____<br>_____ | [Specify] | | |
| Improve oral language through: | | | |
| Social interaction with others: (Check the targets selected) | | | |
| 1. ✓ verbally respond when spoken to<br>2. ✓ verbally express feelings and needs<br>3. ✓ give personal information upon request<br>4. ✓ ask and answer questions<br>5. ✓ initiate conversation<br>6. ✓ share personal experiences<br>7. ✓ describe events in detail<br>8. ✓ report factual information<br>9. ✓ interact verbally with others<br>10. ✓ give sequential, accurate verbal directions<br>11. ✓ take part in class discussions and reports<br>12. ✓ other _____ | [Specify] | | |

## C.7.2. IEP: Treatment of Speech Sound Disorder

**Atlantic Unified School District
Language, Speech, and Hearing
Individualized Educational Program Objectives
Treatment of Speech Sound Disorder**

Pupil _____

Speech-Language and Hearing Specialist _____

Date _____

School _____      Services started on _____

**Goal:** Improved intelligibility of speech through correct production of phonemes at 90% accuracy.

| Target Date | Objectives (Check the Ones Selected) | Evaluation and Treatment Procedures | Date Objectives Met |
|---|---|---|---|
| | **Speech Sound Production** | | |
| [Specify] | Correct production of the following phonemes:<br><br>/d/, /t/, /p/, /z/, and /l/<br><br>✓ in isolation<br>✓ in syllables<br>✓ in words<br>　✓ initial<br>　✓ medial<br>　✓ final<br>✓ in phrases<br>✓ in sentences<br>✓ conversational speech<br>✓ in natural settings<br><br>*increased intelligibility* | Paired stimuli method of treatment<br><br>Probes to assess production in untrained contexts | [Specify] |

## C.7.3. IEP: Treatment of Voice Disorder

**Gulf Coast Unified School District**
**Department of Special Educational Services**
**Language, Speech, and Hearing**
**Individualized Educational Program**
**Treatment of Voice Disorders**

Student's Name _____

Speech-Language and Hearing Specialist _____

School _____

Program Initiation Date _____  Date _____

**Goal:** By *x/xx* [specify the date], the student will complete the following objectives with 80% accuracy.

| Target Date | Objectives (Check The Ones Selected) | Evaluation And Treatment Procedures | Target Met On (Date) |
|---|---|---|---|
| | **Voice** Overall objective: Improved voice quality and appropriate use of voice | | |
| [Specify] | **Pitch** <br> ✓ lower <br> __ higher <br> __ in school <br> __ in other settings <br><br> **Intensity** <br> __ lower (softer voice) <br> ✓ higher (louder voice) <br> __ in school <br> __ in other settings <br><br> **Nasal resonance** <br> __ decrease <br> __ increase <br><br> **Voice quality** <br> ✓ reduce hoarseness <br> ✓ reduce harshness <br> ✓ reduce breathiness <br><br> Other voice objectives (specify): | Successive approximation with the help of Visi-Pitch <br><br> Conversational probes to assess generalization and maintenance | [Specify] |

## C.7.4. IEP: Treatment of Fluency Disorder

**North Central Unified School District**
**Speech, Language, and Hearing Services**
**Individualized Educational Plan**
**Treatment of Fluency Disorders**

Student's Name _____

Speech-Language and Hearing Specialist _____

School _____

Treatment Began On _____   Date _____

**Goal:** Improved fluency in conversational speech produced in extraclinical settings with a dysfluency rate under 5%.

| Target Date | Objectives (Check the Ones Selected) | Evaluation and Treatment Procedures | Objectives Met On |
|---|---|---|---|
| | FLUENCY | | |
| [Specify] | Target Skills:<br>✓ Appropriate management of airflow<br>✓ Gentle phonatory onset<br>✓ Reduced rate of speech<br>   ✓ in words and phrases<br>   ✓ in sentences<br>   ✓ in conversational speech<br>   ✓ in extraclinical situations<br>✓ Normal prosody and fluency | Teaching fluency skills with modeling, successive approximation, and verbal reinforcement; fading the slow rate; shaping normal prosodic features<br><br>Conversational probes to assess generalization and maintenance of fluency in clinical and extraclinical situations | [Specify] |

# C.8. Practice in Writing Treatment Plans

On the following pages, you will find opportunities to practice writing treatment plans. Clinical data are given on the left-hand page. Use these data to write your treatment plans on the right-hand page.

You may wish to consult the corresponding exemplars in sections C.6 and C.7 before you write the reports in this section. Make sure that you vary your sentences.

Clinics vary in their format of treatment plans. The format used in this book does not include formally arranged identifying information that was included in assessment (diagnostic reports). However, if required by your clinic, you can place the identifying information at the beginning of the report in the following (or any other accepted) format:

**Treatment Plan**

Client:                              Date of Birth:

Address:                             Clinic File Number:

City:                                Date:

Telephone Number:                    Diagnosis:

Referred By:                         Clinician:

Supervisor:

## C.8.1. Comprehensive Treatment Plan: *Child Language Disorder*

**University Speech and Hearing Center**
**Pan Pacific University**
**Pacific, California**

> Data Sheet. Use these data to write your report on the opposite page. Use the correct headings.

Harvey Brokert, 6 years, 5 months

Talks in two- to three-word phrases

No sentences; no bound morphemes

Treatment was recommended

Mother brings the child to treatment

Good prognosis for improved language skills, suggested by good imitation of selected language targets

Final target behaviors: Functional grammatical, syntactic, and pragmatic language skills produced in natural settings

Initial target behaviors: Teaching nouns, auxiliary *is* and verb + *ing*; prepositions *in*, *on*, and *under*; and pronouns *he* and *she*; all taught in the context of simple sentences

Baserated on a set of modeled and evoked trials; 20 stimulus sentences for each target; baserates between 0 and 10%

---

*Sidebar:*

Background Information (L1H)
Who, how old, when, to where referred? What were the results of evaluation? (Summarize the disorder.) Was treatment recommended?

Target behaviors? (L1H)

## C.8 Practice in Writing Treatment Plans

> Write your report. Use the information on the data sheet. Invent information as needed.

> Data Sheet. Use these data to write your report on the opposite page. Use the correct headings.

Discrete trial procedure:

    Show the stimulus, ask a question, model the response, reinforce or give corrective feedback, record the response, represent the stimulus for the next trial.

Modeling, verbal praise, natural consequences

Five consecutively and correctly imitated responses: shift to evoked trials

Two incorrect responses on evoked trials: reinstate modeling

Training criterion: Ten consecutively correct, non-imitated responses for each target exemplar (phrase or sentence)

Intermixed probe procedure: Will consist of trained and untrained sentences; trained responses will be reinforced; untrained responses will not be.

Correct probe response rate calculated based only on responses given to untrained (probe) stimuli.

Ninety percent correct probe response rate: Shift training to another stimulus item, a more complex response topography, or another target behavior.

Probe criterion not met: Give more training on the same target behavior.

Eventually, train the target structures in conversational speech with social reinforcers.

*Treatment and probe procedures? (L1H)*

*Various training and probe criteria*

### C.8 Practice in Writing Treatment Plans

> Write your report. Use the information on the data sheet. Invent information as needed.

> Data Sheet. Use these data to write your report on the opposite page. Use the correct headings.

Teaching the mother to evoke and reinforce the target language structures at home

Initially, the mother observes sessions.

Then she learns to present stimulus items.

Then she learns to reinforce or give corrective feedback.

An older brother to be taught to reinforce target responses

---

Maintenance program (L1H)]

Training family members and others

> Write your report. Use the information on the data sheet. Invent information as needed.

> Data Sheet. Use these data to write your report on the opposite page. Use the correct headings.

Informal training in nonclinical settings (specify a few settings) | Training in informal settings

Recorded home samples for probe analysis; 90% correct production at home is the maintenance criterion. | Home samples

Additional training on other language structures to be determined later | Additional training

Signature lines
Student clinician
Client
Supervisor

### C.8 Practice in Writing Treatment Plans

> Write your report. Use the information on the data sheet. Invent information as needed.

## C.8.2. Brief Treatment Plan: *Fluency Disorder*

**Speech and Hearing Clinic**
**Eastern State University**
**Bedford, California**

> Data Sheet. Use these data to write your report on the opposite page. Use the correct headings.

| | |
|---|---|
| James Higginbothams, 27-year-old engineer | Who, how old, when, to where referred? |
| Self-referred | |
| Two speech samples; 23% and 25% dysfluency rate in conversational speech (part-word repetitions, sound prolongations, word and phrase interjections, and broken words) | What were the results of evaluation? (Summarize the disorder.) |
| Treatment was recommended | Was treatment recommended? |
| Prognosis judged to be good because of expressed high motivation for treatment | |
| Normal-sounding fluency with no more than 5% dysfluency rate in non-clinical settings | Final treatment objective? |
| Appropriate management of airflow (inhalation, a slight exhalation, sustained airflow), gentle phonatory onset, reduced speech rate with prolonged syllables, continuous phonation, and normal prosodic features | Target behaviors? (L1H) |

## C.8 Practice in Writing Treatment Plans

Write your report. Use the information on the data sheet. Invent information as needed.

> Data Sheet. Use these data to write your report on the opposite page. Use the correct headings.

Initial baserating in conversational speech

Training to begin at phrase and short sentence levels

Each target to be trained one at a time and then integrated

Instructions and modeling

Verbal reinforcement for the production of all target behaviors

Corrective feedback for incorrect responses and dysfluencies

Normal prosodic features to be trained when 2% or less dysfluency rate is sustained

Wife and a colleague to be trained in fluency maintenance; training in extraclinical situations

Self-monitoring skills to be trained

Home speech samples to evaluate maintenance of fluency

A schedule of follow-up; booster treatment

---

Treatment procedures? (L1H)

Signature lines

Student clinician

Client

Supervisor

## C.8 Practice in Writing Treatment Plans

Write your report. Use the information on the data sheet. Invent information as needed.

## C.8.3. Brief Treatment Plan: *Speech Sound Disorder*

**Valley Speech and Hearing Center**
**Nordstrom, Maine**

> Data Sheet. Use these data to write your report on the opposite page. Use the correct headings.

Beth Hazleton, 9 years of age

Speech sound disorder; omissions: (specify four to six phonemes); substitutions: (specify a few)

Treatment recommended

Mother to participate in treatment

Ninety percent correct production in conversational speech in extraclinical situations

Objective 1. Correct production in all word positions (specify) with 90% accuracy

Procedures: Instructions, demonstrations, modeling, visual feedback, shaping, verbal reinforcement, corrective feedback

Objective 2. Correct production in phrases and sentences

Procedures: Picture description and controlled conversation; modeling, reinforcement, corrective feedback

---

*Sidebar:*

Who, how old, when, to where referred? What were the results of evaluation? (Summarize the disorder.) Was treatment recommended?

Final treatment objective? **(Paragraph heading)**

Objectives? Procedures? **(Paragraph headings)**

Write your report. Use the information on the data sheet. Invent information as needed.

> Data Sheet. Use these data to write your report on the opposite page. Use the correct headings.

Objective 3. Correct production, conversational speech, varied audience

Procedures: Reinforcement, varied audience

Objective 4. Correct production in extraclinical situations

Procedures: Prompting and reinforcing correct production in extraclinical settings (specify)

Objective 5. Teaching the mother (*specify what you teach her*)

Procedures: Initial observation, recognition of the target responses, reinforcement, home treatment sessions, taped home samples to be submitted

Dismissal criterion, follow-up, booster treatment

---

**Paragraph headings** for objectives and procedures

Signature lines

Student clinician

Parent

Supervisor

### C.8 Practice in Writing Treatment Plans

> Write your report. Use the information on the data sheet. Invent information as needed.

## C.8.4. Brief Treatment Plan: *Child Language Disorder*

**Speech and Hearing Clinic**
**Southern State University**
**Johnstonville, Louisiana**

Data Sheet. Use these data to write your report on the opposite page. Use the correct headings.

Harold Ford, 5 years, 7 months; developmentally delayed

Says only six to eight words

No phrases, no sentences, no bound morphemes

Treatment was recommended

Correct production of 20 functional words or two-word phrases at 90% accuracy (invent words or phrases)

Baserates: 5% to 10% correct

Additional words

Expansion of single words into phrases and sentences

Bound morphemes (specify four)

---

Who, how old, when, to where referred?

What were the results of evaluation? (Summarize the disorder.)

Was treatment recommended?

Initial treatment objectives?
**Select a heading style**

Subsequent treatment objectives?
**Repeat the selected heading style**

> Write your report. Use the information on the data sheet. Invent information as needed.

> Data Sheet. Use these data to write your report on the opposite page. Use the correct headings.

Stimuli to include pictures and so forth (expand)

Clinician and the mother to evoke the target language structures

Initially, approximations accepted; subsequently, more accurate productions required

Verbal praise and natural reinforcers

Measurement of responses in each session

Training criterion: 90% accuracy across two sessions for words; then an intermixed probe to be conducted

Phrases formed out of words that meet the 90% accurate probe criterion

Similar progression for sentences (describe)

Home treatment sessions

Taped home samples to monitor home treatment

Subsequent treatment procedures

The same procedure described under initial treatment procedures

Additional words expanded into phrases and sentences

Teaching bound morphemes initially in words, which are later expanded into phrases and sentences

---

Initial treatment procedures?
**Repeat the selected heading style**

Subsequent treatment procedures
**Repeat the selected heading style**

Signature lines

Student clinician

Client

Supervisor

> Write your report. Use the information on the data sheet. Invent information as needed.

## C.8.5. Brief Treatment Plan: *Voice Disorder*

### The Sunshine Speech and Hearing Center
### Zingsville, Vermont

> Data Sheet. Use these data to write your report on the opposite page. Use the correct headings.

Thomas Benson, Jr., 28 years of age

Long history of high-pitched voice

Laryngologist has cleared for voice treatment


Treatment was recommended


Treatment targets

Vocal pitch judged appropriate for age and gender

Lowered pitch level in words, phrases, sentences, and conversational speech (write them as separate goals)

---

Who, how old, when, to where referred?

What were the results of evaluation? (Summarize the disorder.)

Was treatment recommended?

Use the format given in C.6.4. Brief Treatment Plan: Voice Disorder

**Select a heading style and use it consistently**

### C.8 Practice in Writing Treatment Plans

> Write your report. Use the information on the data sheet. Invent information as needed.

> Data Sheet. Use these data to write your report on the opposite page. Use the correct headings.

| | |
|---|---|
| Shaping lower-pitched voice through modeling and verbal feedback | **Treatment procedures**<br>**Use the selected heading style** |
| Starting with words and progressing to conversational speech | |
| Other procedures you select | |
| | |
| Ninety percent accuracy at each level of training | |
| Ninety percent probe criterion in natural settings | |
| Home samples to monitor voice at home | |
| | |
| Self-monitoring skills | |
| | |
| Teaching Ms. Moline Benson (the client's wife) to monitor and reinforce appropriate pitch at home and to conduct informal home treatment sessions | Teach family members and others |
| Home sample to evaluate the home treatment sessions | |
| Standard follow-up and booster treatment | |
| | Signature lines |
| | Student clinician |
| | Supervisor |
| | Client |

C.8 Practice in Writing Treatment Plans

> Write your report. Use the information on the data sheet. Invent information as needed.

## Note to Student Clinicians

Clinical supervisors tend to have their preferred formats for writing treatment plans. Talk to your supervisor before you write treatment plans for your clients.

# C.9. Progress Reports

Progress reports summarize the methods and results of treatment given during a specified period of time. In academic degree programs, progress reports are typically written at the end of a quarter or semester. In some university programs, progress reports also may be known as *final summaries*. In hospitals and private clinics, they are written according to a setting-specific policy. Generally, insurance companies and government or private agencies write them to support payment for services. In such cases, they may be written on a monthly basis. Progress reports are written invariably when the clients are dismissed from services.

Progress reports that students write under clinical practicum or internship are more likely to give additional information such as the number and duration of sessions and the clock hours of clinical practicum. Such information is not a part of reports that professional clinicians write.

Most progress reports are formal documents written for the file. In some settings, especially in hospitals and private clinics, progress reports may be written in the form of a letter to a referring physician or to a funding agency.

Formats used for progress reports vary across clinics. The reports that follow in this section show a few variations. For example, the first report on a fluency disorder refers the reader to a treatment plan in the folder and, therefore, does not summarize the procedures. Compared to the first report, the next report on an articulation disorder makes no mention of a treatment plan; instead, it summarizes the procedures and results (progress).

Student clinicians should consult their clinic director or clinical supervisor to find out the format adopted for the clinic or setting.

### C.9.1. Progress Report: *Treatment of Stuttering*

**University Speech and Hearing Clinic**
**Freemont University**
**Valleyville, California**

**Progress Report**

Name: Matt Dexter                                File Number: Rs92019
Date of Birth: January xx, xxxx                  Diagnosis: Stuttering
Address: Graves 312 B                            Date of Report: May xx, xxxx
City: Valleyville, CA 90710-3342                 Period Covered: xx/xx/xx to xx/xx/xx
Telephone Number: 555-3235                       Clinician: Meena Wong
Supervisor: Linda Hensley, Ph.D., CCC-SLP

**Clinic Schedule**

Sessions per week: 2                             Clock hr of individual therapy: 25
Length of sessions: 50 min                       Clock hr of group therapy: 0
Number of clinic visits: 24                      Total clock hr of therapy: 25

Matt Dexter, a 21-year-old male college student, was enrolled for his first semester of treatment at the University Speech and Hearing Clinic on February xx, xxxx. The presenting complaint was stuttering. An assessment done on February x, xxxx, had revealed a conversational dysfluency rate of 21% in the clinic. A home speech sample had revealed a dysfluency rate of 18.6%. He exhibited interjections, pauses, part-word and whole-word repetitions, silent and audible prolongations, pauses, revisions, and incomplete phrases.

Treatment began on February x, xxxx. An assessment report may be found in Mr. Dexter's folder.

**Summary of Treatment**

*Final Treatment Objective*

Maintenance of fluent speech with a dysfluency rate that does not exceed 5% in natural settings

*Target Behaviors*

Fluency skills described in the treatment plan were taught: appropriate management of airflow, gentle onset of phonation, reduced speech rate, continuous phonation, and normal prosodic features. Please see Mr. Dexter's file for his treatment plan for details.

*Treatment Procedures*

In two clinic baseline samples of conversational speech and a home baseline sample, Mr. Dexter's dysfluency rates were 22%, 21%, and 19%.

Initially, Mr. Dexter was taught the skills of fluent speech: nasal inhalation, minimal amount of oral exhalation prior to initiation of phonation, easy phonatory onset, and vowel prolongation. Therapy was started at the modeled word level and progressed to words, phrases, sentences, and conversational speech in the clinic. At each level, 98% fluency was required. Verbal reinforcement was provided on an $FR_1$ schedule. Corrective feedback was given for dysfluencies or failure to manage a target behavior. Mr. Dexter was then required to correctly repeat his utterance.

After Mr. Dexter had progressed to conversational speech, he was taught to chart his dysfluencies and failure to use a target behavior. Periodically, Mr. Dexter orally read printed stories and then summarized what he had read. Student observers periodically participated in treatment sessions to engage in conversation with the client.

Normal prosodic features were not targeted this semester, as the establishment of stutter-free speech was not completed.

Mr. Dexter's wife attended four treatment sessions, and a colleague of his attended two sessions. Both were taught to prompt Mr. Dexter to use the fluency skills and to reinforce him when he did.

## Progress

Two clinic probes and a home probe were obtained after the client began using the target fluency skills in conversational speech in the clinic (probes #1 and #2). Each probe consisted of 50 utterances sampled from the client's conversational speech. The results were as follows:

Probe #1: 15% dysfluent (Clinic Sample)

Probe #2: 12% dysfluent (Clinic Sample)

Probe #3: 10% dysfluent (Home Sample)

A final conversational speech sample containing 852 words in 102 utterances was obtained in the semester's final treatment session. This sample was obtained through a conversation with a student observer in the absence of the clinician. Results were as follows:

| **Dysfluency Types** | **Frequency** |
| --- | --- |
| Interjections | 23 |
| Pauses | 17 |
| Part-Word Repetitions | 1 |
| Whole-Word Repetitions | 3 |
| Phrase Repetitions | 2 |
| Sound Prolongations | 20 |
| Silent Prolongations | 6 |
| Incomplete Phrases | 2 |
| **Total Dysfluencies** | **74** |
| **Percent Dysfluency Rate** | **8.7** |

The results show that Mr. Dexter's fluency improved over the course of the semester. He was about 21% dysfluent at the beginning of treatment compared to 8.7% dysfluent at the end of the semester.

### *Recommendations*

Although Mr. Dexter's dysfluencies have decreased, he continues to exhibit difficulty in consistently managing the target behaviors. Therefore, it is recommended that Mr. Foxx continue to receive treatment next semester. The clinician should concentrate on the following:

1. Improved management of fluency skills
2. Generalization and maintenance of fluent speech

Submitted By _____
        Layang Chan, B.A.
        Student Clinician

Client's Signature _____ Date: _____
        Mr. Matt Dexter

Approved By _____
        Linda Hensley, Ph.D., CCC-SLP
        Speech-Language Pathologist
        Clinical Supervisor

## C.9.2. Progress Report: *Treatment of Speech Sound Disorder*

**Speech and Hearing Center**
**Henry Higgins Children's Hospital**
**Burlington, Vermont**

**Progress Report**

Period Covered: xx/xx/xxxx to xx/xx/xxxx

### Background Information

Joe Villa, a 6-year and 3-month-old boy, was seen for a speech and language evaluation at the Speech and Hearing Center of the Henry Higgins Children's Hospital on September xx, xxxx. Joe has an articulation disorder characterized mostly by omissions of /s/, /t/, /k/, /b/, and /l/ in the initial and final position of words. An articulation treatment program was recommended. He has received treatment at this facility for four months.

The final treatment objective for Joe was to produce the phonemes he omits with 90% accuracy in conversational speech in extraclinical situations.

### Progress

**Objective 1.** Correct production of /s/, /t/, /k/, /b/, and /l/ in word initial position with 90% accuracy

**Method and Results:** The target phoneme production in word initial positions was baserated on a set of modeled and evoked trials with 20 words for each phoneme. Joe's correct response rate ranged from 0 to 10%. Treatment was begun with the discrete trial procedure involving modeling, imitation, successive approximation, and immediate verbal feedback for correct and incorrect responses. Whenever necessary, the tongue positions were shown with the help of a mirror. Each target sound was trained to a criterion of 10 consecutively correct responses. When four words with a target sound met the training criterion, at least 10 probe words were presented to assess generalization.

Joe has met this training objective. His correct response rates on these phonemes in word initial positions varied between 95 and 100%.

**Objective 2.** Correct production of /s/, /t/, /k/, /b/, and /l/ in word final position with 90% accuracy

**Methods and Results:** The same procedures used to train the phonemes in the word initial position were used. Joe has met this objective. His correct response rates on the phonemes in word final position varied between 92 and 96%.

**Objective 3.** Production of the target sounds in phrases and sentences with 90% accuracy in all word positions

**Method and Results:** Joe's correct productions were initially reinforced in phrases that were prepared for training. Soon, he was asked to use the target words in sentences he formulated. Later, Joe's conversational speech was monitored to strengthen the correct production of the phonemes. Verbal reinforcement was used on an FR4 schedule.

Joe has met this objective as his correct production of the target phonemes in conversational speech varied between 90 and 95%.

**Objective 4.** The development and implementation of a home program to maintain the production of his new speech skills in natural settings with 90% accuracy

**Methods and Results**: Joe's parents, who attended most of the treatment sessions, were taught to recognize, prompt, and reinforce the correct production of target sounds. His parents were asked to hold home treatment sessions twice a week and to tape-record the sessions. These taped samples were analyzed to give feedback to the parents. Three conversational probes recorded at home have revealed a 90% correct response rate.

Overall, Joe has made excellent progress in producing the targeted sounds. All treatment objectives have been met. Therefore, it is recommended that Joe be dismissed from treatment. A follow-up assessment in three months is recommended.

Signed By _____
                Monica Mendoza, M.A., CCC-SLP
                Speech-Language Pathologist

### C.9.3. Progress Report: *Treatment of Child Language Disorder*

**University Speech and Hearing Center**
**Bellview University**
**Bellview, Washington**

### Progress Report

Client: William Shakespeare

Date of Birth: January xx, xxxx

Period Covered: xx/xx through xx/xx, xxxx

Clinician: Noah Webster

### Clinic Schedule

Sessions per week: 2

Clock hr of individual therapy: 25

Length of sessions: 40 min

Clock hr of group therapy: 0

Number of clinic visits: 24

Total clock hr of therapy: 25

William Shakespeare, a 7-year, 3-month-old boy, was assessed at the University Speech and Hearing Center of Bellview University for a language disorder. The assessment suggested that his language disorder primarily involved some syntactic structures and pragmatic functions. Treatment was recommended. He has received treatment for one semester. Please see his clinic file for an assessment report and a complete treatment program.

### Summary of Treatment

William was cooperative in most treatment sessions. The following treatment procedures and objectives were used.

#### Objective 1. Asking wh *questions*

William was taught to ask the following types of *wh* questions:

What do you mean?

What is it?

What are you doing?

What time is it?

What is your name?

**Methods and Results:** Baserating showed that William typically did not ask the target questions even when the situation demanded them. In a conversational role-playing situation, William was taught to ask the target questions. Conversational situations were created such that questions of the kind targeted would be appropriate. Conversation was manipulated in various ways to prompt the target question. For example, William was asked, "Do you live in a condo?" and the correct question was immediately modeled for him to imitate: "William, ask me *what do you mean*?" Or he was shown a picture he did not know anything about and immediately the question "What is it?" was modeled for him to imitate. When William imitated modeled questions or asked similar questions without modeling, the clinician correctly answered them. These answers and verbal praise for asking appropriate questions were the reinforcers.

When William's question-asking reached 90% accuracy, probes were conducted to assess generalized question-asking. The probe results showed that William learned to ask the targeted questions in untrained (probe) contexts with 90% accuracy.

### *Objective 2. Topic maintenance*

William was taught to maintain a topic of conversation for progressively increasing durations with 90% accuracy.

**Methods and Results:** Baserating showed that William typically changed the topic in less than a minute. He was taught to maintain a topic of conversation for progressively longer durations. One-minute increments were used. Starting with a duration of 1 min, he was taught to talk about the same topic for a maximum duration of 5 min. Every time he deviated from the topic, the clinician asked him to stop and prompted him to resume the target topic. He was periodically praised for continuing on the same topic.

William learned to maintain a topic of conversation for a minimum of 5 min. On certain probe topics, he continued to talk for up to 10 min.

### *Objective 3. Conversational turn taking*

William was taught to take appropriate conversational turns with 90% accuracy.

**Methods and Results:** During the baserating, William typically interrupted the clinician every 30 sec. He was initially asked to speak only when told, "It is your turn to talk." The clinician gave William his turn every 1 min or so. William also was taught to say, "It is your turn to talk" when he had spoken for a min or so. If he did not, he was asked to stop at the end of a sentence. The prompt "It is your turn to talk" was withdrawn in the later training sessions. If he interrupted, the clinician gave a hand signal to stop. This signal also was faded. In the last four sessions, a variable time interval of 1 to 3 min of talking before yielding the floor was allowed.

William learned to take conversational turns. On a final probe with no verbal or manual prompt, he took turns on the variable time schedule of 1 to 3 min of talking with 90% accuracy. Occasionally, he appropriately exceeded the range.

A final spontaneous language sample was analyzed to determine the need for further clinical services. The analysis revealed normal language use. Therefore, it is recommended that William be dismissed from treatment.

Signed By _____
        Noah Webster, B.A.
        Student Clinician

Client's Signature _____
        Mrs. Tara Shakespeare

Signed By _____
        Lakshmi Shanker, Ph.D., CCC-SLP
        Speech-Language Pathologist and Clinical Supervisor

## C.9.4. Progress Report: *Treatment of Voice Disorder*

### Sunshine Speech and Hearing Center
### Zingsville, Vermont

### Progress Report

| | |
|---|---|
| Name: Roshana Hersh | File Number: Axxcqxxx |
| Date of Birth: January xx, xxxx | Diagnosis: Voice Disorder |
| Address: 7915 Vishon | Date of Report: May xx, xxxx |
| City: Clovis, CA 93611 | Period Covered: April xx Through May xx, xxxx |
| Telephone Number: (xxx) xxx-xxxx | Clinician: Pero Boss |
| Supervisor: Moss Nero, M.A., CCC-SLP | |

Roshana Hersh, a 21-year-old female college student, was seen at the Sunshine Speech and Hearing Center on March xx, xxxx, for a voice evaluation. The evaluation suggested a pattern of vocal abuse associated with a persistent hoarseness of voice and low pitch. A treatment program to improve her voice quality was recommended. The assessment report and a description of her treatment program may be found in her clinical file.

### Treatment Targets

*Goal 1:*

Production of clear voice at least 90% of the time Roshana speaks by reducing the hoarseness of voice
    Objective 1a. Reduced amount of talking over the phone
    Objective 1b. Reduced amount of shouting at school

*Goal 2:*

Increased vocal pitch
    Objective 2a. Higher pitch at the level of words and phrases
    Objective 2b. Higher pitch at the level of conversational speech

### Treatment Procedures and Results

*Objectives 1a and 1b*

During the first week, the durations of Ms. Hersh's telephone conversation were baserated. The diary record she kept showed that Roshana spoke between 8 to 10 times over the phone each day and that the duration of her phone calls ranged from 10 to 20 min. Sixty percent of her phone calls typically exceeded 15 min.

    During the second week, Ms. Hersh was asked to reduce by 10% the amount of telephone conversation time. She continued to record the amount of time she spent talking over the phone. In subsequent weeks, she was asked to progressively decrease the amount of time spent on the telephone with a goal of reducing the duration by about 50%.

The frequency of shouting also was similarly baserated. On an average day, she tended to shout 8 to 10 times. Ms. Hersh was asked to reduce the frequency of shouting behavior in 10% decrements until the frequency approached zero.

Ms. Hersh made excellent progress in reducing the frequency and duration of phone calls and in reducing the frequency of shouting. At the end of the semester, her phone calls averaged from 3 to 7 min. Only an occasional phone call exceeded this range. Her shouting behavior was reduced to no more than two incidents per day. According to Ms. Hersh, her shouts are not as loud as they used to be.

## *Objectives 2a and 2b*

The Visi-Pitch was used to shape a higher pitch consistent with Ms. Hersh's gender and age. The treatment was started at the word and phrase level and moved to the conversational speech level.

Ms. Hersh's speaking fundamental frequency in the clinic increased from a baserate of 157 Hz to 200 Hz toward the end of the semester. However, she still reports a much lower pitch outside the clinic.

It is recommended that Ms. Hersh continue to receive voice therapy next semester. The emphasis should be on generalization and maintenance of appropriate target vocal characteristics in extraclinical situations. Ms. Hersh needs training in self-monitoring skills.

Signed By _____
      Pero Boss, B.A.
      Student Clinician

Client's Signature _____
      Ms. Roshana Hersh

Signed By _____    Date _____
      Moss Nero, M.A., CCC-SP
      Speech-Language Pathologist
      Clinical Supervisor

C.9 Progress Reports

## Note to Student Clinicians

Contact your clinic director to find out how progress reports vary in your clinic. Contact a private speech and hearing clinic to find out how clinicians there write progress reports they send to health insurance companies.

# C.10. Practice in Writing Progress Reports

## C.10.1. Progress Report: *Treatment of Stuttering*

**University Speech and Hearing Clinic**
**Freemont University**
**Valleyville, California**

**Progress Report**

Name: Winston Churchill                     File Number:

Date of Birth:                              Diagnosis: Stuttering

Address:                                    Date of Report:

City:                                       Period Covered:

Telephone Number:                           Clinician:

**Clinic Schedule**

Sessions per week:                          Clock hr of individual therapy:

Length of sessions:                         Clock hr of group therapy:

Number of clinic visits:                    Total clock hr of therapy:

---

Data Sheet. Use these data to write your report on the opposite page. Use the correct headings.

---

| | |
|---|---|
| Winston Churchill, 22 years of age | Who, how old, came to which clinic, and with what problem? |
| Stuttering since early childhood days; various ineffective treatments in the past | |
| Two conversational speech samples (9 and 11% dysfluency rate) | (Summarize the assessment data in one or two sentences.) |
| One reading sample (22% dysfluency rate) | |
| Received treatment for stuttering for one semester at the same facility; the same treatment as described next | Received treatment for what and for how long? |

C.10 Practice in Writing Progress Reports

> Write your report. Use the information on the data sheet. Invent information as needed.

> Data Sheet. Use these data to write your report on the opposite page. Use the correct headings.

*Select a heading style and use it consistently.*

Final treatment goal: Normal-sounding fluency in natural settings with less than 5% dysfluency rate (or any other objectives you select)

Two conversational speech baselines of 10 and 11% dysfluency or stuttering rate — Baselines

Airflow management (specify the components)
Gentle phonatory onset
Continuous phonation
Rate reduction through syllable stretching
Normal prosodic features

— Treatment targets

Modeling and imitation; controlled utterances; movement from words to phrases and conversational speech; verbal praise; corrective feedback for mismanagement of the target behaviors or for dysfluencies; 98% or better fluency at all stages; periodic probes with no treatment contingencies to assess generalized fluency; twice-a-week sessions of 50 minutes; dysfluencies and errors in target skills measured in all sessions

Roommate taught to prompt and reinforce the production of fluency skills in three treatment sessions.

— Treatment, probe, and measurement procedures

C.10  Practice in Writing Progress Reports

> Write your report. Use the information on the data sheet. Invent information as needed.

> Data Sheet. Use these data to write your report on the opposite page. Use the correct headings.

Results or Progress

Good progress: Dysfluency rates reduced to 5% in conversational probes in the clinic (two probe conversational speech samples), about 6 to 7% at home (one home speech sample).

Continued treatment recommended to further reduce the dysfluencies and to stabilize fluency in naturalistic settings through informal treatment in various nonclinical settings (specify a few).

Your name, degree, and title

Client's name

Your supervisor's name, degree, certification, and title

---

**Continue with the selected heading style**

What were the results? Recommendations

Signature lines

Student clinician

Client

Supervisor

### C.10 Practice in Writing Progress Reports

Write your report. Use the information on the data sheet. Invent information as needed.

## C.10.2. Progress Report: *Treatment of Speech Sound Disorder*

**University Speech and Hearing Center**
**Bloom, Illinois**

**Progress Report**

Name: Jimmy Jones                                File Number:

Date of Birth:                                            Diagnosis: Speech Sound Disorder

Address:                                                    Date of Report:

City:                                                           Period Covered:

Telephone Number:                                 Clinician:

**Clinic Schedule**

Sessions per week:                                   Clock hr of individual therapy:

Length of sessions:                                   Clock hr of group therapy:

Number of clinic visits:                            Total clock hr of therapy:

---

Data Sheet. Use these data to write your report on the opposite page. Use the correct headings.

---

| | |
|---|---|
| Jimmy Jones, 6 years, 7 months | Who, how old, came to which clinic, and with what problem? |
| Speech sound disorder<br>Omissions of initial and final /k, s, t, p, b/ | (Summarize the assessment data in one or two sentences.) |
| No prior treatment | Received treatment for what and for how long? |

### C.10 Practice in Writing Progress Reports

> Write your report. Use the information on the data sheet. Invent information as needed.

> Data Sheet. Use these data to write your report on the opposite page. Use the correct headings.

Treatment objective 1: Teaching the phonemes in word initial and final positions

Baserated: 0 to 5% correct response rate on evoked; 5 to 10% correct response rate on modeled trials

Treatment procedures: Modeling, imitation, successive approximation, visual feedback (phonetic placement); positive reinforcement for correct responses and corrective feedback for wrong responses

Training criterion: Ninety percent correct for any phoneme in any position

Probe criterion: Ninety-five percent correct (intermixed probe: trained and untrained words; reinforcement only for the trained words)

Met the probe criterion for initial and final positions

Production of phonemes in phrases and sentences

Probe: Ninety-five percent correct

Treatment objective 2: Production of target phonemes in phrases and sentences

The same training and probe criteria (specify)

Met the probe criterion for phrases and sentences

Treatment objective 3: Production of target phonemes in conversational speech

The same training and probe criteria (specify)

Did not meet the probe criterion (showed only 70% correct in conversational speech).

---

**Continue with the selected heading style**

Progress or Methods and Results

## C.10 Practice in Writing Progress Reports

> Write your report. Use the information on the data sheet. Invent information as needed.

> Data Sheet. Use these data to write your report on the opposite page. Use the correct headings.

**Continue with the selected heading style**

Development of a home treatment program for maintenance

Teaching the father to evoke and reinforce the phonemes in conversational speech at home

Additional treatment to obtain and stabilize correct productions in conversational speech at 90% accuracy

*Maintenance program*

*Recommendations*

*Signature lines*

Your name, degree, and title

*Student clinician*

The client's father's name

*Parent*

Your supervisor's name, degree, certification, and title

*Supervisor*

## C.10 Practice in Writing Progress Reports

> Write your report. Use the information on the data sheet. Invent information as needed.

## C.10.3. Progress Report: *Treatment of Child Language Disorder*

**University Speech and Hearing Center**
**Bellview University**
**Bellview, Washington**

**Progress Report**

Name: Tanya Tucker                     File Number:

Date of Birth:                          Diagnosis: Language Disorder

Address:                                Date of Report:

City:                                   Period Covered:

Telephone Number:                       Clinician:

**Clinic Schedule**

Sessions per week:                      Clock hr of individual therapy:

Length of sessions:                     Clock hr of group therapy:

Number of clinic visits:                Total clock hr of therapy:

---

Data Sheet. Use these data to write your report on the opposite page. Use the correct headings.

---

Tanya Tucker, 6 years and 8 months

Language disorders. Does not produce *ing*, auxiliary *is*, regular and irregular plurals, regular past tense, prepositions, and pronouns.

Two semesters of treatment on teaching functional words and expansion of words into phrases; has met most probe criteria on these.

> **Select a heading style and use it consistently**
>
> Who, how old, came to which clinic, and with what problem?
>
> Summarize the assessment data in one or two sentences.
>
> Received treatment for what and for how long?

> Write your report. Use the information on the data sheet. Invent information as needed.

> Data Sheet. Use these data to write your report on the opposite page. Use the correct headings.

Treatment targets: Present progressive *ing*, auxiliary *is*, and regular plural morpheme *s* (e.g., *books* and *cups*) in sentences during the current semester of treatment

**Use the selected heading style consistently**

Pictures to evoke the target structures

Training criterion: Ninety percent correct in words, phrases, and sentences

Probe criterion: Ninety percent correct on a set of 10 untrained words, and untrained words used in phrases and sentences

Twenty words, phrases, and sentences for each target. Baserate: 0 to 10% correct

Discrete trial training at the level of words, phrases, and sentences

Treatment procedures included stimulus presentation, appropriate question asking, modeling, reinforcement, and corrective feedback.

### C.10 Practice in Writing Progress Reports

Write your report. Use the information on the data sheet. Invent information as needed.

> Data Sheet. Use these data to write your report on the opposite page. Use the correct headings.

Results or Progress

Tanya made good progress in learning the language structures.

Met the probe criteria for words and phrases for all targets.

For sentences: Present progressive *ing*: Eight sentences trained; probe response rate: 90% correct probe response rate (thus has met the probe criterion)

Auxiliary *is*: Six sentences trained; 70% correct probe response rate

Regular plural *s* morpheme: four sentences trained; 80% correct probe response rate

Mother has received training in evoking and reinforcing the target structures at home.

A home sample showed: 87% correct for the *ing*; 65% for the auxiliary *is*; and 70% for the plural *s*

Recommendations:

Continued treatment on the auxiliary and the plural morpheme to meet the probe criterion

Training to be shifted to conversational speech level for the present progressive *ing*

Training on additional grammatic morphemes Tanya does not produce

Continue to promote home training

Your name, degree, and title

Parent's name

Your supervisor's name, degree, certification, and title

**Use the selected heading style consistently**

Signature lines

Student clinician

Parent

Supervisor

> Write your report. Use the information on the data sheet. Invent information as needed.

## C.10.4. Progress Report: *Treatment of Voice Disorder*

### The Sunshine Speech and Hearing Center
### Zingsville, Vermont

### Progress Report

| | |
|---|---|
| Name: Raj Mohan | File Number: |
| Date of Birth: | Diagnosis: Voice Disorder |
| Address: | Date of Report: |
| City: | Period Covered: |
| Telephone Number: | Clinician: |

### Clinic Schedule

| | |
|---|---|
| Sessions per week: | Clock hr of individual therapy: |
| Length of sessions: | Clock hr of group therapy: |
| Number of clinic visits: | Total clock hr of therapy: |

---

Data Sheet. Use these data to write your report on the opposite page. Use the correct headings.

---

Raj Mohan, 35 years of age

High school teacher

*Select a heading style and use it consistently*

Inadequate loudness; voice too soft; students complain; his voice gets tired; ENT report negative; no contraindications for voice therapy

No prior treatment

## C.10 Practice in Writing Progress Reports

> Write your report. Use the information on the data sheet. Invent information as needed.

**Data Sheet.** Use these data to write your report on the opposite page. Use the correct headings.

Treatment targets:

> Use the selected heading style consistently

Increased vocal loudness; adequate loudness for classroom teaching as rated by the clinician and his students across a minimum of four teaching sessions

Baseline of loudness established by: The clinician's and students' rating of loudness on a 5-point rating scale in three class periods

Recording the frequency of student requests for louder speech (invent baseline data)

Treatment procedures

Included verbal reinforcement of progressively louder speech

Masking noise to increase vocal intensity (Lombard effect)

Visi-Pitch feedback to shape progressively louder voice

## C.10 Practice in Writing Progress Reports

> Write your report. Use the information on the data sheet. Invent information as needed.

> Data Sheet. Use these data to write your report on the opposite page. Use the correct headings.

Results or Progress

Excellent progress; clinician's rating of loudness in three class periods showed adequate loudness; no student requests for louder speech in the three observed class periods (compare this to baseline data)

Schedule a follow-up in 3 months to assess maintenance of adequate loudness

Recommendations: Dismissal from treatment; 3 and 6 month follow-up and booster treatment if necessary

Your name, degree, and title — Student clinician

Client's name — Client

Supervisor's name, degree, certification, and title — Supervisor

**Use the selected heading style consistently**

## C.10 Practice in Writing Progress Reports

> Write your report. Use the information on the data sheet. Invent information as needed.

## Note to Student Clinicians

Obtain samples of progress reports from your clinic director. Practice writing reports on other disorders of communication.

# Selected References

## Sources on Clinical Report Writing

The clinical assessment, treatment, and progress reports outlined in this coursebook are based on information presented in the textbooks listed here. If you are not sure of clinical terms, assessment techniques, or treatment procedures, consult the following sources. You also may use textbooks you used in courses on clinical methods, including diagnostic procedures. Ask your clinic director, clinic supervisors, or course instructors to recommend other sources.

Hegde, M. N. (1998). *Treatment procedures in communicative disorders* (3rd ed.). Austin, TX: Pro-Ed.

Hegde, M. N., & Freed, F. (2017). *Assessment of communication disorders in adults* (2nd ed.). San Diego, CA: Plural.

Hegde, M. N., & Pomaville, F. (2017). *Assessment of communication disorders in children* (3rd ed.). San Diego, CA: Plural.

Hegde, M. N. (in press, 2018). *Hegde's PocketGuide to assessment in speech-language pathology* (4th ed.). San Diego, CA: Plural.

Hegde, M. N. (in press, 2018). *Hegde's PocketGuide to treatment in speech-language pathology* (4th ed.). San Diego, CA: Plural.

Hegde, M. N., & Davis, D. (2010). *Clinical methods and practicum in speech-language pathology* (5th ed.). Clifton Park, NY: Thomson Delmar Learning.

## Selected Books on Writing

Many excellent sources on general, technical, and professional writing are available. Besides the APA *Manual*, students should consult a few of the following books.

American Medical Association. (2007). *American Medical Association manual of style* (10th ed.). Baltimore, MD: Williams & Wilkins.

American Psychological Association. (2010). *Publication manual of the American Psychological Association* (6th ed.). Washington, DC: Author.

American Psychological Association. (2012). *APA style guide to electronic references* (6th ed.). Washington, DC: Author.

Bates, J. D. (2000). *Writing with precision*. New York, NY: Penguin Books.

Burchfield, R. W. (1996). *The new Fowler's modern English usage* (3rd ed.). New York, NY: Oxford University Press.

Butterfield, J. (2015). *Fowler's dictionary of modern English usage* (4th ed.). New York, NY: Oxford University Press.

Follett, W. (1998). *Modern American usage: A guide* (1st Rev. ed.). New York, NY: Hill & Wang.

Kane, T. S. (1988). *The new Oxford guide to writing*. New York, NY: Oxford University Press.

Kirszner, L. G., & Mandell, S. R. (2002). *The Holt handbook* (6th ed.). New York, NY: Harcourt College.

Modern Language Association. (2016). *MLA handbook for writers of research papers, theses, and dissertations* (8th ed.). New York, NY: Author.

Morris, W., & Morris, M. (1992). *Harper dictionary of contemporary usage* (2nd ed.). New York, NY: Harper.

Newman, E. (1976). *A civil tongue.* New York, NY: Bobbs-Merrill.

Strunk, W., Jr., & White, E. B. (1999). *The elements of style* (3rd ed.). Boston, MA: Pearson.

Thomas, F., & Turner, M. (1994). *Clear and simple as the truth: Writing classic prose.* Princeton, NJ: Princeton University Press.

University of Chicago Press. (2010). *The Chicago manual of style* (16th ed.). Chicago, IL: Author.

Zinsser, W. (1980). *On writing well: An informal guide to writing nonfiction* (2nd ed.). New York, NY: Harper & Row.

# Glossary

In composing your scientific and professional writing, use the terms as defined in this glossary or *as defined by your instructor* or *clinical supervisor*. Also, consult books on clinical methods that your instructors and clinical supervisors recommend.

**Abstract:** A brief summary of a research paper manuscript printed on a separate page (page 2); in the published articles, the abstract is printed on the title page, below the authors' names and their affiliation.

**Ampersand:** The character & used in place of *and;* used in reference lists to connect names; not used in regular text except for inside parentheses for multiple authors.

**Appendixes:** Materials placed at the end of a paper or a chapter to give additional details on selected aspects of what is written in the body of the paper; the preferred plural spelling is appendixes, not appendices.

**Arabic Numerals:** The widely used numbering system (e.g., 0, 1 through 9) in many parts of the world including most countries in Europe and the United States; also known as the Hindu-Arabic numerals because of their origin in India; contrasted with roman numerals; the terms *arabic* and *roman*, when used to refer to number systems, are not capitalized except when they start a sentence.

**Assessment:** Clinical procedures designed to diagnose a disorder or evaluate a client's existing and nonexisting communicative behaviors, communicative problems, and potential factors associated with these problems.

**Baselines:** Measures of communicative or other behaviors before the treatment is started; they help evaluate the client's improvement in treatment; they may be taken on evoked and modeled trials or in conversational speech. Baselines and baserates can both be nouns, but only baserate can be used as a verb (baserated, not baselined). Baselines of various communicative behaviors may be established by either using discrete trials or by taking conversational speech and language samples. See **Discrete Baseline Trial**.

**Bibliography:** A list of all relevant publications on a given topic or field of research; much more comprehensive than a reference list; not attached to a paper or a chapter; may be free-standing; the format may be the same as that of a reference list.

**Block Quotation:** A quotation of 40 or more words reproduced verbatim from another source, including the author's own words published elsewhere; does not contain quotation marks and is set as a separate paragraph with a rigidly specified format.

**Booster Treatment:** Treatment given anytime after the client is dismissed from the original treatment to maintain clinically established skills; given after a follow-up assessment indicates a need for additional treatment.

**CD-ROM:** Compact Disk Read-Only Memory; a compact disk that stores a vast amount of information, including graphics and sound.

**Clichés:** Popular, overused, and dull expressions.

**Conditioned Generalized Reinforcers:** Tokens, money, and such other reinforcers that are effective in a wide range of conditions and are not subjected satiation effect; in therapy, tokens may be exchanged for a variety of back-up reinforcers.

**Conditioned Reinforcers:** Events that reinforce behaviors because of past learning experiences; same as secondary reinforcers.

**Continuous Reinforcement:** A schedule in which the clinician reinforces all correct responses.

**Conversational Turn Taking:** Switching from the role of a speaker to that of a listener and vice versa; a conversational skill taught to persons with language disorders.

**Copyediting:** Editing of a manuscript by the publisher's editor for clarity, style, coverage, and so forth; the editor also may process the manuscript for typesetting.

**Corrective Feedback:** Consequences that decrease behaviors; for example, saying "No," "Not correct," "Wrong," and so forth when a client's response is unacceptable.

**Criteria:** Rules to make various clinical judgments including when to model, when to stop modeling, and when a behavior is trained (e.g., the target is 90% correct production of the regular plural *s* in words).

**Diagnostic Report:** A report on the methods and results of an assessment done on a client with a disorder or disease; description of diagnostic procedures and their results; also known as an assessment report.

**Discrete Baseline Trial:** An opportunity to produce a target response when no reinforcers or corrective feedback is given; may be modeled or evoked; steps are the same as those described under *discrete training trial, evoked* and *discrete training trial, modeled* except that no reinforcement or corrective feedback is provided for the correct and incorrect responses, respectively; the client may be periodically reinforced for being cooperative and responsive; used to determined the target response rate before introducing treatment.

**Discrete Training Trial, Evoked:** An opportunity to produce a target response when the clinician does not model that response; in administering an evoked trial, the clinician:

1. Places the stimulus item in front of the client, or demonstrates the action or event with the help of objects.
2. Asks the predetermined question.
3. Waits a few seconds for the client to respond.

4. If the client's response is correct, reinforces it immediately by verbal praise and any other potential reinforcer.
   5. If the client's response is incorrect, immediately gives corrective feedback.
   6. Records the response on the recording sheet.
   7. Pulls the stimulus item toward herself, or removes it from the client's view.
   8. Waits a few seconds to mark the end of the trial.
   9. Initiates the next trial.

**Discrete Training Trial, Modeled:** An opportunity to produce a target response when the clinician models that response; in administering a modeled trial, the clinician:

   1. Places the stimulus item in front of the client, or demonstrates the action or event with the help of objects.
   2. Asks the predetermined question.
   3. Immediately models the correct response.
   4. Waits a few seconds for the client to respond.
   5. If the client's response is correct, reinforces it immediately by verbal praise and any other potential reinforcer.
   6. If the client's response is incorrect, immediately gives corrective feedback.
   7. Records the response on the recording sheet.
   8. Pulls the stimulus item toward herself, or removes it from the client's view.
   9. Waits a few seconds to mark the end of the trial.
   10. Initiates the next trial.

**Electronic Editing:** Revising manuscript in such a way as to show the original and subsequent versions of the document; interactive method of manuscript processing by two or more individuals who review, comment, and respond to each other's revisions and comments.

**Electronic Proofreading:** Reading and correcting typeset manuscripts; typically in the PDF format.

**Electronic Manuscript Submission:** Preparation and submission of manuscripts as computer files, not as printed papers, usually attached to e-mails; journal articles and conference presentations typically submitted on a dedicated website maintained by the journal or an organization.

**E-mail (e-mail):** Electronic mail; sending messages electronically, via a network of computers.

**Euphemism:** Hiding negative meanings by positive-sounding words. For example, the term *residentially challenged* is a positive-sounding term for the *homeless*.

**Evoked Trial:** A structured opportunity to produce a response when the clinician does not model; presenting a picture and asking a question (e.g., "What is this?") is an example of an evoking trial.

**Exemplar:** A response that illustrates a target behavior (e.g., *These are two cups* is an exemplar of the regular plural *s*).

**Fading:** A method of reducing the controlling power of a stimulus while still maintaining the response.

**Fixed Interval Schedule:** An intermittent schedule of reinforcement in which a response produced after a fixed duration is reinforced.

**Fixed Ratio Schedule:** An intermittent schedule of reinforcement in which a certain number of responses are required to earn a reinforcer.

**Flush-left:** Typing the first character flush with the left margin, with no indentation.

**Follow-up:** Probe or assessment of response maintenance after dismissal from treatment; usually involves taking a new speech and language sample to assess the production of previously taught responses or skills.

**Footers:** A feature of computer word processors; a full or abbreviated title of a paper or a chapter automatically printed at the bottom of a page; may contain other information such as the chapter number, time and date of printing, and the author name; may be flush-left, centered, or right-aligned; not used in the APA style.

**FTP:** File Transfer Protocol; electronic means of transferring data from one computer to another via a network of computers.

**Functional Outcome:** Generalized, broader, and socially and personally meaningful effects of treatment; an overall improvement in communication between clients, their families, and their caregivers.

**Generalized Production of Target Responses:** Production of responses when the treatment procedure is not in effect; for example, the clinician may take a speech sample without implementing any treatment procedures to see if a child who has been taught various language structures uses them; this procedure of assessing generalized production is called a probe.

**Headers:** A feature of computer word processors; an abbreviated or full title of a paper or a chapter automatically printed on top of each page of a manuscript; may contain additional information including the author name and time and date of printing; depending on the style used, may be flush left, centered, or right-aligned; in the APA style, abbreviated and typed right-aligned; contrasts with *footers*.

**Headings:** Subtitles within a paper or a chapter that suggest the subtopic that follows; classified into levels (e.g., level 1 and level 2 headings); not to be confused with a title, headers, page headers (of a manuscript), or running heads.

**IEPs:** Individual Educational Plans for children with disabilities or special needs; typically written in educational settings; similar to target behaviors and treatment procedures specified in clinical settings.

**IFSPs:** Individualized Family Service Plans developed for infants and toddlers and their family members; typically written in educational settings.

**Imitation:** Learning in which responses take the same form as their stimuli; modeling provides the stimuli; often necessary in the initial stages of treatment.

**Informant:** A person who gives case history and related information to the clinician; it may be the client himself or herself or another person (e.g., a family member).

**Initial Response:** The first, simplified component of a target response used in shaping.

**Instructions:** Verbal stimuli that gain control over other persons' actions; description of how to perform certain actions; often given before modeling a skill for the client.

**Intermediate Response:** Responses other than the initial and final, used in shaping.

**Intermittent Reinforcement:** Reinforcing only some responses or responses produced with some delay between reinforcers.

**Intermixed Probes:** Procedures of assessing generalized production by alternating trained and untrained stimulus items; typically administered on discrete trials; one trial involves a previously trained stimulus (e.g., the picture of *two cups,* used in training the plural *s*), and the next trial involves an untrained (novel) stimulus (e.g., the picture of *two books,* not used in training); correct responses given to untrained stimuli are counted to calculate the percentage correct probe response rate. See also **Probe** and **Pure Probes.**

**Internet:** A high-speed network of computers linked to transfer data from one computer to another; computers may be linked locally, nationally, and internationally; they share standard communication protocols.

**Maintenance Strategy:** Extension of treatment to natural settings; a collection of methods to help maintain clinically established skills over time; includes such procedures as teaching the client to self-monitor his or her behaviors and training the significant others to prompt and reinforce those behaviors in natural settings.

**Manual Guidance:** Physical guidance provided to shape a response; gently guiding a child's tongue tip toward the alveolar ridge with a tongue depressor to help the child produce a speech sound is an example of manual guidance; taking the client's hand and pointing to a correct picture is another example.

**Mean Length of Utterance (MLU):** A measure of language development; measured as the number of morphemes or words in each utterance and averaged across a collection of utterances.

**Modeled Trial:** An opportunity to imitate a response when the clinician models it; see **Discrete Trial, Modeled.**

**Modeling:** The clinician's production of the target response the client is expected to learn; used to teach imitation (e.g., the clinician might show a picture of a boy running and ask *"What is the boy doing?"* and immediately model the response by saying, *"Say the boy is running."*).

**Mood:** In grammar, mood refers to various verb forms that indicate whether implied or expressed actions are more or less likely; indicative mood expresses factual statements; subjunctive mood suggests uncertainty; and imperative mood suggests a command or request.

**Negative Reinforcers:** Aversive events that are removed, reduced, postponed, or prevented by specific responses; such responses then increase in frequency. See also **Positive Reinforcers**.

**Online:** A format of storing information that can be retrieved in an interactive manner; many journals now are online, meaning that they can be searched through the Internet.

**Operational Definitions:** Scientific definitions that describe how what is defined is measured; clinical treatment targets should be defined operationally (e.g., "I will teach language competence" is not an operational description of a target; "I will teach the following four grammatical morphemes in sentences" followed by a list, is).

**Orofacial Examination:** A visual examination of the oral and facial structures to detect gross abnormality; includes several tasks (such as producing certain vowels, moving the tongue, lifting the soft palate) to assess functional integrity of the oral and facial structures; also known as oral-peripheral examination.

**Page Header:** A brief header printed on each page of a research article (including the title page) except for those containing figures; consists of two or three words taken from the title of the paper and printed on the upper-right corner above or five spaces left of the page number; not to be confused with the running head.

**Parallelism:** Expressing similar ideas or a series of ideas in similar forms; expressing similar ideas or a series of ideas in different forms violates parallelism, resulting in nonparallel constructions.

**Parenthetic Constructions:** Phrases within sentences that express ideas that are not integral to those sentences; enclosed within parentheses.

**PDF:** Portable Document Format; a method of converting documents prepared on various computer platforms and operating systems into a single format; when PDFs are exchanged across computers, the original and the converted formats are retained.

**Peer Training:** Training peers of clients to evoke and reinforce target behaviors in natural settings; a maintenance strategy.

**Positive Reinforcers:** Events that, when presented immediately after a response is made, increase the future probability of that response. See also **Negative Reinforcers**.

**Pragmatic Features:** Aspects of language use in social contexts; targets of language treatment; pragmatic language targets for treatment include skills such as conversational turn-taking and topic maintenance.

**Primary Reinforcers:** Unconditioned reinforcers whose effects do not depend on past learning (e.g., food).

**Probe:** Procedure to assess generalized production of responses. See also **Intermixed Probes** and **Pure Probes**.

**Probe Criterion:** A rule that says that a trained response is satisfactorily produced without the treatment variables; for example, *95 percent fluency maintained in conversational speech when the clinician does not reinforce or prompt the target fluency* describes a probe criterion.

**Prompts:** Special stimuli that increase the probability of a response; prompts may be verbal or nonverbal; similar to hints.

**Proofs:** Also known as page proofs; the typeset manuscript sent to the author for final review; previously printed, and currently, in the PDF format.

**Pure Probes:** Procedures for assessing generalized production with only untrained stimulus items; contrasted with intermixed probes in which trained and untrained stimuli are alternated; for example, in administering pure probes, a clinician may present 20 untrained pictures that show plural objects to assess whether the child will produce the plural *s* without reinforcement.

**Reference List:** A list of all and only the works cited in the body of text; follows a prescribed format; always attached to a paper, a chapter, or an entire book; not free-standing; not to be confused with a bibliography.

**Reinforcers:** Events that follow behaviors and thereby increase the future probability of those behaviors. See also **Positive** and **Negative Reinforcers**.

**Response Cost:** A method of directly reducing an undesirable behavior by presenting a reinforcer for a desirable (alternative) behavior (e.g., fluent speech) and withdrawing a reinforcer for every undesirable behavior (e.g., stuttered speech).

**Right-Justification:** Printing lines to align with the right margin, as in most printed books; when computer-printed, the words may have uneven spaces between them; not accepted in the APA style.

**Running Head:** An abbreviated title of a research paper printed flush-left at the top of the title page, but below the page header; printed in all capitals; it does not exceed 50 character spaces including letters, punctuation marks, and spaces between letters.

**Schedules of Reinforcement:** Different patterns of reinforcement that generate different patterns of responses; includes such schedules as continuous reinforcement (every response is reinforced) and intermittent reinforcement (some responses are not reinforced).

**Self-Control:** A behavior that monitors other behaviors of the same person; a maintenance strategy; clients who are taught to count their errors, for example, have learned to monitor their responses.

**Serial Comma:** The comma that is used in a series of similar elements including before *and* and *or*, as in *clients, their families, and employers; roses, gardenias, or magnolias.*

**Shaping:** A method of teaching nonexistent responses that are not even imitated. The responses are simplified and taught in an ascending sequence. Also known as successive approximations.

**Significant Others:** People who are important in the lives of clients; includes family members, peers, colleagues, and teachers; training them in prompting and reinforcing a client's target behavior is a maintenance strategy.

**Social Reinforcers:** A variety of conditioned reinforcers, which include verbal praise.

**Subscript:** A character or a number printed lower than the rest of the printed line; the 1 in $X_1$ is a subscript character.

**Superscript:** A character or a number printed higher than the rest of the printed line; the D in $S^D$ is a superscript character.

**Targets:** Behaviors a client is taught; communicative skills that are trained.

**Terminal Response:** The final response targeted in shaping.

**Time-out:** A period of nonreinforcement imposed response-contingently; the typical effect is reduced rate of that response.

**Title:** The name given to a paper or a chapter; printed on the title page; repeated on every page of a book chapter; printed, in an abbreviated form, on all pages of a research paper; not to be confused with headings in a paper or chapter.

**Tokens:** Objects that are earned during treatment and exchanged later for back-up reinforcers.

**Topic Maintenance:** Talking on a single topic for an extended period of time; a language skill taught to persons with language disorders.

**Training Criterion:** A rule that says that a given target response has been trained; for example, 90% correct responses over a block of trials for a given target response may mean that the response has been trained.

**Treatment:** In communicative disorders, it is the management of contingent relations between antecedents, responses, and consequences; it is a rearrangement of communicative relationships between a speaker and his or her listener.

**Trial:** A structured opportunity to produce a response; see **Discrete Training Trial, Evoked** and **Discrete Training Trial, Modeled**.

**Variable Interval Schedule:** An intermittent reinforcement schedule in which the time duration between reinforcers is varied around an average.

**Variable Ratio Schedule:** An intermittent reinforcement schedule in which the number of responses needed to earn a reinforcer is varied around an average.

**Vocal Wetness:** An impression that the voice is wet, often noticed in patients with dysphagia and is due to pharyngeal residue of food or liquid.

**World Wide Web (WWW):** A vast structure of interconnected computers that stores electronic files of data that can be retrieved; information is transmitted across the Internet; a graphical environment for creating, storing, and transferring information.

# Index

# A

Abbreviations, 180–185
    ampersand and, 2–3
    first time use, 180
    hyphens and, 179
    Latin, 182–183
    parenthesis and, 180–181
    period, using correctly, 184–185
    plural, 184–185
    starting a sentence with, 180–181
    units of measurement, 184–185
Abrupt break, 22
Absolute possessive pronouns, 12
Abstract, 228–229
    page, 160
Accept
    and except, 124–125
Active voice, 56–57
Adjective, 38–39
    as participial phrase, 40
Adobe Acrobat Professional, 247, 259–262
Adobe Acrobat Reader, 260
Adult client report, outline of, 268–269
Advocacy groups, citation from, 212
Affect
    and effect, 124
Agreement, rules for, 24–31
Allusion
    and illusion, 126
Alphabetical,
    order of authors within parentheses, 204–205
    suffixes, 202–203
Alternate
    and alternative, 126
Alternative
    and alternate, 126
American Psychological Association (APA), 143
American Speech-Language-Hearing Association (ASHA), 143
    print journals, 248–249

Ampersand (&), 2–3
    joining multiple authors with, 200–201
Analysis (study), 132–133
Anatomy of a diagnostic report, 270–275
And, joining multiple names with, 200–201
And/or, 126
Antecedents, 34–35 (*see also*, Pronouns)
*APA Manual*, 143–144, 170, 175, 179–180, 208, 213, 241, 245–246, 434
APA Style Guide to Electronic References, 213–215
Aphasia and apraxia sample diagnostic report, 284–287
Apostrophe, 2–3
    with abbreviations,
    with plurals, 6–8
    with possessives, 12–13
    used unnecessarily, 4
Appendixes, 16, 438
Appositives, 36–37
Arabic numerals, 186–187
Articulation disorders (*see* Speech sound disorders)
Author citations in text, 194–211 (*see also* Reference list)
    classical works, 208
    different first authors with the same surname, 200
    initials, adding to last names, 200
    last name citation, 194
    multiple authors, joining with *and* or &, 200
    multiple authors within parentheses, alphabetical order, 204
    multiple works of the same author, 202
    multiple works of the same author, published in the same year, 202
    no author or anonymous author, 206
    secondary sources, 204
    six or more authors, 196
    specific parts of a source, 210
    three to five authors, 196
    two authors, 194

## Index

works of multiple authors published in the same year, 198
year of publication in parenthetical text, 210

## B

Baseline
   and baserate, 128
Basic rules of usage, 2–41
Because
   and since, 138
Beginning of text, 161
Bias, writing without, 145–155
   without gender bias, 146
   without prejudicial reference to disabilities, 148
   without prejudicial reference to ethnic and racial background, 150
   without prejudicial reference to sexual orientations, 152
   use of appropriate gender identity terms, 154
Bibliography, vs. reference list, 216
Block quotation, 112, 178
Boldface, 163, 164, 165, 166, 168
Books and book chapters, 230–232
   capitalization of, 174
   edited and chapters in edited, 232
   editorial process of, 254–258
   italicizing the titles of, in the body of text, 174
   italicizing the titles of, in the reference list, 174
   manuscripts, 250
   review and revision of, 256–258
Brackets, 110, 114, 226, 228
Break, abrupt, 23
Brief treatment plans, 353–368, 369–394
Broad outline, research paper, 42
Bulleted lists, parallelism in, 88

## C

Capitalization, 150, 171–173
   book and article titles, 171
   first words, 171
   headings, 172
   journal names, 171
   nouns followed by a number, 173
   words in headings, 162
   words that contain four words, 162
Child language disorder, 306–319, 358–360, 364, 370–377, 401–402, 420–425
   brief treatment plan for, 358–359
   individualized educational programs for, 364
   practice writing diagnostic report, 306–319
   practice writing progress reports, 420–425
   practice writing brief treatment plan, 386–389
   progress reports, 401–402
   sample diagnostic report, 306–319
Citations, reference. *See* Author citations in text, and Reference list
Class paper title page, 158
Clause, joining them with a semicolon, 22
   dependent, 22
   independent, 22
Cliché, avoiding, 122
Colloquial or informal expressions, avoiding, 122
Comma, 18–21
   serial, 18–19
Commonly misused words and phrases, 124–138
Composition, basic rules of, 42–122
Concise writing, 54–84
Concrete language, 62
Conference proceedings, published as a book, 234
Conjunctions, 200, 202,
   ampersand, 2
   joining multiple author names with, 200
Contractions, 12
   distinguishing from possessives, 12
   avoiding as colloquial or informal, 122
Convention presentation, 228, 262
   unpublished, 234

Copyediting, 255–258
Copyeditor, 255–256
Copyedited manuscripts, review of, 256–258
Criteria, as a plural, 14
Cultural factors, 146
Currency of information, 212

## D

Diagnostic reports, 266–347 (*see also* Sample diagnostic reports)
    anatomy of, 270–275
    elements of, 265
    formats of, 265–275
    outline of, 266–269
    practice writing, 291–347
    samples of, 287–290
Daily newspapers, referencing, 228
Dangling modifiers, avoiding misplaced, 90
    participial, 40
Dash, 22
Declarative statement, as sentence fragments, 36
Digital Object Identifier (DOI), 214
Disabilities, writing without prejudicial reference to, 148–149
Discussion, in research reports, 241, 245
Disproved, usage of, 136
Double quotation marks, 108, 112, 206, 228

## E

Edited books, citation format, 232
Editorial process, for electronic submissions, 253–258
Educational programs, individualized, 363–368
Effect
    and affect, 124
    and impact, 128
Electronic manuscripts, 247–262
    book and book chapters, 249
    copy editing, 255
    editorial process of, 253
    editorial process of book manuscripts, 254
    editorial process of journal articles, 253
    evolving practices, 247
    general guidelines on, 251
    print and online journals, 247
    print journals of the American Speech-Language-Hearing Association, 248
    preparation, 247–253
    review and revision of copyedited, 256
    revision of manuscripts, 255
    review task bar on computer screens, 257
    submission to conventions and conferences, 249
Electronic proof reading, 259–262
    page proofs, 259
    PDF documents, 259–260
    proof reading PDF versions, 261–262
Electronic sources, referencing
    general guidance, 213–215
Elicit
    and evoke, 130
    and illicit, 130
Ellipsis marks
    to show changes in quotations, 114
E-mail, 255, 261, 440
Em dash, 22, 179
Empirical reports
    heading levels for, 162
    writing sections of, 241–246
Encyclopedia, online, 213
Et al., 182
    adding to works with three to five authors, 196
    adding to works with six or more authors, 196
Ethnic background, writing without prejudicial reference to, 150–151
Euphemism, avoiding, 82
Evaluation reports (*see* Diagnostic reports)
Evidence, 136
Evoke
    and elicit, 130

Except
  and accept, 124
Expressions, parenthetic, 20

## F

Farther
  and further, 132
Final summaries, 395
First, use of, 138
Focus
  and analysis, 132
Former, 136
Fragments, sentence, 36
Fresh language, use of, 122
Further
  and farther, 132

## G

Gender bias, (*see also* Bias, writing without)
  writing without, 146
Government agencies, referencing reports from, 236

## H

Hanging indents, 222
*He* or *she*, usage, 24, 94, 146
Headers and footers, 251
Headings, 162–166
  and subheadings, 243, 251
  boldfaces for, 168
  double spacing, 170
  capitalizing, 172
  indentations for, 178
  levels of, 163–166
  numbers in, 192
  within the text, 162
Host name, in URLs, 214
http (hypertext transfer protocol), 214
Hyphenation, 175–176

  creating an *em dash* with, 179
  hyphenated compounds, 173
  misuse of, 177
  overuse of, 177
  serving as a minus sign, 179

## I

-*ics* terms, correct usage, 120
Ideas, related in paragraphs, 46
Idioms, 122
IEPs, 363–368
Illicit
  and elicit, 130
Illusion
  and allusion, 126
Impact
  and effect, 128
Incidence
  and prevalence, 134
Indentation, 178, 264
Independent clause, 20
  joining, 22
Individualized educational programs, 363
  IEP: Treatment of child language disorder, 364
  IEP: Treatment of fluency disorder, 367
  IEP: Treatment of speech sound disorder, 365
  IEP: Treatment of voice disorder, 366
In press, 202, 224
Inter-
  and intra, 134
Internet, 212
  online journals, 248–249
  quoting the sources from, 116
  referencing electronic sources available on, 213–215
  referencing online oriented reference works, 236
  unpublished articles, theses, and dissertations retrieved from, 238

Interruptions, setting them off with dashes, 22
Intra-
    and inter, 134
Introduction
    untitled, 162
    to research papers, 242
Islands of quotations, 100
Italicization, 174
    book titles and journal names, 106, 446
    level 4 headings, 165
    level 5 headings, 166
    terms in the body of text, 174
    to add emphasis, 114

## J

Jargon, avoiding, 80
Journal articles
    editorial process, 248–249
    format for in reference lists, 224

## L

Language
    definite, specific, and concrete, 62–63
    fresh, use of, 122
Language disorders, *see* Child language disorder
Later, 136
    and latter, 137
Latter
    and later, 136
Line spacing, single, double, or triple, 170
List, maintaining parallelism in, 88

## M

Magazines and newspaper articles, referencing, 228
Margins, 156

Materials, subsection of a research paper, 243–244
Method, section of a research paper, 243
*Merriam-Webster's Collegiate Dictionary*, 218
Modifiers,
    back-to-back, 192
    dangling, avoiding, 91
    misplaced, avoiding, 90–92
Monograph, reference format, 226
Mood, grammatical, shift in avoiding, 94
MS Word, editing features, 256–258

## N

Negative comments, making them directly, 58
Newspaper articles and magazines, referencing, 226
Nonparenthetical written sentences, 182
    Latin abbreviations, not using, 182
Nouns, 38–39
    agreement and, 24
    and adjectives, 38
    capitalizing, 172–173
    plural, not turning them into possessives, 4
    possessive, 6
    unusual singulars and plurals, 14
Numbers and numerals, 186–193
    Arabic numerals, for 10 and above, 186
    avoid beginning a sentence with, 192
    below 10, 188–190
    combining words and numerals, 192
    in words or numerals, 186
    Roman numerals, use of 186
    units of measurement when a number is not specified, 186

## O

*ology*-terms, using correctly, 118
One-sentence paragraphs, 50
Outline, of research papers, 42

Outline of diagnostic reports, 266–269
    adult client, 268–269
    child client, 266–267
Organizations, referencing reports from, 236

# P

Page
    numbers, 157, 169
    running head, 157
Papers, structure of research, 42–44
Paragraphs, composing, 46–52
    as expression of related ideas, 46
    one sentence, 50
    too long, 48
    writing transitory sentences for, 52
Parallelism, 86–88
    bulleted or numbered lists, 88
    in a series, 18
    terms, writing in, 19, 86
Parentheses, as plural, 14
    to enclose abbreviations in, 180
    to enclose page numbers of quotations, 112
    to separate parenthetic expressions, 20
Parenthetical constructions, 182
Participial phrase, 40
Passive voice, 56
Path name, 215
PDF files (documents), 247, 259–262
Period
    after closing parenthesis, 236
    ending the reference entry with, 224
    in electronic citations, 214
    in reference list, after the year in parentheses, 224
Phrase
    commonly misused, 124–138
    eliminate or replace unnecessary, 64–71
    participial, 40
    redundant, avoiding, 72
Plural, unusual, 14–15
    possessives and, 3–4, 6
Portable Document Format, *see* PDF files
Possessives, 12
    distinguishing them from contractions, 12
Prevalence
    and incidence, 134
Practice writing
    diagnostic reports, 291–347
    progress reports, 407–431
    treatment plans, 369–393
Prejudicial reference to
    disabilities, avoiding, 148
    ethnic or racial background, avoiding, 150
    sexual orientation, avoiding, 152
Presentations, 234–235
Print journals
    American Speech-Language-Hearing Association, 248–245
    file formats for, 248–249
    and online journals, 247–248
Print media, and serial comma, 18
Procedures, subsection of a paper, 244
Proceedings of conference and symposia, referencing, 234
Progress reports, samples of, 395–404
    practice writing, 407–431
Pronouns, 34–35
    absolute possessive, 12
    case of, 34–35
    clarify referents, 34–35
Proof, 136–137 (*see also* Electronic proof reading)
Proposal, research, 241–245
Protocol, URL, 213–214
*Publication Manual of the American Psychological Association*, 143, 157
Publication title page, 157
Punctuation
    in electronic citation, 214
    space after, 179
    with quotations, 104

## Q

Qualifications, avoiding too many, 60
Quotations, 96–117
    block, arranging, 112
    exact reproductions of, 110
    integrating into text, 110
    islands of, avoiding, 100
    making them count, 96
    misuse of, 106
    not beginning a sentence with, 102
    overuse, avoiding, 98
    punctuation marks and, 104
    references for, 108

## R

Racial and ethnic background
    writing without prejudicial reference to, 150–151
Redundant phrases, avoiding 72–77
Reference citations in text, *see* Author citations in text
Reference list, (*see also* Author citations in text)
    abbreviations in, 222
    abstracts international, theses and dissertations in, 238
    abstracts used as the primary sources, 228
    alphabetizing the titles of multiple works of the same author, 220
    arranging multiple works of the same single author, 218
    arranging names in alphabetical order, 218
    articles with multiple authors, 226
    books and book chapters, 230
    convention paper and poster presentation, unpublished, 234
    different forms of journal publications, 226
    dissertations, unpublished, 238
    edited books and chapters in edited books, 232
    first page format, 216
    general guidelines, using electronic sources, 212–215
    guidelines on referencing electronic sources, 213–215
    hanging indent for each entry, 222
    heading format, 216
    journal articles, format for, 224
    magazines and newspaper articles, 228
    organization and government reports, 236
    printed and online reference works, 236
    proceedings of conferences and symposia, 234
    same last surname of different authors, 220
    temporally ascending order for multiple works of the same author published in a different year, 220
    theses, unpublished, 238
    unpublished articles, 238
Referents of pronouns, 34
Related words, keeping them together, 84–85
Reports
    diagnostic, 265–347
    empirical, 241–246
    organizations and government agencies, 236
    progress, 395–431
    writing sections of, 241–246
Research papers, writing the sections of, 241–245
    abstract, 241
    introduction, 242
    method, 243
    participants, 243
    materials, 244
    procedures, 244
    results, 244–245
    discussion, 245
    references, 245
    general guidelines on completed and proposed, 241
Research proposals, *see* Research papers
Results, section of research papers, 244–245

Right alignment, of page numbers, 157
Roman numerals, 186
Rules
    of agreement, 24–31
    usage, basic, 2–41
Running head, 159

## S

Secondary sources, citing, 294
Secondly, usage of, 138–139
Semicolon, 22
Since
    and because, 138
Sample diagnostic reports
    aphasia and apraxia, 284–287
    speech sound disorders, 278–280
    stuttering, 288–290
    voice disorders, 281–283
Sample progress reports
    child language disorders, 401–402
    speech sound disorders, 399–400
    stuttering, 396–398
    voice disorders, 403–404
Sentence
    fragments, 36–37
    preferring shorter to longer, 54
    shifts within and between, 94
    transitionary, 52
Serial comma, 18
Sexual orientation, writing about without prejudicial reference to, 152
*She* or *he* usage, 146–147
Shifts within and between sentences, 94
Since
    and because, 138
Singulars, 14–17
Six or more authors, citation of, 196
Space after punctuation, 179
Spacing, line, 170
Specific language, 62

Sponsors, of electronic sources, 212
Statements
    declarative as sentence fragments, 36
Speech sound disorder, 278–280, 292–305, 356–357, 399–400, 414–419
    brief treatment plan for, 356–357
    comprehensive treatment plan for, 350–352
    individualized educational programs for, 365
    practice writing diagnostic report, 292–305
    practice writing progress reports, 399–400
    practice writing treatment plan, 382–385
    progress reports, 399–400
    sample diagnostic report, 278–280
Structure of research papers, 42–44, 241–246
Stuttering, 288–290, 320–333, 354–355, 367, 378–381, 396–398, 408–413
    brief treatment plan for, 354–355
    individualized educational programs for, 367
    practice writing diagnostic report, 320–333
    practice writing progress reports, 408–413
    practice writing brief treatment plan, 378–381
    progress reports, 396–398
    sample diagnostic report, 288–290
Style menu in word processors, 162
Subheadings, 162, 241, 243, 261, 265
    design, 44
Suffixes, alphabetical, 202
Support and proof, 136–137
Symposia proceedings published as a book, 234

## T

Technical writing, and jargon, 80
Tense, shifting, 94
    future tense for proposals, 241
    past tense for completed studies, 241
Term paper, 143–144, 250
    Heading styles for, 158
    title page of, 158

Terms, 18, 38
   boldface for defined, 168
   ending in -ics
   ending in -ology
   grammatical in headings, 172
   hyphenated, 175, 177
   linguistic exemplars, 174
Text, beginning of, 161
Their
   and there, 138
There
   and their, 138
Theses and dissertations in *Abstracts International*, 238
   italicizing the titles of, 106
   prescribed formats, 143
   unpublished, 238
Thirdly, usage of, 138–139
Three to five authors, reference citation of, 196
Title, 157
   alphabetizing newspaper article, 228
   capitalizing and italicizing book, 230
   dissertation, not italicizing, 238
   journal title, italicizing, 224
   paper for publication
   presentation, italicizing
   proceedings, published as book, 234
   quotation marks and, 106
   term paper, 158
Trade names, capitalization, 172
Transitory sentences between paragraphs, 52
Treatment plans
   brief, 353–361
   comprehensive, 349–351
   individualized education programs, 363–368
   practice in writing, 369–391
Two authors, reference citation for, 194
Typeface and size, 168

## U

Underlining, 144, 174, 261

Uniform Resource Locators, URLs, 213–214
Units of
   abbreviations of, 184
   measurement, 184, 186, 188
   when a number not specified, 186
Unnecessary phrases, eliminate or replace, 64
Unpublished
   articles, theses, and dissertation, 238
   convention presentations, 234
Untitled introduction, 42, 161, 162
U.S. government publications, citing, 236
Usage, basic rules of, 2–41

## V

Variables, 172, 244
Verb, 38, 39
   agreement with subject, 24
   use of effect as, 124
Versus, use of, 182
Voice disorders, 281–283, 334–347, 360–362, 366, 390–394, 403–404, 426–431
   brief treatment plan for, 360–361
   individualized educational programs for, 366
   practice writing diagnostic report, 334–347
   practice writing progress reports, 426–431
   practice writing brief treatment plan, 390–393
   progress reports, 403–404
   sample diagnostic report, 288–290

## W

*Webster's New International Dictionary*, 175, 177, 178, 180,
White and Black, as racial references, 150
Word, see MS Word, editing features
Wordiness, avoiding, 78
Writing
   diagnostic reports, 291–347
   progress reports, 407–431
   treatment plans, 369–393